OXR

3 200357 020

C000153280

P. 140.00

A HUNDRED YEARS OF
BRITISH FOOD
& FARMING
A STATISTICAL SURVEY

by H F Marks

(Former Chief Economist, Meat and Livestock Commission)

edited by D K Britton

*(Emeritus Professor of Agricultural Economics,
University of London)*

Taylor & Francis
London, New York and Philadelphia
1989

UK   Taylor & Francis Ltd, 4 John St., London WC1N 2ET

USA   Taylor & Francis Inc., 242 Cherry St., Philadelphia,
PA 19106–1906

British Library Cataloguing in Publication Data

Marks, H. F. (Hilary F)
  A hundred years of British food & farming: a statistical survey.
  1. Great Britain. Agricultural industries, 1889–1989
  I. Title   II. Britton, D. K. (Denis King), *1920–*
  338.1′0941

  ISBN 0-85066-452-7

Library of Congress Cataloging in Publication Data

Marks, H. F. (Hilary F.)
  A hundred years of British food & farming: a statistical survey/
  by H. F. Marks; edited by D. K. Britton.
  ISBN 0-85066-452-7
  1. Agriculture – Great Britain – Statistics.   I. Britton, Denis K.,
  1920–   .   II. Title.
  S217.M37 1989
  338.1′0941′021 – dc19

Graphs prepared by Sarah Waddell, Adrian Baker and Tracey Wright.
Cover design by Russell Beech.
Cover photograph is reproduced by kind permission of the University of
Reading, Institute of Agricultural History and Museum of English Rural Life.
Typeset by Cambridge Photosetting Services.
Printed in Great Britain by Taylor & Francis (Printers) Ltd, Rankine Road,
Basingstoke, Hants.

Contents

Some wag is reported to have said that "There are lies, damned lies and statistics". I very much doubt that compilers of statistics set out deliberately to deceive. It is much more likely to be a case of drawing the wrong conclusions from the figures.

The 'Introduction' to this remarkable collection of facts and figures sets out the background and suggests how the statistics should be interpreted. I believe it would be quite reasonable to draw the conclusion that over the last forty years British farmers have responded magnificently to the encouragement and inducements to adopt new techniques and machinery. It is ironical that their productivity has grown to such an extent that today there is anxiety about over-production of certain commodities.

Forty years ago the economics of farming were a national concern within a world market system. With membership of the European Economic Community and the demolition of all trade barriers in 1992, the situation will change dramatically and British farmers will find themselves part of a much wider system. It will be interesting to see comparable statistics for the whole Community ten years from now.

1988

NFU MUTUAL

GENERAL INSURANCE

LIFE ASSURANCE

PENSION PLANS

INVESTMENT PLANS

DOMESTIC MORTGAGES

INHERITANCE TAX PLANNING

SCHOOL FEES

LOAN REPAYMENT

A Major Sponsor and Official Insurer of

NFU Mutual Insurance Society Ltd
Head Office: Tiddington Road, Stratford-upon-Avon,
Warwickshire CV37 7BJ.
A member of LAUTRO.

A FINANCIAL FORCE
IN THE COUNTRY

Preface

British Food and Farming is being celebrated in 1989 to mark the 150th anniversary of the founding of the Royal Agricultural Society of England and the centenary of the Ministry of Agriculture, Fisheries and Food. It is therefore an appropriate time to take a fresh look at the record of British agriculture over the past hundred and fifty years or so. The aim of this book is not so much to describe the great progress which has been made but rather to assemble the statistical facts and figures and use them to highlight what has happened.

This is not the first attempt of its kind. In 1968 the Ministry of Agriculture, Fisheries and Food published *A Century of Agricultural Statistics* which has well fulfilled its purpose of providing 'a permanent and useful work of reference'. However, no one connected with agriculture will need to be reminded that much has happened since 1968. Far-reaching changes have occurred in technology, policy and social structure, and the pace of change seems to be accelerating. The story so ably presented 20 years ago now needs to be brought up to date. We have also attempted to widen its scope.

The task of selection has been formidable. Both the breadth of coverage and the weight of detail of agricultural statistics have greatly increased in our time. The annual census has not surrendered its central position, but it cannot of itself provide the national account for agriculture which can now claim to be the primary purpose of the statistical activities of the Agricultural Departments. Prices and incomes are at least as important in the field of policy as crop areas, harvests and livestock numbers.

Taking the long-term view brings its own problems. Nearly all the major series of annual data have undergone changes in definition and these can distort trends. In particular, when looking at any long series expressed in money terms it is essential to keep in mind that the purchasing power of the pound has undergone great changes, especially in the 1970s. We have therefore deflated such series, using a Long-Term Index of Prices of Consumer Goods and Services in UK, published by the Central Statistical Office. Bold attempts can be made to splice together series which are known to be dissimilar in important respects, and these may then result in biassed conclusions. A more rigorous approach would treat the earlier series as non-comparable and therefore obsolete. We have tried to steer a prudent course through these difficulties.

We hope that this record of the major long-term developments which have occurred in British food and farming will be of interest not only to those concerned with the formulation and evaluation of agricultural policy but also to farmers, the food industries and the general public. It gives an insight into the historical changes in response to adversity and opportunity which have led to the present deployment of agricultural land, labour and capital and to current patterns of consumer expenditure and food demand.

We should like to record our thanks to those in various organisations, but especially in the Ministry of Agriculture, Fisheries and Food, for the valuable help and advice which they have given. However, any remaining errors must, as always, be the sole responsibility of the authors.

Denis Britton
Hilary Marks

Introduction

Historical

The period since the first agricultural census was taken in 1866 is of interest not only from an agricultural point of view but also because it highlights the difficulties with which agricultural policy makers have to contend. They face the challenge of formulating policies which ensure that the nation is adequately fed but which also take into account the interests of both consumers and the agricultural industry.

In order to understand how the present situation has come about it is necessary to go back to the mid 1870s, about 30 years after the repeal of the Corn Laws when agriculture began to suffer from a major depression which lasted, with some temporary breaks, until the outbreak of World War I. During this period farm production did not increase year by year as has been the case since 1939. Farm wages were very low and farmers could seldom invest for expansion. Within this general stagnation there was a switch from crop to livestock production.

Imports of cheap grain increased rapidly, but farmers producing meat and dairy produce were less severely hit than arable farmers because of the rapidly expanding market brought about by an increasing population, greater wealth and an improved transport system. The last quarter of the 19th century also saw the development of the refrigerated cargo ship, and from then onwards imports of beef and lamb as well as dairy produce began to increase rapidly.

After the outbreak of World War I the heavy reliance on imported food supplies produced a rapid rise in prices, but it was not until 1916 that a Food Controller was appointed to take over the supplies, distribution, consumption and prices of basic foods. Farmers were offered a variety of incentives to increase production, particularly of crops. The 1918 harvest saw the peak of the agricultural war effort and no further measures were introduced to increase crop production.

The post World War I years were again unsatisfactory from the arable farmer's point of view and by 1929 the total tillage area had fallen by 20%. The rise in the cost of labour and the cheapness of cereals encouraged the intensive production of livestock and livestock products for a comparatively sheltered market.

The Great Depression began in 1929, and by 1933 agricultural prices had fallen by about a quarter. Food imports had continued to increase, particularly as other importing countries closed their frontiers in order to protect their own farmers.

Although farmers were already being given some assistance in the 1920s it was not until the early 1930s that a new approach to agricultural policy began to take shape, with a more positive role to stabilise and strengthen the industry.

The Agricultural Marketing Acts of 1931 and 1933 resulted in the setting up of Marketing Boards for milk, potatoes, hops and bacon pigs, while the Board of Trade was permitted to restrict imports of these commodities.

The Wheat Act of 1932 enabled wheat producers to receive a standard price linked to a standard quantity financed by a levy on all wheat flour, both home milled and imported. The subsidy on sugar beet was put on a permanent basis and the factories were required to combine into the British Sugar Corporation.

From 1934 onwards a subsidy was also paid on fat cattle which reached certain standards of weight and conformation. Imports of store and fat cattle, mainly from the Irish Republic, were also restricted.

The policy measures to increase agricultural production during World War II and the control and rationing of food supplies, which lasted until 1954, represented a further extension of the powers of the government to support agriculture and to stabilise markets. It was also during this period that the mechanisation of agriculture became of major importance.

The Agriculture Act 1947 formed the basis of post-war agricultural policy. It provided for guaranteed prices and deficiency payments, but by the early 1960s there was already concern about the overproduction of certain commodities.

Entry into the European Community in 1973 provided a strong incentive for British farmers, particularly cereal producers, to expand production. Efforts to contain the European surpluses in the 1980s have so far been only partially successful in spite of sharp reductions in real product prices. This has resulted from the rapid increase in agricultural productivity brought about by animal and plant breeders and from improved methods of cultivation and husbandry.

The imbalance between supply and demand has not yet been corrected and British agriculture is once again facing a period in which difficult readjustments will be needed.

Within the context of the Common Agricultural Policy, the UK government and the farming industry are having to give serious consideration to ways and means of transferring land from food production to other uses. In retrospect this is a situation which could have been foreseen as production was persistently overtaking demand, but in the event neither the government nor the industry were well prepared for the transition to the next phase of British agricultural history.

Main statistical trends

Output increased after 1950 to much higher levels than had previously been attained. This expansion has been fairly steadily maintained for about 40 years and does not yet show any real signs of abating. A main cause of the expansion has been rising yields (production per hectare and per animal). Another cause has been the almost complete displacement of horses by tractors and other machines. This released a great deal of land for the production of marketable output. At the same time it increased agriculture's dependence on industry.

Rising production has not generated any increase in employment on farms: indeed, the reverse has been the case. There are not only fewer workers on farms, but also fewer farmers. Farms have become larger and more specialised.

For a time the increase in production was accompanied by a closely corresponding increase in purchased inputs such as fertilisers, feeding stuffs, pesticides and machinery, but more recently, output has increased without any appreciable increase in dependence on inputs.

Changes in prices and incomes can be properly appreciated only if allowance is made for changes in the value of money. In 1946 the pound sterling was worth about 13 times more than in 1986 in terms of purchasing power over consumers' goods and services in the UK market. It is necessary to deflate the annual statistics by a general price index to see what has happened to 'real' prices and incomes.

For a long period real prices received by producers for their farm products have been falling, with a few interruptions, notably in 1973–77.

On average real incomes from farming are now considerably lower than they were in the best times, which occurred for most farms in the mid–1970s. While other sources of income are being developed, farmers have been caught in the squeeze between the prices of what they sell and the prices of what they buy.

To some extent individual farmers have been able to maintain their incomes by enlarging the size of their businesses so that their greater output compensated for their reduced profit margins per tonne.

There has been a substantial increase in the real value of farm workers' weekly earnings. Contrasting this with the decline in farming real incomes, it is evident that the gap between the farmers' and farm workers' earnings from agriculture has been reduced.

In real terms the market value of agricultural land rose to unprecedented heights during the 1960s and 1970s but has been sharply reduced since then. Movements in rents have been similar in direction but less volatile.

The trading position of UK in agricultural products has been transformed by the expansion of home output. The UK's self-sufficiency has been greatly increased compared with 1939 and in recent years a considerable export trade has been developed.

As can be seen from the contents of this book, agriculture is particularly well served statistically. The main statistical sources and a summary of the changes in the thresholds below which minor holdings in England and Wales have been excluded from the agricultural census since 1955 are presented after the Appendices. It is necessary to bear these in mind when interpreting the tables.

General notes

1. In general, metric measurements have been used throughout. However, where the official sources still use other systems these are reproduced.
2. Calendar years have been shown wherever possible. However, until about 1970 official agricultural statistics were not shown in calendar years but in other 'agricultural' years. It has therefore not been possible to show the complete series in calendar years.
3. It has not been possible to provide statistical series for the United Kingdom of Great Britain and Northern Ireland before 1923. Figures were then available for the whole of Ireland, not for Northern and Southern Ireland separately. In general the statistics therefore relate to Great Britain prior to 1923 and to the United Kingdom thereafter.
4. The term 'supply' used in the tables is defined as home production plus imports.
5. The term 'new supply' used in the tables is defined as home production plus imports less exports.
6. Because of some rounding of figures the columns in the tables may not always add up to the totals shown.
7. Calculations in 1986 money values have been carried out by the authors.

8. The following acronyms and abbreviations have been used:
   MAFF: Ministry of Agriculture, Fisheries and Food.
   HMSO: Her Majesty's Stationery Office.
   HGCA: Home Grown Cereals Authority.
   MLC: Meat and Livestock Commission.
   MMB: Milk Marketing Board.
   EC: European Community.
   FEOGA: French acronym for the European Guidance and Guarantee Fund.
   DAFS: Department of Agriculture for Scotland.
   DANI: Department of Agriculture for Northern Ireland.
   ADAS: Agricultural Development and Advisory Service.
   AWU: Annual Work Unit.
   ALU: Annual Labour Unit.
   SMD: Standard Man Days.
   MCA: Monetary Compensatory Amounts.
   CAP: Common Agricultural Policy

CHAPTER 1

Agriculture in the national economy

Agriculture is one of the United Kingdom's major industries. The 593 000 persons engaged in farming contribute about £5 600 million to the national gross domestic product and produce almost 60% of the nation's food and about 75% of the indigenous food which is consumed.

Although agriculture's gross domestic product has increased by almost 400% since 1970, partly because of increased production and partly because of higher prices, its contribution as a proportion of the national gross domestic product has fallen almost continuously because of major increases in the economy as a whole. By 1987 its contribution was only 1.7%.

Agriculture's net product at constant 1980 prices increased by about 95% between 1976 and 1987; this indicates the substantial increase in agricultural production which has occurred since the mid 1970s.

Such an increase would not have been possible without a high level of capital investment. Fixed capital formation for agriculture reached a peak in 1983 when it accounted for 2.8% of the national share. Investment has fallen since then because of the decline in farming profitability. Capital formation in 1986, at £1 033 million, accounted for only 1.6% of the total. Of the £1 033 million invested in 1986, £440 million was on buildings and works and £593 million on plant, vehicles and machinery.

The high level of capital investment has not only resulted in higher agricultural production but has also enabled considerable labour economies to be made. In 1987 there were only 593 000 persons engaged in agriculture, about 2.4% of the working population. Of these 287 000 were farmers, partners and directors; 142 000 were regular whole-time workers and 61 000 were part-time workers. The number of people engaged in agriculture as a proportion of those in all occupations has fallen almost continuously since the 1950s, the normal characteristic of economic development in any country.

Spending on food, including caterers', has increased continuously during the past 20 years. This has been due mainly to increased prices, though even at constant prices there has been some increase in expenditure on certain types of food such as fruit and vegetables, preserves and confectionery. In spite of this, spending on food has fallen sharply as a percentage of total consumer expenditure; by 1987 it accounted for only about 16% of the total.

The value of home-produced food as a percentage of all food consumed in the United Kingdom reached a peak in 1982 but has since fallen slightly, because of increased imports. The value of home production as a percentage of indigenous type food consumed, has also fallen since 1984 because of increased imports. Imports of food, feed and beverages have risen by about 16% in terms of volume since 1982. Exports of agricultural products have become an important feature of UK trade.

Contribution to gross domestic product

The gross domestic product of the agriculture, forestry and fishing industry has at current prices increased almost six-fold since 1964. But as a proportion of the national gross domestic product, it has fallen from 3.4% in 1964 to only 1.8% in 1986. In terms of 1980 constant prices, agriculture, forestry and fishing gross domestic product increased by 66% between 1965 and 1986.

The gross domestic product statistics for agriculture on its own have only been available since 1970. At current prices there was a five-fold rise between 1970 and 1987.

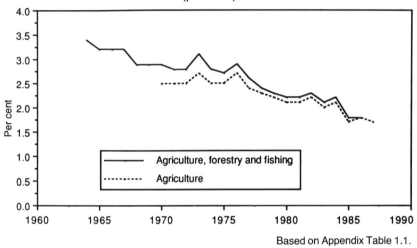

The percentage contribution of agriculture to gross domestic product (per cent)

Based on Appendix Table 1.1.

Capital formation

In the period immediately after World War II when food was in short supply, agriculture's share of gross fixed capital formation accounted for 6% of the national total. As other investment began to rise, agriculture's share fell sharply and by 1954 had declined to 3.8%. This trend has continued, the agricultural share falling to 2.8% in 1983. A sharp reduction in agriculture's capital formation since then has meant that by 1986 agriculture's share was only 1.6% of the national total.

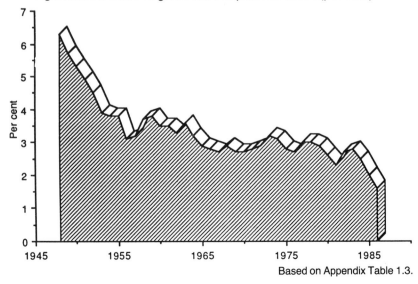

Agriculture's share of gross fixed capital formation (per cent)

Based on Appendix Table 1.3.

Manpower

The number of people engaged in agriculture, as a proportion of those engaged in all occupations, has been declining gradually. In 1987 the proportion was only 2.4% compared with 3% in 1970. Chapter 4, *Labour*, deals with this more fully.

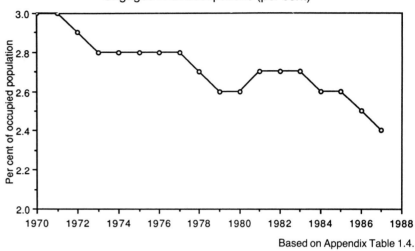

Manpower engaged in agriculture as a proportion of manpower engaged in all occupations (per cent)

Based on Appendix Table 1.4.

Imports

In spite of the rise in agricultural production, the United Kingdom continues to be a major importer of food, feed and beverages. Imports in 1986 totalled £10 475 million and have risen continuously since the mid–1960s. In terms of volume there has been relatively little change in the level of imports since the mid–1970s, but prices have doubled.

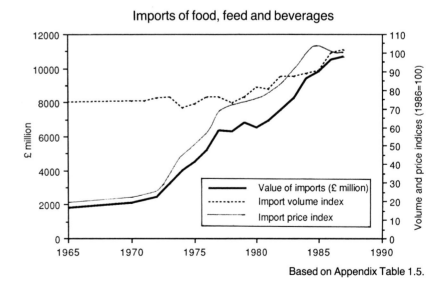

Imports of food, feed and beverages

Based on Appendix Table 1.5.

Exports

Exports of food, feed and beverages have become a major feature of UK trade, both in terms of volume and value. Exports of food, feed and beverages (excluding alcohol) in 1986 totalled £5 368 million. In terms of volume exports have been increasing continuously since the mid-1960s and rose by 95% between 1974 and 1986. Export prices have almost trebled during this period.

Exports of food, feed and beverages

Based on Appendix Table 1.6.

Expenditure

The Central Statistical Office's household food expenditure series, which goes back before World War II, shows that in 1938 household food expenditure accounted for almost 30% of total consumer spending. It fell to about 25% during the war and did not rise again until the mid-1950s when it again reached about 30%. It then went into a steady decline and by 1987 had fallen to 12.7%.

Statistics on food expenditure including caterers', have been available since 1967. These show that in 1967–69 expenditure on food accounted for 24.1% of total consumers' spending. By 1986 this had fallen to 16.1% in spite of an increase in catering food expenditure until 1980, when the catering industry was affected, at least temporarily, by the recession.

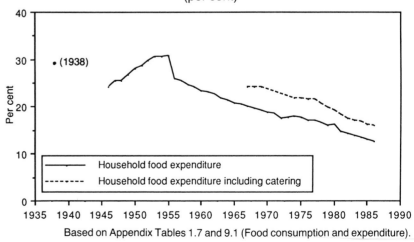

Expenditure on food as a proportion of total consumers' expenditure (per cent)

Based on Appendix Tables 1.7 and 9.1 (Food consumption and expenditure).

Self-sufficiency

The statistics relating to the value of home produced food as a percentage of all food consumed have only been available since the mid–1960s when approximately half the total food consumed in terms of value was produced in the UK. This was probably very similar to the mid–19th century before the agricultural depression in the latter part of the century reduced self-sufficiency to only about 33% by the outbreak of World War I. This percentage remained the same during the 1920s and 1930s.

The increase in agricultural production from the mid–1970s has increased self-sufficiency. Home production as a percentage of all food consumed rose from 50% in 1973 to 63% in 1982. Since then there has been a reduction to 57% in 1987. Home production as a percentage of indigenous type food consumed increased from 62% in 1973 to 83% in 1984, but by 1987 had again fallen to 73%.

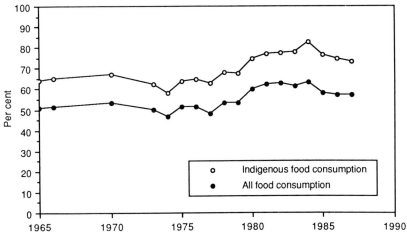

Self-sufficiency in food (per cent)

Based on Appendix Table 1.8.

CHAPTER 2
British agriculture in the European Community

The United Kingdom, the Irish Republic and Denmark became members of the European Community on 1 January 1973. As the six founder member states had originally set their institutional prices at relatively high levels in order to encourage food production after the devastation of World War II, the Treaty of Accession provided for a transitional period of five years during which it was intended that the United Kingdom and the Irish Republic should raise their institutional prices to the level of the original six.

Denmark decided to adopt the Community level of prices from the date of joining and did not have a transitional period. Other aspects such as international trade policy, support for capital and other farm improvements as well as support for agriculture in special areas also needed to be harmonised. It was therefore not until 1 January 1978 that the United Kingdom achieved full membership.

Wherever possible the statistics given in this chapter relate to the present 12 member states, but if this has not been possible EC10 statistics (which exclude Spain and Portugal) are used.

Many of the difficulties in negotiating EC agricultural policy since entry into the European Community have been due to the United Kingdom's imbalance between its financial contributions and receipts. Agriculture is also less important in the UK than in most other member states, both from an economic and political point of view.

Although the United Kingdom has the highest proportion of land devoted to agriculture and the largest average size of holding, less than 3% of the population is engaged in agriculture compared with about 8% in the EC12. The proportion of gross domestic product derived from agriculture in the UK is also much lower than in most other member states.

Household expenditure on food, beverages and tobacco, as a proportion of total consumer expenditure, is also lower in the UK than in other countries, with the exception of the Federal Republic of Germany.

Cereal production has risen rapidly in the UK since entry into the EC. This has been the result of a sharp rise in real prices, the development of more productive varieties and improved methods of cultivation, which were perhaps more readily adopted in this country than in some other member states. The United Kingdom's share of EC cereal production has increased significantly in recent years.

The most dramatic change since entry into the European Community has been the increased production of oilseed rape. In 1986 The United Kingdom accounted for over a quarter of total EC12 production compared with only about 3% in 1973. The share of total EC fruit production has fallen but there has been less change in fresh vegetables.

The United Kingdom's share of beef, sheep and poultry meat production in relation to total EC10 production has shown little change since entry, but its share of pigmeat production has fallen. Eggs have become relatively less important. The United Kingdom's share of total EC milk production since 1973 has shown little change, but there has been a major rise in the proportion of home produced butter.

British agriculture as a whole has almost certainly benefited from entry into the Community. In terms of gross value added (in ECUs) there has been an increase of over 50% since 1973; this was only exceeded by the Netherlands and Denmark.

There has also been a major shift in the pattern of trade in food and agricultural products. More than half the United Kingdom's imports, in terms of value, now come from other member states compared with less than 30% in 1973. Almost 60% of its food and agricultural exports are sent to the EC compared with only 40% in 1973.

The European Community

In 1986 the United Kingdom contributed 4825 million ECUs to the European Community's financial resources, about 15% of the total revenue. The level of the United Kingdom's contribution is in sharp contrast with its share of FEOGA[1] expenditure which in 1986 accounted for only 9% of the total guarantee fund's expenditure. In 1973 the UK contributed 9% of the EC's total revenue but its FEOGA expenditure only accounted for 4% of the total.

The United Kingdom has only a relatively small area of forest (9% of the total land area compared with 30% in the Federal Republic of Germany). Much of the land is suitable for agricultural production, and 76% is in fact devoted to farming. Only the Irish Republic has a higher proportion (81%).

The average size of agricultural holding in the United Kingdom is larger than in any other EC state, 69 hectares compared with an EC12 average of 16.5 hectares.

The number of people in agricultural production has been falling rapidly. In 1986 only 2.6% of the working population was involved in farming in this country, the lowest in the European Community. United Kingdom farmers, however, employ the highest proportion of hired workers, 52% compared with an EC10 average of 25%.

In the UK, agriculture's share of the total national gross domestic product has also shown a steady decline, to only 1.8% in 1986. This is the lowest in the EC, with the exception of the Federal Republic of Germany (also 1.8%).

In 1984 the British spent about 20% of their total consumer expenditure on food, beverages and tobacco; only the Federal Republic of Germany spent proportionately less.

[1]FEOGA is the French acronym for the European Guidance and Guarantee Fund (EAGGF) which is responsible for financing agricultural activities in the European Community. The guarantee section finances expenditure arising from the common agricultural market and prices policy, e.g. export refunds, MCAs, intervention, storage and premium payments. The guidance section finances the agricultural structures policy. This covers aid for investment projects such as those concerned with marketing and processing of agricultural products, modernisation, restructuring and development of farming, fisheries, aid for agricultural infrastructure and aid for agriculture in less favoured areas.

The United Kingdom in the European Community

UK financial contribution to EC, 1986 (%)		14.5	
UK FEOGA Expenditure – Guarantee Fund, 1986%		9.0	
– Guidance Fund, 1986%		10.7	

	United Kingdom	EC10	EC12
Land use for agriculture, 1986	76.2%	58.6%	57.2%
Average size of holding, 1985	69.4 ha	17.4 ha	16.5 ha
Employment in agriculture, 1986	2.6%	7.0%	8.3%
Proportion of hired agricultural workers, 1985	52.4%	24.6%	
Proportion of national GDP from agriculture, 1986	1.8	3.4	3.5
Expenditure on food, tobacco and beverages, 1984[1]	19.9	21.3	21.9

[1]As a % of total expenditure

Crops

Cereal production has increased rapidly since the United Kingdom's entry into the EC. Whereas in 1973 UK wheat accounted for only 11.4% of EC12 production, by 1986 it had risen to an estimated 21.3%. The rise in barley production has been much less, the UK continuing to grow 19–23% of the barley produced in EC12. Total cereal production increased by about 60% between 1973 and 1986 and in 1986 accounted for about 16% of the EC12 production compared with only 13% in 1973.

There has also been a rapid rise in oilseed rape production in the UK because of increased profitability. Whereas the United Kingdom contributed only 2.9% at the time of entering the EC, this had risen to 26.3% in 1986.

Sugar production, in terms of white sugar value, has risen by about 25% since entry into the European Community. There has, however, been little change in the UK's share of about 9% of the EC12 total. Production is regulated by quotas.

Potato production can vary considerably from year to year depending on seasonal factors. There has been some increase in United Kingdom production since entry into the EC while the total for the EC has fallen. In 1986 the UK accounted for 16% of EC12 production.

British fruit growing is relatively unimportant in an EC context. In 1986 British growers produced only 3.8% of the EC12's apples and 1.9% of the pears.

UK crop production in relation to the European Community (%)

	UK production as % EC10			UK production as % EC12		
	1973	1985	1986	1973	1985	1986
Common wheat	12.6	20.0	22.9	11.4	18.4	21.3
Barley	25.5	23.9	25.4	22.6	18.9	21.4
Total cereals[1]	14.0	16.2	17.9	12.6	14.0	15.9
Oilseed rape	2.9	24.0	26.4	2.9	23.9	26.3
Sugar	10.0	10.1	10.0	9.2	9.4	9.2
Potatoes	16.2	19.3	19.0		16.1	16.1
Fruit (area)	4.7	2.9	2.9	2.6	1.8	1.8
Fresh vegetables (area)	12.9	12.5	12.2	9.2	8.8	8.7

[1]Excluding rice.
Based on Appendix Tables 2.15 to 2.28.

The vegetable area has fallen only slightly since 1973 and in 1986 accounted for 8.7% of the EC12 total. Cauliflower production has shown a small increase, although there are considerable seasonal variations. The United Kingdom continues to produce 17–19% of EC12 cauliflowers. There has been little change in the quantity of tomatoes produced in this country, production amounting to only about 1% of EC12 production.

Meat

In 1986 British farmers produced about 14% of the EC10's beef and veal production, slightly less than in 1973. The proportion of sheepmeat has shown virtually no change. Pigmeat production is currently at about the same level as in 1973, while production has risen sharply in some other member states, particularly the Netherlands, reducing the proportion of pigmeat produced in the UK from 11.8% of the EC10 total in 1973 to only 9.2% in 1986. Poultry meat production has risen both in this country and the EC10. The United Kingdom accounts for about 20% of the EC10's production; there has been little change in this proportion since 1973.

UK meat production in relation to the European Community (%)

	UK production as % EC10			UK production as % EC12		
	1973	1985	1986	1973	1985	1986
Beef and veal	15.3	15.4	13.9			13.0
Sheepmeat	40.4	40.9	41.4			34.2
Pigmeat	11.8	9.2	9.2		8.3	8.2
Poultry meat	20.5	20.0	20.3		16.3	16.9

Based on Appendix Tables 2.29 to 2.32.

Milk, dairy products and eggs

In spite of the rapid rise in milk production since 1973 the United Kingdom's share of total EC10 milk production has fallen slightly from 15.6% in 1973 to 14.7% in 1986. In 1986 this country also accounted for 14.0% of EC12 production. Since 1984 there have been EC milk quotas.

There has been an increase of about 130% in butter production since entry into the EC. This means that the United Kingdom in 1986 produced 10.3% of the EC10's production compared with only 5.7% in 1973.

Cheese production has risen rapidly as more manufacturing milk has become available. In 1986 the United Kingdom accounted for about 6.8% of total EC10 cheese production and about 6.2% of EC12 production.

United Kingdom egg production has fallen since 1973 and in 1986 only accounted for 15.6% of EC12 production. As a proportion of EC10 production its share has declined from 22.7% in 1973 to 18.7% in 1986.

Milk, dairy products and egg production (%)

	UK production as % EC10			UK production as % EC12		
	1973	1985	1986	1973	1985	1986
Milk	15.6	14.8	14.7		13.9	
Butter	5.7	9.9	10.3			
Cheese		6.6	6.8			6.2
Eggs	22.7	18.6	18.7		15.8	15.6

Based on Appendix Tables 2.33 to 2.36.

CHAPTER 3
Farm structure and land use

About 77% of the United Kingdom's total land area is currently used for agricultural purposes. This includes rough grazings and common land. The total area of agricultural land, which has only been recorded from the mid-1960s, has been falling continuously as a result of increasing urban development, roads, reservoirs, afforestation and recreational uses. Much of the reduction occurred up to the mid-1970s.

Statistics relating to the area of crops and grass have been available since 1866. They show a continuous decline in Great Britain since the mid-1880s, which was accelerated during the 1930s because of the depressed state of British agriculture. There has been an apparent further reduction since the mid-1960s, but this was partly due to changes in methods of enumeration with the result that small holdings are no longer included in the agricultural census.

In the United Kingdom there was a sharp rise in the arable area during World War II as farmers were encouraged to expand food production. Although the total arable area has remained virtually stable since the mid-1970s, crop production has increased as a result of improved productivity and there has been an increase in tillage area at the expense of short-term grassland.

There have also been significant changes within the tillage area itself since the mid-1970s. The areas of cereals and oilseed rape have risen while potatoes and horticultural produce have fallen. Tillage and cereal areas expanded in England and Scotland, but contracted elsewhere.

Permanent grassland was sharply reduced during World War II as farmers were encouraged to plough. There has been very little change since the mid-1970s. Woodland on farms has shown some increase since the mid-1970s.

A Century of Agricultural Statistics 1866 to 1966 and more recent statistics suggest that a trend towards amalgamation has resulted in an increasing proportion of crops and grass being on larger holdings. Scottish statistics show a similar trend.

The trend towards larger holdings is confirmed by other statistics which show farm size in terms of standard man days and British Size Units. Although the rate of growth has slowed down recently, there is no doubt that the increase in farm size constitutes a major structural change for the agricultural industry.

The proportion of rented land has continued to decline slowly. The proportion of land farmed by its owner has risen since 1960. In Northern Ireland virtually all farmers are owner-occupiers.

Part-time farming appears to be increasing in England, Wales and Scotland but has shown a slight reduction in Northern Ireland. In the United Kingdom as a whole 30% of the agricultural holdings have a standard gross margin of less than 4 British Standard Units, or 8000 ECU at 1978–80 values.

Agricultural land prices throughout the United Kingdom rose six- or seven-fold between 1970 and 1984. They have, however, fallen since.

Crops and grass

The area of crops and grass in Great Britain was at a peak in the mid-1880s but has since fallen almost continuously. Since the late 1920s there has been an eight per cent reduction in the area of crops and grass in the United Kingdom, mainly because of the depressed state of British agriculture in the 1930s. Since 1955 the area has fallen from 12.6 million to 12.1 million hectares.

The total area of agricultural land in the United Kingdom, which includes rough grazing and woodland, has fallen from 19.6 million hectares in 1965 to 18.7 million hectares in 1987. The proportion of land used for crops tends to vary with the economic prosperity of crop production. It was highest at 45.5% prior to the agricultural depression at the end of the 19th century and the beginning of the 20th century. After a recovery during and immediately after World War II it fell again until after the United Kingdom's entry into the European Community. By 1987 almost 44% of the total area of crops and grass consisted of crops and fallow.

The proportion of land with grasses less than five years old (temporary grass) was highest in the 1950s and 1960s; in 1987 it only accounted for 14% of the area of crops and grass. The proportion of land used for permanent grass (grass over five years old) has shown little change since the mid-1970s and accounts for about 42% of the total.

Area of crops and grass (million hectares)

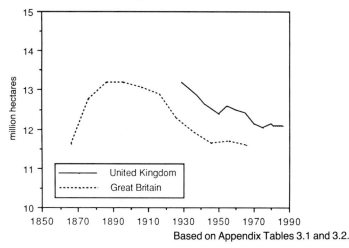

Based on Appendix Tables 3.1 and 3.2.

Changes in the balance of tillage and grassland

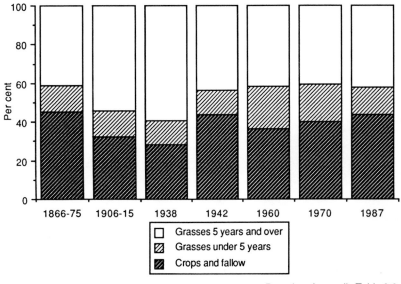

Based on Appendix Table 3.3.

Farm size

From 1885 to 1944 there appears to have been a decline in the proportion of crops and grass on holdings of about 200 hectares and over but an increase on holdings with 20 to 121 hectares. Since the end of World War II agricultural holdings have become fewer and larger. In 1944 only 24% of the total area of crops and grass in England and Wales was on holdings with more than 121 hectares of crops and grass, but by 1966 this had risen to 34%.

The United Kingdom figures, which are based on the total land area of the holdings, show that there has been a further small increase in the proportion of land on the larger holdings since 1977. Changes in farm size can also be measured in standard man days (SMD) for the various enterprises on the farm. This is a standard measure of labour needed to farm the crops and livestock on the holding. The figures from 1978 onwards are not directly comparable with the earlier figures.

The average number of standard man days on holdings with 275 SMD and over increased from 944 in 1967 to 1114 in 1974. The standard man days were revised in 1978 to take account of the changes in farming which had occurred, and between 1978 and 1985 the average for holdings with 250 SMD and over increased from 898 to 928. In terms of British Size Units (BSU) (which measures the financial potential of farms) the average has risen from 105.1 in 1984 to 106.3 in 1987.

Area of crops and grass by holding size (per cent)

	England and Wales (per cent)						United Kingdom[1] (per cent)	
Hectares	1885	1895	1915	1944	1966	Hectares	1977	1986
Under 2.5	1.2	1.2	1.1	0.8	0.8	Under 2	0.1	0.1
2.0–20.2	14.2	14.2	15.1	13.2	10.2	2–29.9	10.4	9.4
20.3–40.4	14.4	15.2	15.9	17.7	15.2	30–49.9	8.7	8.2
40.5–121.4	41.6	42.1	43.5	44.4	40.2	50–199.9	36.5	37.0
121.5–202.3	16.3	15.5 }	24.4	13.6	16.0	200–299.9	9.2	9.8
202.3 and over	12.3	11.9 }		10.3	17.6	300 and over	35.1	35.5
Total	100.0	100.0	100.0	100.0	100.0	Total	100.0	100.0

[1]Total land area of holdings.

Size of business in terms of standard man days % of holdings

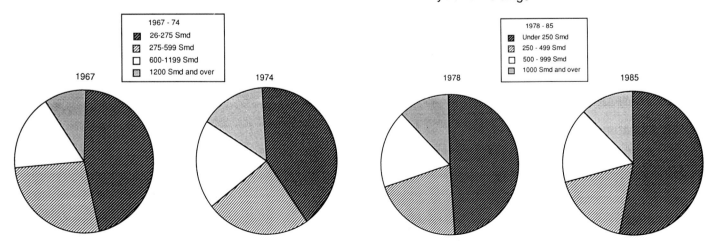

1967 — 74
▨ 26-275 Smd
▨ 275-599 Smd
☐ 600-1199 Smd
▨ 1200 Smd and over

1978 — 85
▨ Under 250 Smd
▨ 250 - 499 Smd
☐ 500 - 999 Smd
▨ 1000 Smd and over

1967 1974 1978 1985

Type of business

In terms of British Size Units, 44% of the agricultural holdings in the United Kingdom are small, 36% medium and only 20% large. The livestock farms, both hill and upland (LFA) and lowland livestock have the highest proportion of small farms while the cropping farms have the highest proportion of large farms. About 47% of dairy farms are in the medium size category. Only about 25% of the less favoured area holdings in the United Kingdom are in England. There is some evidence that part-time farming may be showing some increase.

Proportion of full-time businesses by farm type and size group 1986 (per cent)

	Dairying	Hill and upland (LFA)[1] livestock	Lowland livestock	Cropping	Total[2]
Small[3]	35.2	61.1	69.6	29.2	43.8
Medium[4]	47.0	31.5	23.5	33.2	35.9
Large[5]	17.8	7.4	6.9	37.6	20.3
All sizes[6]	100.0	100.0	100.0	100.0	100.0

[1]Less farmed area.   [2]Not including pigs and poultry and horticulture.   [3]4 to under 16 BSU.   [4]16 to under 40 BSU.   [5]40 BSU and over.   [6]4 BSU and over.
Note. The British Size Unit (BSU) measures the financial potential of the farm in terms of margins which might be expected from its crops and stock. For a detailed definition, see Appendix Table 3.12.

Part-time agricultural holdings[1] (%)

	England	Wales	Scotland	Northern Ireland	United Kingdom
1978	45	54	51	64	49
1980	46	54	53	63	50
1985	51	56	56	61	53

[1]Number of holdings needing less than 250 standard man days to operate.

Land tenure

There have been considerable changes in the proportions of land which are owner occupied and rented. In Great Britain the area which was owner occupied increased from 15% in 1887 to about 18% in 1922. Statistics based on the total land area of farms available since 1970 show that the area owner occupied has risen from 57% in 1970 to 61% in 1986. Virtually all the land is owner occupied in Northern Ireland.

Area of land by tenure Great Britain (per cent)

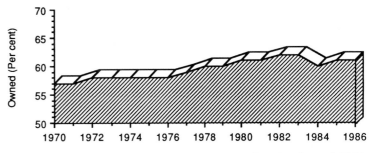

Based on Appendix Table 3.13

Land prices

The data in this section is based on figures compiled by the Oxford Institute of Agricultural Economics as the official price series for England and Wales only distinguishes between prices for land which is tenanted and land offered for sale with vacant possession.

Agricultural land prices (with vacant possession) increased continuously from the mid 1940s until 1983, the increase being particularly rapid during the 1970s. Since 1983 there has been some reduction although there were some signs of recovery in 1987. In 1986 money values, prices increased more than five-fold between 1945 and 1979, but since then there has been a sharp decline.

Agricultural land prices: England and Wales (£ per hectare)[1]

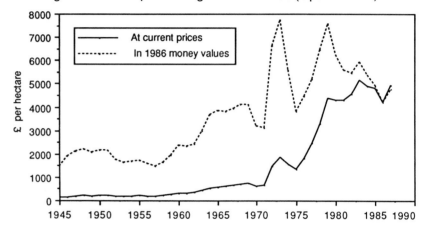

[1]With vacant possession

CHAPTER 4

Labour

One hundred years ago, the only information available about the total number of people working in British agriculture was obtained at ten-year intervals from the Population Census. It was not until 1921 that all occupiers of over one acre of agricultural land were required to state the number of workers employed on the day of the Agricultural Census. These numbers have been collected annually since 1923.

Regular full-time workers have been distinguished from part-time, seasonal and casual workers since the series began. Later, further sub-divisions were introduced to give separate figures for males and females and for hired and family workers. Farmers themselves were not included until 1970. Since 1977 spouses of farmers, partners and directors engaged in farm work have also been recorded.

The Population Census of 1851 recorded two million persons as being engaged in agriculture in Great Britain. By 1951 this figure had fallen to 1.1 million, and by 1986 to 0.6 million, reflecting one of the most profound changes which have occurred in British agriculture throughout its history.

Since the 19th century much of the work which used to be done on farms has been transferred to food manufacturing and other enterprises which are outside agriculture, and this partly accounts for the reduction in the farm labour force. However, its main cause has been the introduction of mechanical power in the fields and farmsteads.

There are fewer farmers than there were 100 years ago, but the greater part of the decline in the total labour force has been in the number of hired workers. Farmers and family workers now make up nearly two thirds of the total, after allowing for seasonal part-time help.

Since 1970 the rate of decline of the labour force has slowed down, as the substitution of machinery for labour has not persisted at its former rate. The annual decline is now only about one per cent.

The long-term decline has been due not only to the attraction of higher wages in other occupations but also to the rising wage rates secured by farm workers themselves, causing many farmers to look for ways of reducing their wage bills. Average farm wages are still well below the average earnings in other occupations, but the gap has gradually been narrowed.

Many farmers no longer employ any full-time workers. They are doing most of the work themselves with some help from the family and from casual workers at busy seasons. There has also been an increase in the use of outside firms for contract work.

The combined effect of rising wages and falling numbers of workers has meant that the total wage bill of farmers has remained fairly constant in real terms. On many farms it is the largest item in total costs.

The agricultural workforce

The number of farmers in Great Britain has fallen by about one sixth since the middle of the nineteenth century, but the number of farm workers has fallen by over 80% in the same period. Since 1970 there has been a noticeable slowing down in the rate of decline.

These figures were obtained by a counting of heads. They take no account of the extent to which some of the people concerned were employed only part-time . The proportion of these has tended to increase. At the same time, the number of holdings employing full-time workers has declined steadily while the number of family members counting as part of the workforce is showing an increase. There are other series of statistics in which an attempt is made to convert part-time farmers and workers to their equivalent full-time units (Appendix Table 4.3).

The agricultural workforce: United Kingdom ('000)

	1976	1981	1986	1987
Farmers, partners and directors				
of which full-time	219	204	197	194
part-time	80	91	94	94
Regular hired workers				
of which full-time	163	139	112	106
part-time	47	43	41	40
Regular family workers				
of which full-time	51	35	37	35
part-time	32	20	20	20
Seasonal or casual workers	83	97	97	96
Salaried managers	7	8	8	8
Total	682	637	606	593
Spouses of farmers, partners and directors		75	78	77

The agricultural workforce in Great Britain

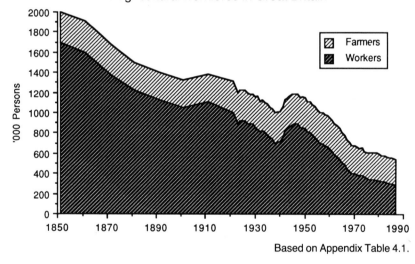

Based on Appendix Table 4.1.

Holdings by number of full-time workers: England and Wales ('000)

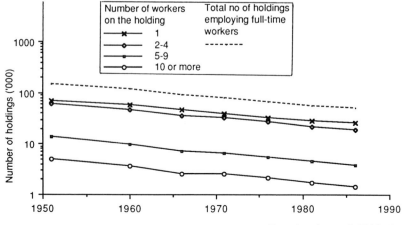

Based on Appendix Table 4.7.

Agricultural wages

The real value of the weekly earnings of farm workers has shown a strong upward trend since 1939. Earnings are now at a level about three times what they were worth in 1939. At the same time, the number of hours worked per week has fallen, so that the improvement in earnings per hour has been greater than in weekly earnings.

The figures shown for 1939 are estimates, based on the statutory minimum wage, adjusted for the change in the standard working week and allowing for 'premium' payments above the minimum wage in a proportion similar to the immediate post-war years. Studies of wage rates in the second half of the nineteenth century showed that in the United Kingdom agricultural weekly wages were generally at a level which was only about 50% of average weekly wages in industry. This disparity has been greatly reduced. By the end of World War II the ratio had reached nearly 70%. It showed a further marked improvement in the mid-1970s, and has now reached over 80%.

As will be seen in the section on incomes, there has been a sharp fall in the incomes of farmers in recent years, which is in striking contrast to the steady increase in the wages of farm workers. The income gap between farmers and their workers has been closing even more rapidly than the gap between agricultural and industrial workers.

Earnings of hired regular adult male workers

	Average earnings (£ per week)	In 1986 money values (£ per week)	Average hours worked per week	Average earnings (£ per hour)	In 1986 money values (£ per hour)
1939	2.15	46.74			
1950	5.83	63.20	51.0	0.11	1.20
1960	10.32	80.29	51.2	0.20	1.57
1970	18.61	98.26	48.3	0.39	2.03
1980	86.48	126.26	46.2	1.87	2.73
1986	140.76	140.76	46.7	3.01	3.01

Average weekly earnings of full-time men in agriculture and in all industries and services (£ per week)

	Agriculture[1]	Industry and services	Agricultural earnings as % of earnings in industry and services
1960	10.32	14.10	73
1970	18.61	26.90	69
1980	86.48	111.40	78
1985	136.09	163.60	83
1986	142.77	176.56	81

[1] In England and Wales.

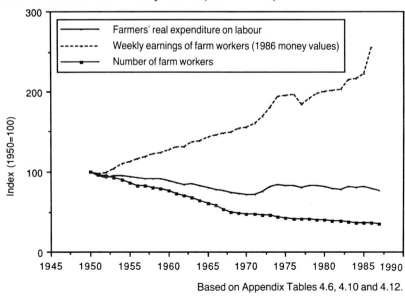

Indices of farmers' expenditure on labour; numbers and real earnings of farm workers in 1986 money values (1950 = 100)

Based on Appendix Tables 4.6, 4.10 and 4.12.

CHAPTER 5

Mechanisation

Mechanisation has been the prime cause of the decline in the number of people working in agriculture. Statistics showing the decline in the number of horses on farms and the increase in numbers of machines show this dramatically.

The number of horses used in agriculture reached a peak before the outbreak of World War I and then fell continuously from 1920 onwards. By the mid-1960s there were so few horses they were no longer recorded in the agricultural census. By 1960 the number of horses on farms used for non-agricultural purposes had exceeded those used in farming. That trend is probably continuing.

Tracing the trends in machinery numbers is complicated by the fact that there have been numerous changes in the precise definition of the different categories of machinery. Some such as binders are no longer used while other machines like complete potato harvesters have only become important since the mid-1960s or early 1970s. The situation is further complicated by the fact that there are differences in the way individual countries collect machinery statistics. At the time of writing there are no Scottish statistics after 1980.

The estimated balance sheet for British agriculture, in 1986 money values, gives some indication of the overall change in the United Kingdom's machinery inventory. Unfortunately there are no statistics prior to 1970. The asset value of machinery in 1986 money values reached a peak in 1979 but has since declined by almost a third.

Horses

The number of horses used for agricultural purposes in Great Britain reached a peak of about 1.1 million in about 1910, after which there was a steady fall as the use of tractors increased. Horses were no longer recorded as a matter of routine in the agricultural census after 1958 and by 1965 there were only 21 000 still being used for agricultural purposes.

In addition to the horses used for agricultural purposes, there were a large number of other horses on farms. Prior to 1950 these were mostly unbroken horses.

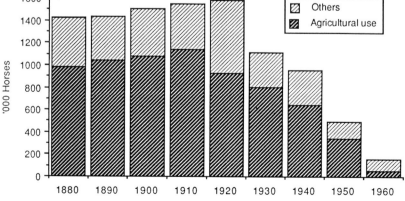

Number of horses in Great Britain ('000)

Based on Appendix Table 5.1.

Value of assets

The statistics on the asset value of farmers' machinery in real terms give some indication of the changes which have occurred in the total value of the machinery inventory. The asset value rose to a peak in 1978 after increasing by almost 40% since 1970. Since then there has been a continuous decline and by 1986 the asset value had fallen by almost 30% to well under £5000 million.

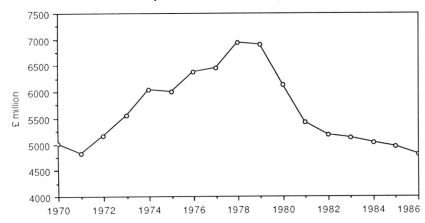

Farmers' machinery assets in 1986 money values (£ million)

Machinery

The gradual process by which agricultural machinery replaced the labour of men and horses had already begun by the first half of the 19th century, and, as with other technological developments, was greatly accelerated by two world wars. Unfortunately the beginning of these developments cannot be illustrated statistically as regular censuses of machines on farms only began in 1942.

In 1944 there were about 168 000 tractors in the United Kingdom; by 1961 there were 512 000 and since then there has been surprisingly little change. Corn drills peaked at 135 000 in 1961 and have fallen rapidly since. Combine harvesters reached a peak of 67 000 in 1966 and their numbers have also dropped. For potatoes and root crops mechanisation was long delayed and it was not until the 1960s that potato harvesters were to be found on farms in significant numbers.

The number of farms with milking machines reached a peak in the mid-1960s and then declined because of fewer milk producers. Milking machine installations have not been recorded in the census since the mid-1970s.

Estimated number of agricultural machines ('000)

	1944	1952	1961	1966	1970	1977	1980	1986
Tractors	168	387	512	517	511	519	530	532
Corn drills	94	100	135	124	132			101
Tractor ploughs		99	359	323	308	246	287	258
Combine harvesters	2	17	55	67	66	58	57	55

CHAPTER 6

Capital and investment

The Ministry of Agriculture estimates of capital formation consist of three components:

- Investment in plant, machinery, works and vehicles. These are based primarily on returns by agricultural machinery manufacturers and on expenditure on grant aid for buildings and works under various grant schemes.
- Breeding livestock capital formation is a measure of the investment or disinvestment in breeding livestock and dairy cattle.
- Stock appreciation. This measures the value of the physical increase in stocks and work in progress. This, together with stock appreciation equals the increase in the book value of stocks and work in progress.

Estimates of capital formation are made on the basis of current prices and constant prices. Estimates of capital formation at 1980 prices are available from 1975 onwards.

Gross fixed capital formation on plant machinery, buildings, works and vehicles totalled only £910 million in 1987. This was the lowest figure since 1981 and reflects the decline in the profitability of agricultural production in real terms since the early 1980s. Of the £910 million, £430 million was spent on plant and machinery, £380 million on buildings and works, and £100 million on vehicles. Gross fixed capital formation at constant 1980 prices totalled £725 million. This is the lowest level since 1975, the first year when capital formation was valued at constant 1980 prices. In 1987 there was negative capital formation for breeding livestock at both current and constant prices, as well as a reduction in the value of stocks and work in progress.

Also of interest is the 'Balance Sheet of British Agriculture' (see Appendix Table 6.4). These figures are available since 1970 and show the aggregate end-year market value of the assets and liabilities of the industry. They cover the complete range of business capital and current assets employed, together with the loans outstanding to the industry. Personal non-agricultural assets are excluded.

The total assets of agriculture increased almost continuously between 1975 and 1983, but have since fallen. Liabilities rose to a peak in 1984 and have shown relatively little change. The net worth of agriculture rose to a peak of almost £50 000 million in 1983, but has fallen by almost a fifth since then.

In real terms assets have been falling since 1979 and by 1986 the fall had amounted to 40% mainly due to the fall in land prices. Liabilities increased continuously between 1980 and 1984, but have since shown a considerable reduction. In real terms the net worth of agriculture declined by about a third between 1980 and 1986.

Plant and machinery

Gross capital formation on plant and machinery rose to a peak of £599 million in 1983 but has fallen to only £430 million in 1987. At 1980 constant prices investment was highest in 1977. In 1987, investment at £337 million was 47% less than in 1977. Investment on plant and machinery at constant prices has been declining continuously since 1983.

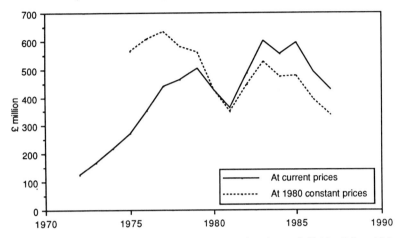

Capital formation, plant and machinery (£ million)

Based on Appendix Tables 6.2 and 6.3.

Buildings and works

Gross capital formation on buildings and works has been rising rapidly since the early 1970s, reaching a peak of £684 million in 1984. Since then there has been a sharp decline; investment totalled only £380 million in 1987.

Investment in buildings and works at constant 1980 prices also reached a peak in 1984, but fell sharply from 1985 onwards. Investment in 1987 at only £325 million was the lowest since the constant price series began in 1975.

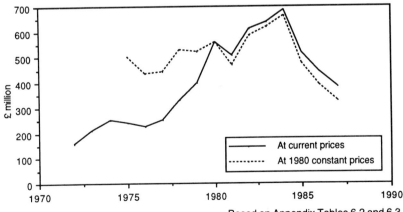

Capital formation, buildings and works (£ million)

Based on Appendix Tables 6.2 and 6.3.

Vehicles

Gross capital formation on vehicles at current prices has been increasing almost continuously since the early 1970s, peaking at £129 million in 1984. There was a reduction to £100 million in 1987.

Investment on vehicles at constant 1980 prices was at its highest level in the second half of the 1970s but has since fallen. Investment at only £63 million in 1987 was the lowest recorded since the beginning of the series in 1975, with the exception of 1980.

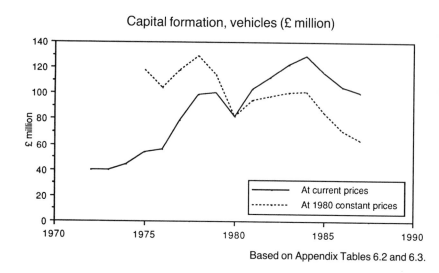

Capital formation, vehicles (£ million)

Based on Appendix Tables 6.2 and 6.3.

Balance sheet for agriculture

Agriculture's assets increased almost continuously between 1970 and 1983, primarily because of an eight-fold increase in land and building values. Other assets such as machinery, livestock, crops and stores only increased five-fold during this period. Since 1983 the total asset value has fallen by about 13% because of the fall in land values.

The high level of bank borrowing meant that total liabilities were at a peak in 1984; since then there has been some reduction.

The net worth of agriculture has fallen by 17% since 1983 and in 1986 accounted for only 2.3% of the United Kingdom's national wealth compared with 3.6% in 1983. In real terms, after allowing for inflation, the net worth of agriculture declined by almost 50% between 1979 and 1986. Asset value has fallen by 43% while liabilities have risen by 17%.

Index numbers of value of assets and liabilities in real terms (1980 = 100)[3]

	Total assets	Total liabilities	Net worth
1970	64	105	59
1971	70	100	67
1972	125	100	128
1973	126	112	127
1974	92	107	91
1975	81	90	79
1976	86	84	87
1977	98	88	99
1978	112	95	114
1979	122	104	124
1980	100	100	100
1981	91	103	90
1982	88	108	86
1983	94	117	91
1984	85	119	81
1985	74	122	69
1986[1]	70	121	64
1987[2]	68	119	62

[1]Provisional. [2]Forecast. [3]At end of December.

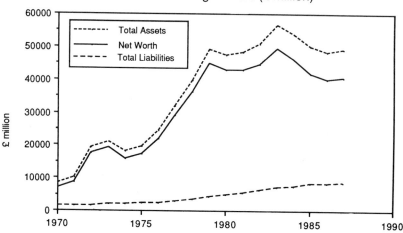

Balance sheet for agriculture (£ million)

CHAPTER 7

Output, expenses and income

Annual estimates of the total value of output from agricultural holdings are made by the Agricultural Departments. Production grants and compensation payments to farmers are added in to give estimates of total receipts from farming. Out of these receipts, farmers have to meet the cost of the inputs used in production, including purchase of feedingstuffs, fertilisers, seeds, fuel, repairs to machinery and miscellaneous expenses. The sum available to pay for labour, rent of tenanted land and interest on commercial debt (but not on debts incurred in land purchase) is net product. What remains after meeting all these outgoings is the farming income for the year.

The proportion of output which is used to pay for inputs has remained within the range of 50–55% since 1958. Before then, purchases of many of the inputs such as fertilisers and machinery were on a much smaller scale. Farmers were less dependent on the supplying industries than they are today.

Figures for input, output and income at current prices are influenced from year to year by changes in prices and quantities bought and sold. In particular, farming income is adversely affected if output prices change less favourably than input prices.

The total value of UK agricultural output has increased 40-fold in the past 50 years, but long-term comparisons are meaningless without taking into account the general rise in prices and incomes and the fall in the value of money. The figures have therefore been converted into their approximate 1986 monetary equivalents by using a general price index of goods and services.

In these 'real' terms, the value of output moved strongly upward from 1938 until 1955, as a result of favourable price movements during World War II and immediately post-war, combined with a significant expansion of the volume of output. After 1955 prices began to move against the farmer and, despite the continuing growth of output, real receipts showed little increase. There was a brief boom in 1973–74 but since then the prices of farm products have fallen behind the general rate of inflation. In 1987 the real value of gross output was less than at any time since 1953.

Various factors have contributed to an even more marked decline in the real value of the total UK farming income. Input prices have generally risen faster than output prices; depreciation of farm machinery and buildings absorbs an increasing proportion of total receipts; farm wages have risen rapidly in real terms; and farmers have had to pay higher rates of interest on a rising commercial debt.

After the spectacular but short-lived rise in farming income in 1973, the economic situation of many farm businesses has deteriorated sharply, and the figures suggest that a relapse to something like the pre-World War II situation has occurred. However, a more complete view would have to take account of farmers' wealth as distinct from income, of the reduced number of full-time farmers and of the increasing amounts of income accruing to farmers from non-farm sources.

Output and income

There have, as might be expected, been many major changes in the value of farm output and income during the past 50 years. Farming income has risen from only £67 million in 1938–39 to £1305 million in 1985–87. Gross output has increased from £321 million to £12 190 million as a result of increases in the quantities produced and higher prices.

These figures do not, however, mean a great deal given the general rise in prices and the fall in the value of money. To enable meaningful comparisons to be made, the figures have been converted into 1986 money values. On this basis gross output in real terms has risen by 72% since 1938–39 while gross inputs have increased by 116%. The net product of agriculture (which takes into account depreciation) has shown an increase of 10%. Farming income has fallen by 12% in real terms between 1938–39 and 1985–87.

Agricultural output, input and income at current prices (£ million)

Average of years	Gross output	Gross input	Gross product	Net product	Farming income
1938–39	321	137	184	174	67
1945–47	664	210	454	425	196
1955–57	1520	722	732	645	316
1965–67	2043	1059	984	845	448
1975–77	6007	3167	2839	2224	1178
1985–87	12 190	6523	5667	4212	1305

Based on Appendix Table 7.2.

Real agricultural output and income in 1986 money values (£ million)

Average of years	Gross output	Gross input	Gross product	Net product	Farming income
1938–39	7043	3006	4038	3810	1472
1945–47	8543	2698	5845	5472	2526
1955–57	12 234	6076	6159	5423	2652
1965–67	13 040	6761	6279	5390	2682
1975–77	14 665	7715	6950	5450	2886
1985–87	12 147	6502	5644	4195	1298

Based on Appendix Table 7.3.

Gross output

The volume of gross agricultural output is a measure of the total quantity of products sold from farms, excluding inter-farm sales, or used directly in farm households, adjusted for any change in stocks or work in progress. It takes no account of the purchased inputs such as feed and fertiliser which have been used in the process of production.

Gross output in 1986 money values showed no discernible trend upwards or downwards over the period 1885–1947. However, after 1947 British agriculture moved into a sustained phase of expansion of output, interrupted only by temporary setbacks which were attributable to unfavourable weather.

The annual rate of this expansion (from 1946–48 av. to 1984–86 av.) was 2.7%, equivalent to a doubling of output every 26 years. This is much faster than the increase in internal demand for agricultural products, with the result that the UK has become more self-sufficient in these products. Imports have diminished and exports increased.

The increase in output has occurred during a period in which the area of land being used for agricultural production has been reduced. This means that productivity per hectare has increased, due in part to higher yields of crops and in part to more intensive systems of livestock production.

Volume of gross output of UK agriculture (volume index 1970 = 100)

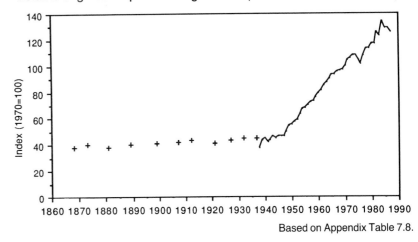

Based on Appendix Table 7.8.

Prices and expenditure

Agricultural product prices have increased four fold during the past 20 years. In real terms product prices increased by 18% between 1972 and 1976; since then there has been a 40% reduction.

The value of gross output of agriculture rose to a peak in real terms in 1973 when it exceeded pre-war gross output by almost 135%. Since then there has been a reduction due to the decline in real prices and in spite of a major further rise in agricultural production.

Prices of agricultural products

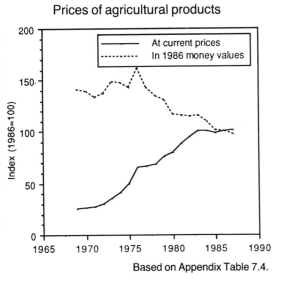

Based on Appendix Table 7.4.

Value of gross output (1986 money values)

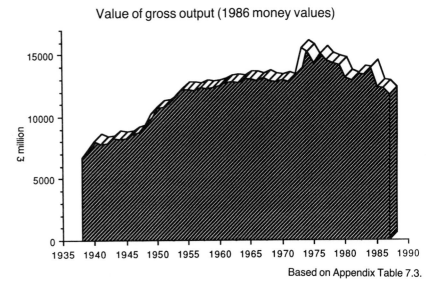

Based on Appendix Table 7.3.

Income

Farming incomes rose in real terms during World War II and during the period of post-war controls which followed. They reached a peak in 1949. There were then considerable annual variations until 1973 when farming incomes rose sharply, partly as a result of UK entry into the EC. Since then they have fallen steeply.

Most types of expenditure have tended to fall in real terms since about 1974, but the reduction has not been sufficient to offset the fall in gross output. Farm incomes have therefore declined sharply in real terms compared with the mid 1970s; in 1985–87 they amounted to only 44% of the 1974–76 level.

Output, expenses and income from farming (1986 money values)

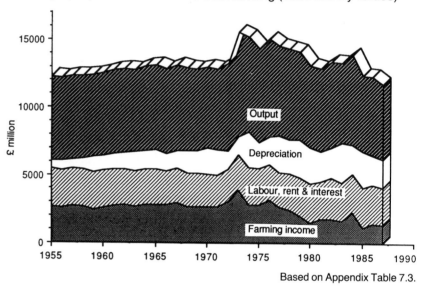

Based on Appendix Table 7.3.

Farming income in real terms (1986 money values)

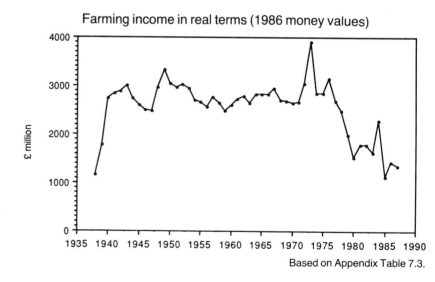

Based on Appendix Table 7.3.

CHAPTER 8

Public expenditure on agriculture

Estimating public expenditure on agriculture is complex and sometimes contentious. This section is based on the tables shown in the Annual Review of Agriculture White Papers and therefore excludes expenditure on the control of pests and diseases research, advice and education. It also excludes expenditure on agriculture in Northern Ireland except for that relating to the Milk Outgoers' Scheme. It does, however, include some expenditure which benefits consumers and trade interests rather than producers.

The changes which have occurred in the methods of supporting agriculture since this country joined the European Community have complicated the estimation of support costs. Prior to the United Kingdom's adoption of the Common Agricultural Policy (CAP), the market prices of agricultural products were mostly dictated by the prices on the world market. If the guaranteed price was above this level, the additional cost was paid by the taxpayer and was fairly easy to quantify.

Since the adoption of the CAP the system has changed. Market prices are often above world prices because of supply restrictions and import taxes. Estimating the benefit to farmers of import controls, support buying and export restitution payments is therefore problematic.

The figures of market regulation under the CAP (from about 1973–74 onwards for most commodities) are made up of several elements and include refunds on trade within the Community, import and export refunds on third country trade, the Beef and Sheep Variable Premium Schemes (net of claw back for sheepmeat and charges on beef exported and sold into intervention), aid for private storage and animal feed, certain other marketing and production subsidies and the cost of purchasing commodities into intervention less proceeds from sales.

The figures are also net of other receipts treated as negative expenditure, i.e. monetary compensatory amounts levied on intra-Community trade (in the case of pigmeat these sometimes exceed expenditure), the coresponsibility and supplementary levies on milk producers and the coresponsibility levy on cereals. Receipts from levies on the production and storage of sugar and isoglucose and on third country exports, which are regarded as the Community's own resources, are excluded. The figures include the EC butter subsidy, which ended in May 1985, and the United Kingdom share of the EC School Milk Subsidy Scheme.

Payments for wool and potatoes relate partly to the clip or crop year indicated and partly to preceding years. The negative figures for wool reflect the stabilisation arrangements with the British Wool Marketing Board whereby advance payments by the exchequer are repayable from later surpluses when auction prices are above the guaranteed price.

The additional assistance available to farmers in special areas under the Agriculture and Horticulture Development Scheme, the Northern Ireland Agriculture Development Programme, the Agriculture and Horticulture Grant Scheme, and the EC and National Agriculture Improvement Schemes, have been included under 'Others' in Appendix Table 8.1.

Apart from a temporary reduction in 1986–87, public expenditure on agriculture has risen sharply since 1980–81. This is due almost entirely to increased expenditure on market regulation and price guarantees, particularly cereals, beef and veal and milk products. Support for capital and other improvements and for agriculture in special areas has changed much less. In 1987–88, 60% of the expenditure was from the European Agricultural Guidance and Guarantee Fund and 40% from national funds.

Public expenditure

Public expenditure on agriculture has risen sharply since the beginning of the 1980s, reaching a record level of £2162 million in 1985–86, because of the unusually high level of cereal support costs. Expenditure on beef and veal and milk products was also at a high level. There was no expenditure on oilseeds until 1976–77, since when, apart from a sharp reduction in 1984–85, it has increased continuously.

The expenditure figures in 1986 money values are also of interest. Public expenditure on agriculture was high from the mid-1950s to the mid-1960s when producers were being encouraged to increase production after the end of food rationing. Expenditure then declined and remained at a relatively low level until 1978, the end of the transitional period which the United Kingdom was allowed in order to adapt to the CAP. Since then expenditure has risen sharply as production has increased, though it declined again in 1986–87.

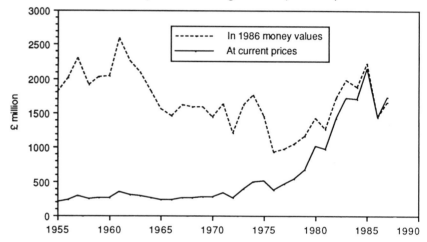

Public expenditure on agriculture (£ million)

Market regulation and price guarantees

Most of the rise in public expenditure on agriculture since the beginning of the 1980s has resulted from increased expenditure on market regulation and price guarantees. This type of expenditure rose to a peak of £1667 million in 1985–86, 162% more than in 1980–81.

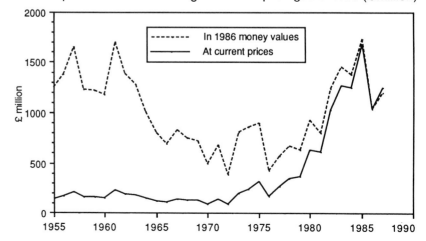

Public expenditure on market regulation and price guarantees (£ million)

In real terms public expenditure on price guarantees was also high from the mid-1950s to the mid-1960s as farmers were encouraged to increase production. Betwen 1980–81 and 1985–86, it increased by 87% in real terms.

Expenditure on market regulation and price guarantees has declined in both actual and real terms since 1985–86.

Cereals

Public expenditure on cereals tends to show considerable annual fluctuations because of seasonal conditions and variations in the world grain market.

In real terms, support levels were high from the mid-1950s to the mid-1960s as farmers were encouraged to produce more grain. They were at relatively low levels in the 1970s, particularly in the period 1976–79, when world market prices were firm because of shortfalls in production in North America and Europe.

Public expenditure on cereals rose to a record level both in actual and real terms in 1985–86. Since then there has been another reduction as attempts were made to cut back intervention, but in spite of this, expenditure rose again in 1987–88.

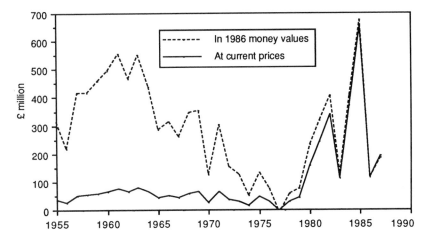

Public expenditure on cereals (£ million)

Milk products

Public expenditure on milk products rose sharply between 1977–78 and 1983–84 to a peak of £557 million. Since then it has fallen and expenditure in 1987–88 is estimated at £282 million.

In real terms public expenditure on milk products has fallen by 58% since the peak level in 1983–84.

Public expenditure on milk products (£ million)

	1972 –73	1975 –76	1980 –81	1981 –82	1982 –83	1983 –84	1984 –85	1985 –86	1986 –87	1987 –88[1]
At current prices	30.9	61.8	187.0	168.8	342.5	556.6	250.6	353.7	299.6	282.1
In 1986 money values	139.1	176.7	273.0	221.1	411.0	640.1	275.6	364.3	299.6	270.5

[1]Forecast.   Based on Appendix Table 8.2.

Beef and veal

Public expenditure on beef and veal has been high since 1983–84, largely because so many dairy cows have been culled in an attempt to cut back milk production, and this has depressed the overall beef market. Prices were also affected by weak demand, partly because of competition from other cheaper meats.

In real terms expenditure on beef was high in 1975–76 when prices were low due to production exceeding 1.2 million tonnes, compared with an annual average production of about 950 000 tonnes during the period 1970–74.

Expenditure has fallen in both actual and real terms since 1985–86.

Expenditure on beef and veal (£ million)

	1955 –56	1960 –61	1972 –73	1975 –76	1980 –81	1981 –82	1982 –83	1983 –84	1984 –85	1985 –86	1986 –87	1987 –88[1]
At current prices	0.4	12.3	1.0	113.0	131.6	41.8	93.8	263.9	343.2	328.3	229.7	243.0
In 1986 money values	3.5	95.7	4.5	323.2	192.1	54.8	112.6	303.4	377.5	338.1	229.7	233.0

[1] Forecast.

Sheepmeat

Public expenditure on sheepmeat, which had been relatively low during most of the 1970s, increased sharply in 1980–81 after the introduction of the CAP regulation for sheepmeat in October 1980. Expenditure rose to £158 million in 1983–84 because of a weak market. Since then there has been some reduction.

In real terms public expenditure was also at a peak in 1983–84.

Public expenditure on sheepmeat (£ million)

	1955 –56	1960 –61	1972 –73	1975 –76	1980 –81	1981 –82	1982 –83	1983 –84	1984 –85	1985 –86	1986 –87	1987 –88[1]
At current prices	5.2	13.9	1.9	7.5	75.2	72.2	126.1	158.3	113.3	110.0	102.3	124.7
In 1986 money values	45.5	108.1	8.6	21.5	109.8	94.6	151.3	182.0	124.3	113.3	102.3	119.6

[1] Forecast.

Oilseeds

The rapid increase since the mid-1970s in the production of oilseed rape has resulted in a major rise in public expenditure. Expenditure has risen from £5.2 million in 1976–77 to a forecast of £196 million in 1987–88. In real terms expenditure has risen from £13 million in 1976–77 to an expected £188 million in 1987–88. The rapid expansion in the area planted is shown in Chapter 11, *Oilseed rape*.

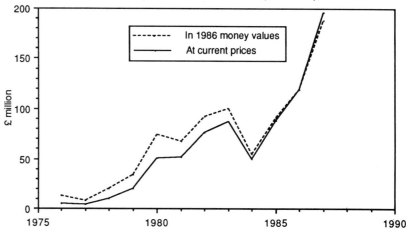

Public expenditure in oilseeds (£ million)

CHAPTER 9

Food consumption and expenditure

Although consumers' total expenditure has risen in both actual and real terms, in relation to it, food expenditure has become relatively less important in the UK. Consumers as they become wealthier will usually purchase more or better quality food, but an increasing proportion of their expenditure will be used for items other than food, such as housing, cars and videos.

On average, about 23% of consumers' total expenditure went on food in the early 1960s; now it has fallen to about 13%. Total expenditure on food has risen continuously since the abolition of rationing in 1954 but, after allowing for inflation, it has fallen since the mid-1970s.

The Ministry of Agriculture's National Food Survey, which only relates to household food consumption, shows that there have been major changes in the national diet. Bread consumption has fallen almost continuously since World War II. Less white bread is being eaten compared with brown, whole wheat and wholemeal.

Less carcase meat is being eaten, mainly due to lower consumption of imported lamb. However, more pork is being used in the household. The consumption of other meat and meat products, particularly poultry meat, has risen since the mid-1960s but bacon consumption has fallen.

Milk consumption has been falling continuously since the mid-1960s, but cheese has become more popular. The consumption of oils and fats has fallen since 1980: the decline in the use of butter has not been offset by the increase in margarine. Sugar consumption has fallen continuously since the early 1960s.

There has been a reduction in the consumption of fresh green vegetables since the early 1960s but more of other fresh vegetables are being eaten and there has been a dramatic rise in processed (primarily frozen) vegetables. Fresh fruit has shown little change but there has been a rapid rise in the use of fruit juice.

Tea consumption continues to fall and instant coffee has shown little change since 1980. The government's Family Expenditure Survey shows a sharp rise in soft drink purchases which now account for about 4% of expenditure on food and beverages.

The number of meals taken outside the home increased during the 1970s, but since then there has been little change. Fewer meals are eaten at school and at places of work, but this appears to have been offset by an increase in the number of meals consumed at restaurants and snack bars.

Most of the changes which have occurred in the national diet are almost certainly due to changes in lifestyle and taste. Fewer people are now engaged in heavy manual work; the traditional cooked breakfast is rapidly disappearing; consumers, particularly younger housewives, are increasingly relying on snacks or made up, often foreign, dishes rather than cooking traditional meals. The switch to supermarket shopping has also had a major impact on consumer behaviour.

Prices, or more importantly, changes in relative prices, have also influenced consumption levels. Pork, eggs and margarine have shown the smallest price rises since 1970. Changes in the prices of foods are, of course, not only due to changes in raw material cost; there may also be quality changes, more packaging and increased marketing costs.

Expenditure

Household expenditure on food has been rising continuously since the end of World War II and in 1986 totalled £29 756 million, accounting for 12.7% of total consumers' expenditure. However, as a proportion of total spending, the amount spent on food has fallen almost continuously as consumers have spent more on items other than food.

In real terms expenditure on food reached a peak in 1955, the year after the end of rationing. It was high during most of the 1970s, but there was some reduction during the early 1980s because of the recession. There was some recovery in 1986. The pattern of expenditure on individual foods and beverages in 1938 was probably not dissimilar to that of 1946 but slightly more was spent on meat, cheese and eggs, oils and fats, fruit, sugar and preserves. Little was spent on soft drinks; tea was of some importance and expenditure on coffee very modest. A lower proportion was probably spent on bread and cereals, milk and vegetables and potatoes.

Since World War II, the proportion spent on bread and cereals has shown surprisingly little change, accounting for about 14% of total expenditure on food and beverages. The proportion spent on meat and bacon rose to a peak of 28.3% in 1980, but fell to 25.3% in 1986; while fish showed an increase to 3.7%.

Since 1980 a smaller proportion has been spent on dairy products and oils and fats, but more on vegetables; in 1986 12.2% of the food and beverage total was spent on vegetables and potatoes. The proportion spent on soft drinks rose to 4.3% in 1986.

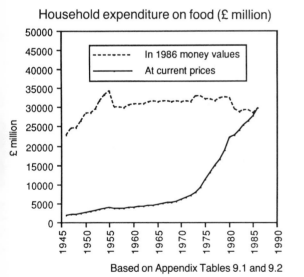

Household expenditure on food (£ million)

In 1986 money values
At current prices

Based on Appendix Tables 9.1 and 9.2

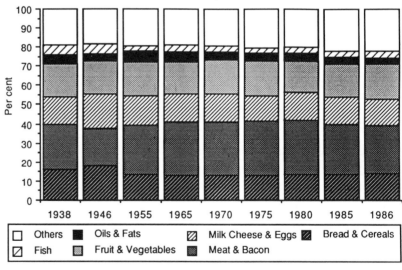

Proportion of food expenditure spent on individual foods and beverages at current prices

	Others		Oils & Fats		Milk Cheese & Eggs		Bread & Cereals
	Fish		Fruit & Vegetables		Meat & Bacon		

Based on Appendix Table 9.3

Consumption

There have been considerable changes in household food and beverage consumption during the past 30 years. Less is eaten of most types of food, the reductions in butter, sugar and eggs being particularly marked. More non-carcase meat (including poultry), cheese, margarine, breakfast cereals and frozen vegetables are being eaten. Less tea is being drunk, but fruit juice has become very popular.

Changes in household food consumption

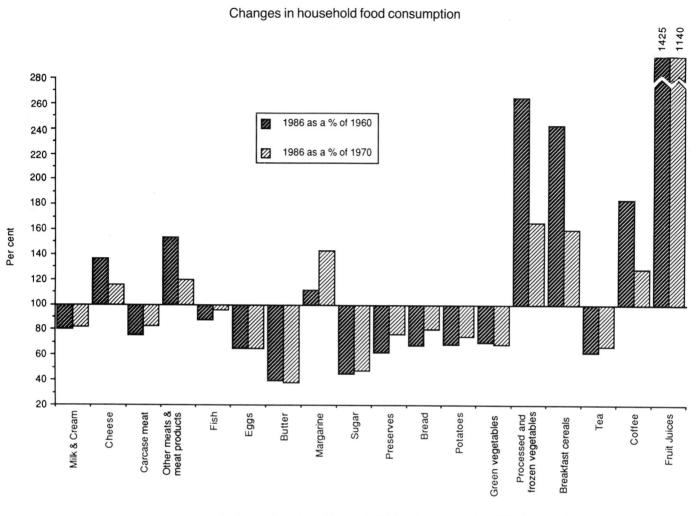

Indices of per head household food consumption (1986 = 100)

	1950	1955	1960	1965	1970	1975	1980	1985	1986
Milk and cream	125.5	122.7	123.9	125.1	122.4	123.4	110.4	99.5	100.0
Cheese	61.1	68.0	73.1	76.9	86.3	91.1	93.5	94.0	100.0
Carcase meat	108.7	137.7	131.3	126.7	119.9	115.6	126.6	99.8	100.0
Other meats and meat products	54.3	56.8	65.0	73.1	83.0	76.6	82.3	82.7	100.0
Fish	128.3	115.3	113.6	112.0	103.7	86.4	93.0	95.0	100.0
Eggs	116.3	139.2	154.2	158.8	154.8	137.5	122.6	109.7	100.0
Butter	200.9	196.9	250.2	268.7	263.9	248.0	178.4	124.7	100.0
Margarine	96.1	114.1	89.3	74.1	69.8	63.4	93.4	91.7	100.0
Sugar	126.0	219.4	220.9	218.4	210.7	140.4	138.9	104.6	100.0
Preserves	318.2	206.6	162.1	151.0	129.8	122.7	103.5	94.4	100.0
Fresh potatoes	160.1	154.5	144.6	137.4	133.7	113.3	105.7	105.7	100.0
Fresh green vegetables	124.3	133.1	142.3	137.0	130.1	104.2	111.8	88.0	100.0
Other fresh vegetables	90.8	87.0	89.5	85.2	82.9	81.9	94.1	93.3	100.0
Fresh fruit	70.9	101.6	90.6	92.4	94.1	86.1	102.4	91.1	100.0
Fruit juices	3.7	4.2	7.0	9.8	8.8	19.4	45.0	76.2	100.0
Bread	180.3	179.1	147.1	131.9	123.8	109.4	101.1	100.6	100.0
Flour	175.1	207.0	163.3	147.1	137.2	124.6	137.0	97.8	100.0
Breakfast cereals	32.0	38.6	41.1	45.0	62.6	69.6	79.9	92.2	100.0
Tea	124.1	160.3	160.9	150.0	148.9	125.3	117.8	100.0	100.0
Coffee	29.2	50.0	54.2	61.1	77.8	90.3	86.1	94.4	100.0

Based on Appendix Table 9.5

Dietary habits are the most important factor in determining consumer behaviour, but price changes also play an important role. The sharp fall in mutton and lamb consumption since the mid 1950s is due not only to the desire to eat leaner meat, but also to the rise in prices.

Of the carcase meats, pork has risen least in price since 1956, and this has resulted in a 92% increase in fresh pork consumption. Pork has also become much leaner. Poultry meat consumption has increased enormously while the price rise has been modest.

The decline in butter consumption, though primarily due to concern about cholesterol levels, is also a result of the sharp rise in price relative to margarine.

Changes in price and per head household consumption

	Price indices						% change in consumption
	1956	1966	1970	1975	1980	1986	1986/1956
Beef and veal	100	152	185	344	661	902	−34
Mutton and lamb	100	131	156	314	591	813	−58
Pork	100	121	149	291	473	630	+92
Poultry meat	100	70	70	132	249	346	+1340
Bacon and ham uncooked	100	111	132	297	482	626	−28
Fish (white)	100	156	185	407	659	1102	−16
Butter	100	100	100	161	408	521	−52
Margarine	100	113	128	265	383	467	−8

Source. Based on MAFF *Household Food Consumption and Expenditure Statistics.*

Relative prices also play an important role in determining the pattern of consumption. Pork and poultry meat have both become relatively much less expensive than beef. Household poultry meat consumption has more than doubled since 1965 while pork has risen by 30%, beef and veal consumption has fallen by 19%.

Butter consumption has fallen by 63% since 1965 while margarine has risen by 35%.

Changes in relative prices and per head household consumption

	1965	1975	1980	1985	1986	% change in consumption 1986/1965
Beef and veal	100	100	100	100	100	−19
Mutton and lamb	76	79	78	77	78	−19
Pork	83	90	76	75	74	+30
Poultry meat	66	53	52	51	53	+104
Bacon and ham, uncooked	82	99	84	80	79	−32
Fish (white)	68	78	65	76	80	−11
Butter	100	100	100	100	100	−63
Margarine	55	85	49	56	46	+35

Source. Based on MAFF *Household Food Consumption and Expenditure Statistics.*

CHAPTER 10

Cereals

Cereal production has risen dramatically since the mid-1970s. The value of output rose to a peak of £2420 million in 1984 but has fallen since then, due in part to lower levels of production as well as reduced prices. Output in 1987 is forecast to be worth £1927 million, accounting for 61% of the value of all farm crops.

Historically, the UK has been a major producer of cereals; in 1866 there were about 3.4 million hectares planted to cereals in Great Britain. The area fell sharply between the late 1870s and the outbreak of World War I due to the collapse of cereal prices. There was some recovery during World War I, but the area declined still further during the 1930s. Producers were encouraged to expand production during World War II but the area sown to cereals again declined in the 1950s. By 1968 the total cereals area had recovered to 3.8 million hectares through a sharp rise in the area sown to barley.

During the past 20 years there has been little change in the area sown to cereals, the total ranging between 3.8 and 4 million hectares. The area sown to oats has fallen continuously since World War II, partly due to the almost complete disappearance of the horse as a draught animal.

Virtually all of the United Kingdom wheat is produced in England (about 94% in 1986). Barley production is more widespread. In 1986, 75% of the total was produced in England, 21% in Scotland and 2% each in Wales and Northern Ireland.

The number of holdings growing cereals in the United Kingdom has fallen sharply during the past 20 years while the average area of cereals per holding has almost doubled. In England and Wales there has been a continuous fall in the number of holdings growing barley during the past decade but those with wheat have been increasing since 1981.

Although there has been little change in the area sown to cereals during the past 20 years, total production has risen dramatically. Wheat production has risen by almost 250% since 1966 and barley by 6%, but oats have fallen from 1.1 million tonnes in 1966 to only 436 000 tonnes in 1987.

The increase in cereal production is due primarily to improved yields brought about by the development of more productive varieties and to improved methods of cultivation, including a switch from spring to winter sowing. The shift to wheat from barley and the cut back in oats has, however, contributed to the increase in total cereals production as wheat tends to have the highest yield.

There has also been a major change in international trading. Since the early 1980s the United Kingdom has become a net exporter of both wheat and barley, whereas in former times it was a net importer.

There have also been changes in the way cereals are used. In 1977 only 42% of the wheat used for milling was home grown; by 1986 this had risen to 64%. Much less Canadian hard wheat is now used for bread making; only 474 000 tonnes were imported in 1986 compared with 1.5 million tonnes in 1980. There has been a sharp rise in the quantity of wheat used for animal feed, increasing from about 1.4 million tonnes in the early 1950s to about 6.4 million tonnes in 1986.

The quantity of barley used for malting, flaking and roasting has remained stable at about 1.6 million tonnes in recent years. Its use as animal feed has fallen in favour of wheat and imported cereal substitutes.

Cereal prices have risen sharply since the mid-1970s, but prices have weakened slightly since 1984 as the EC has attempted to contain the over-production of cereals. After allowing for inflation, wheat prices have fallen by over one third between 1980 and 1987; the reduction in the real price of barley has been slightly less marked.

Area grown

In 1866 there were 3.4 million hectares of cereals in Great Britain, but that level was not reached again until the mid-1960s. There has been little change in total United Kingdom area during the past 20 years. This, however, hides the fact that there has been a switch from barley to wheat and that the area of oats has fallen to a negligible level.

Wheat rose from 1.1 million hectares in 1973 to 2 million hectares in 1987, while the area of barley fell from 2.3 million hectares in 1973 to 1.8 million in 1987. Oats has fallen from a peak of 1.7 million hectares in 1942 to only 99 000 hectares in 1987. The switch from barley to wheat is primarily due to the potentially greater productivity of wheat. More rapid harvesting and autumn cultivation means that more cereals can be planted in the autumn; winter wheat has also become the farmer's first choice because of its higher yielding varieties compared with barley.

Area of cereals (million hectares)

	1866[1]	1900[1]	1910[1]	1920[1]	1930	1940	1950	1960	1970	1980	1985	1986	1987
Wheat	1.4	0.7	0.7	0.8	0.6	0.7	1.0	0.9	1.0	1.4	1.9	2.0	2.0
Barley	0.9	0.8	0.7	0.7	0.5	0.5	0.7	1.4	2.3	2.3	2.0	1.9	1.8
Oats	1.1	1.2	1.2	1.3	1.2	1.4	1.3	0.8	0.4	0.1	0.1	0.1	0.1
Total[2]	3.4	3.0	2.9	3.1	2.3	2.9	3.3	3.1	3.7	3.9	4.0	4.0	3.9

[1]Great Britain only.   [2]Including other cereals.

Based on Appendix Tables 10.2, 10.3, 10.4 and 10.5.

Holdings

The number of holdings with cereals has almost halved during the past 20 years while the average area of cereals per holding has virtually doubled. About three quarters of the total cereal area in 1987 was on holdings with more than 50 hectares of cereals. About two thirds of the English cereals area is in the East Midlands, East Anglia and the South East of England.

Number of holdings with cereals ('000)

Hectares of cereals	1967[1]	1972[1]	1975	1980	1985[2]	1987[2]
0.1–19.9	87.6	58.4	77.6	60.9	49.8	44.7
20–49.9	57.4	46.8	22.7	22.2	21.5	21.1
50 and over	27.0	26.7	21.0	23.0	24.0	23.8
Total	172.0	131.9	121.3	106.1	95.3	89.7
Average area	22.2	28.8	30.1	37.0	42.1	43.9
% of total cereals area on holdings with 50 ha and over				65.9	70.8	73.6	73.7

[1]Size groups in 1967 and 1972: 0.1 ha to 8.0 ha; 8.1 ha to 40.4 ha; 40.5 ha and over.   [2]Provisional.

Yields

Cereal yields per hectare showed relatively little change between the 1880s and pre-World War II.

The development of new varieties of cereals and changes in methods of cultivation have resulted in spectacular increases in cereal yields since World War II. Average wheat yields have risen from 2.81 tonnes per hectare in 1950–54 to over 6.7 tonnes in 1983–87, and there have been major increases in other cereal yields.

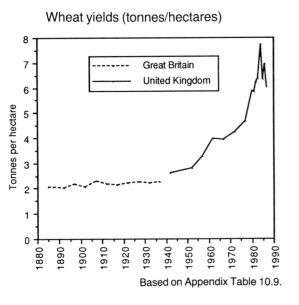

Wheat yields (tonnes/hectares)

Based on Appendix Table 10.9.

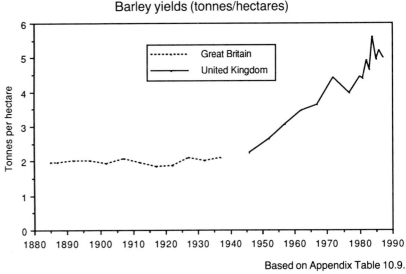

Barley yields (tonnes/hectares)

Based on Appendix Table 10.9.

Production

Wheat production has increased dramatically and in a record year, 1984, amounted to 14.9 million tonnes compared with only 2.2 million tonnes in 1885 and 2.6 million tonnes in 1950. Barley production has also risen sharply, but oats production, which at the beginning of the 20th century was the most important cereal, has fallen to a negligible level. Wheat production in 1987 accounted for 55% of total cereal production compared with only 33% in 1950.

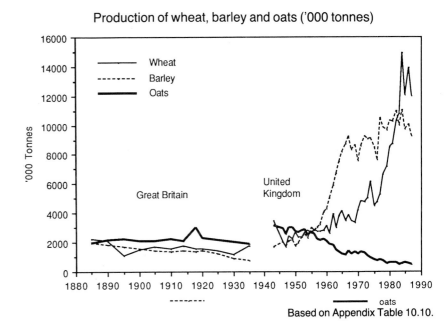

Production of wheat, barley and oats ('000 tonnes)

Based on Appendix Table 10.10.

Area, yield and production

The total area of cereals has risen by only 6% between 1965–1969 and 1985–1987, but total cereal production has increased by 67%. Yields have, on average, risen by over 55%. The spectacular increase in cereal production is therefore primarily due to increased yields brought about by the development of more productive varieties together with improved methods of cultivation, including the switch from spring sowing to higher yielding winter sowing. This has occurred in spite of the substantial fall in real cereal prices since the mid-1970s.

Cereal area, yield and production

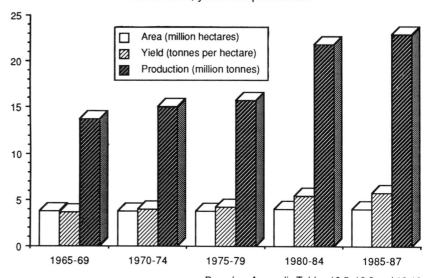

Based on Appendix Tables 10.5, 10.9 and 10.10.

Wheat supplies

Domestic production of wheat has increased from 1.5 million tonnes in 1937–38 to 12.0 million tonnes in 1987, and wheat imports have dropped from about 5 million tonnes pre-World War II to only 1.5 million tonnes in 1987. The United Kingdom has itself become a major exporter of wheat; in 1987 self-sufficiency increased to 131% in marked contrast to the 24% or so pre-World War II.

Wheat supplies ('000 tonnes)

	1937–38	1942–43	1951–52 to 1955–56	1970	1975	1980	1985	1986	1987[1]
Production	1533	2608	2575	4236	4488	8472	12046	13911	12011
Imports	4917	3298	4793	5352	3634	2256	1614	1707	1495
Exports	–	–	26	30	252	1055	1890	3990	4354
New supplies	6450	5906	7342	9557	7870	9633	11770	11628	9152
Production as % of new supplies	24	44	35	44	57	88	102	120	131

[1]Forecast.

Based on Appendix Table 10.15.

Disposal of wheat

The quantity of wheat used for milling has fallen since the 1950s but has remained virtually stable, at about 4.7 to 5.1 million tonnes since the beginning of the 1970s. Both the quantity and proportion used for animal feed has, however, risen dramatically, from less than 20% in the 1950s to over 50% in 1986. In 1986 more wheat (6.4 million tonnes) was used as animal feed than barley (4.7 million tonnes).

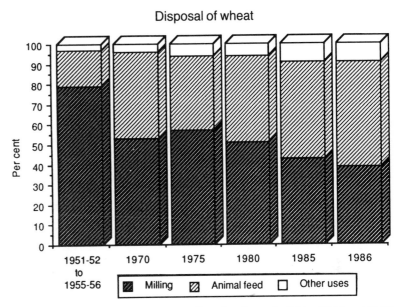

Disposal of wheat

Based on Appendix Tables 10.15 and 10.16.

Barley supplies

There has been a dramatic increase in domestic barley production while imports have fallen sharply. Barley production has increased from 669 000 tonnes pre-World War II to over 11 million tonnes in 1984 (a record year). Imports declined from over a million tonnes to about 175 000 tonnes during this period. The United Kingdom has also become a major exporter of barley: exports rose to over three million tonnes in 1987; there were no exports pre-war. Self-sufficiency increased to 146% in 1987 compared with 40% pre-war.

Barley supplies ('000 tonnes)

	1937–1938	1943–1944	1955–1956	1970	1975	1980	1985	1986	1987[1]
Production	669	1671	3011	7530	8513	10325	9740	10014	9219
Imports	1004	–	664	1050	502	207	198	280	175
Exports	–	–	205	171	1068	1639	3014	4111	3091
New supplies	1673	1671	3470	8409	7947	8839	6924	6183	6303
Production as % of new supplies	40	100	87	90	107	116	141	162	146

[1] Forecast.

Based on Appendix Tables 10.17 and 10.18.

Household consumption

The consumption of the majority of cereal products has fallen in recent years. Bread consumption was at a high level during and after World War II (it was not rationed except for a relatively brief period after the war). However, by 1986 it had fallen to only 31 ounces compared with over 60 ounces during the war and 38 ounces in 1970.

Bun and cake consumption was also at a high level during the war but has fallen sharply, while biscuits have shown relatively little change during the past 30 years. The consumption of breakfast cereals has increased continuously since World War II. That of oatmeal and oats products fell until about 1970 but has since recovered.

Household consumption of cereal products (ounces per head per week[1])

	Bread	Buns etc	Cakes, pastries	Biscuits	Breakfast cereals	Oatmeal and oat products
1942	60.60	7.00[2]		2.60	0.80	1.70
1950	55.56	3.08	3.61	3.68	1.40	1.32
1955	55.13	1.44	4.12	5.12	1.69	1.19
1960	45.44	1.49	4.82	5.67	1.80	0.94
1965	40.60	1.88	4.85	5.83	1.97	0.99
1970	38.11	1.21	4.47	5.76	2.74	0.50
1975	33.67	1.12	3.12	5.59	3.05	0.50
1980	31.12	0.96	2.77	5.40	3.50	0.42
1985	30.99	1.01	2.48	5.22	4.04	0.49
1986	30.75	1.05	2.55	5.21	4.37	0.55
1987	30.60					

[1]National Food Survey statistics are given as ounces, not grams.   [2]Includes cakes and pastries.
Source. MAFF: *Household Food Consumption and Expenditure*

Cereal prices

Cereal prices, which had been relatively high in 1870, fell almost continuously until World War I. There was again a sharp decline until the outbreak of World War II when wheat prices were only slightly higher than they had been in 1900. Prices began to rise rapidly after entry into the EC but, after allowing for inflation, all cereal prices are much lower today than they were in 1950. Wheat prices declined by 29% in real terms between 1980 and 1987 while barley prices were 23% less. There has been a tendency in all major countries in the world for production to run ahead of market demand.

Cereal prices excluding acreage and deficiency payments (£ per tonne)[1]

	Wheat		Barley		Oats	
	At current prices	In 1986 money values	At current prices	In 1986 money values	At current prices	In 1986 money values
1780	8.92		4.98			
1850	9.55		6.71			
1870	11.07		9.86			
1900	6.15	247.5	6.89	277.3	6.23	250.8
1910	7.30	264.4	6.40	231.8	6.15	222.8
1920	18.54	258.2	24.61	342.8	20.09	279.8
1938	6.64	147.2	10.10	222.0	7.46	165.4
1942	15.67	222.7	44.95	638.9	14.68	208.7
1950	25.43	275.6	27.48	297.8	21.24	230.2
1960	21.00	163.4	20.91	162.6	22.14	172.2
1970	27.10	143.0	28.41	150.0	24.68	130.0
1980	104.98	153.6	95.50	139.7	97.00	141.9
1985	112.20	116.0	106.02	109.6	92.95	96.1
1986	112.70	112.7	111.30	111.3	114.10	114.1
1987	113.90	109.2	111.60	107.0	129.13	123.8

[1]England and Wales.   Based on Appendix Table 10.31.

CHAPTER 11

Oilseed rape

Oilseed rape is not a traditional crop. Production in significant quantities began only in the early 1970s, mainly as a break crop in the cereals rotation. The value of output has risen from less than £1 million in 1972 to £291 million in 1987, rapid expansion occurring since entry into the European Community.

Although the EC regime for oilseed rape provides for a target price with the possibility of intervention, such purchases have been negligible. Of more importance is the crushing subsidy which is paid on Community-produced seed processed in the EC. The level of aid is variable and is the difference between the fixed market price and the fluctuating world price.

As is the case for many other commodities, the EC has developed a surplus of oilseed rape to which the United Kingdom is a contributor. Efforts are being made to contain EC support expenditure and it has recently been agreed that a 'stabiliser' should be introduced which would link the level of payments to the quantity produced, thus restricting the total level of support.

Imports of rape seed meal for inclusion in concentrate feeds have also risen sharply from only 30 000 tonnes in 1980 to 220 000 tonnes in 1986.

Area, yield and production

The area of oilseed rape has shown a sharp increase. Very little was grown until the second half of the 1970s, but since then there has been a remarkable rise to almost 390 000 hectares in 1987.

Yields have increased from about 1.8 tonnes per hectare in 1968–70 to almost 3.4 tonnes in 1987. There are, however, considerable annual variations depending on seasonal conditions.

Production of oilseed rape has risen from a negligible quantity in the 1970s to 1.3 million tonnes in 1987.

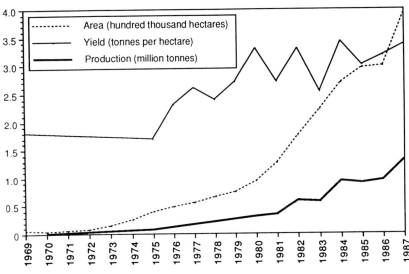

Area, yield and production of oilseed rape

Based on Appendix Tables 11.2, 11.4, 11.5.

Holdings

Although the total area of oilseed rape grown has risen rapidly there are still only a relatively small number of holdings with oilseed rape. Nevertheless, the number of holdings has risen from 3500 in 1979 to 15 600 in 1987. About 32% of total oilseed rape area is on holdings with 50 hectares or more of oilseed rape. In 1986 there were 11 508 holdings growing oilseed rape in England and Wales and 1455 holdings in Scotland.

Number of holdings with oilseed rape ('000)

Hectares of oilseed rape	1979	1983	1985[1]	1987[1]
0.1–19.9	2.1	5.2	7.5	8.9
20–49.9	1.1	3.2	4.0	5.2
50 ha and over	0.2	0.8	1.1	1.5
Total	3.5	9.2	12.6	15.6
Average area (ha)	21.4	24.1	23.4	25.0
% of total oilseed rape area on holdings with 50 ha or more of oilseed rape	24.2	30.6	30.6	32.2

[1] Provisional

Supplies

Not only has the UK become a major producer of oilseed rape during the past two decades but a major international trade has developed. In 1987 production amounted to 1.3 million tonnes; 200 000 tonnes were imported and 293 000 tonnes exported.

Oilseed rape supplies ('000 tonnes)

	1968–69	1970–71	1975–76	1980	1985	1986	1987
Production	–	8	67	300	891	951	1318
Imports	72	57	61	137	60	259	200
Exports	–	1	1	–	295	496	293
New supply	72	63	127	437	656	714	1225
Production as % of new supply	–	13	53	69	130	133	108

Based on Appendix Table 11.5.

Prices

Oilseed rape prices rose sharply during the early 1970s, both in current and in real terms. Since then current prices have continued to increase, but there was a sharp reduction in 1987. In real terms prices have fallen by 43% since 1979.

Oilseed rape prices (£ per tonne)

Based on Appendix Table 11.6.

CHAPTER 12

Potatoes

Potatoes, valued at £538 million in 1987, contribute about 17% of total crop output (excluding horticulture) and 4% of total agricultural output.

There are three main types of production: earlies, maincrop and seed. Earlies are defined as potatoes lifted up to 31 July and in recent years have accounted for about 5% of total production. From 1 August potatoes are regarded as maincrop.

The Potato Marketing Board, which was formed in 1934, is responsible for orderly marketing through production quotas and intervention buying to deal with surpluses. These mechanisms are linked to stock feed programmes. Pre-season contracts have been in operation since 1978. Since 1985 their use to support the market has been supplemented by direct intervention by the Board.

Prior to World War II the area planted to potatoes was fairly constant at about 300 000 hectares. After 1939 the area increased rapidly to help the shortage of food and animal feedstuffs. Since the 1950s there has been a slow but continuing decline in the area planted.

The number of registered producers in Great Britain declined by almost 75% between 1955 and 1986; at the same time there was a considerable increase in the average area per producer. In 1987 39% of the total area planted in the United Kingdom was on holdings with 20 hectares and over of potatoes.

There are considerable variations in annual yields and hence production, mainly because of the weather. There has, however, been a long term upward trend in yields which have more than doubled since before World War II; the rise in maincrop yields has been particularly marked.

Given the steady demand and the variability in annual production levels, potato imports fluctuate but generally account for 10–12% of total supplies for human consumption. Most of the imports consist of early potatoes and processed products, mainly in frozen or dehydrated form, but ware potatoes, which are mainly used for processing, are also imported. Potatoes are also exported.

Potato consumption per head per annum increased sharply during World War II from a pre-war average of 86.2kg to over 100kg, then declined to more normal levels. Since 1980 there has been a notable increase in the use of processed potatoes, resulting in some increase in consumption in all forms.

Potato prices depend on availability. There were exceptionally low yields (only 22 tonnes per hectare) in both 1975 and 1976. This had a spectacular effect on prices which in 1976 averaged more than three times the normal level. A somewhat similar, but less severe market scarcity occurred in 1983 when prices increased by 136% compared with a year earlier. Apart from these exceptions, there has been a downward trend in real prices since 1956.

Area grown

The area planted to potatoes in Great Britain showed relatively little change between the mid-1860s and the outbreak of World War I, when there was a temporary increase. The area planted increased dramatically between 1938 and 1946. There has been a continuous fall since 1948, and by 1987 the area planted had fallen to only 177 000 hectares.

The aim of the Potato Marketing Board is that home production should meet home demand. A national 'target area' is determined each year by the Agricultural Departments; the Board then prescribes a quota on each producer's basic area to achieve that aggregate target. Producers pay a large additional levy for any excess plantings.

Area of potatoes ('000 hectares)

Great Britain								
1866	1870	1880	1890	1900	1910	1914	1920	1925
202	238	223	214	227	219	248	286	257

United Kingdom											
1925	1930	1938	1942	1946	1950	1960	1970	1980	1985	1986	1987
319	277	297	528	576	499	335	271	206	191	178	177

Based on Appendix Table 12.2.

Number of holdings

The number of registered potato producers in Great Britain has shown a steady decline from 86 800 in 1955 to only 21 400 in 1987. In the United Kingdom as a whole the number of holdings with potatoes has fallen from 104 900 in 1967 to 32 800 in 1987 while the average area has doubled. Over 39% of the total potato area is now on holdings with 20 hectares and over of potatoes. In 1986, 65% of the holdings producing potatoes were in England and Wales, 23% in Scotland and 12% in Northern Ireland.

Number of holdings with potatoes ('000)

	1967	1972	1975	1980	1985[4]	1987[4]
Hectares of potatoes						
0.1–9.9	85.8[1]	54.6[1]	50.4	43.1	33.8	27.9
10–19.9	16.7[2]	13.6[2]	3.7	3.6	3.3	3.0
20 and over	2.4[3]	2.0[3]	1.9	2.0	2.1	1.9
Total	104.9	70.3	56.0	48.7	39.2	32.8
Average area	2.7	3.4	3.6	4.2	4.9	5.4
% of total potato area on holdings with 20 ha and over of potatoes	28.9[3]	30.4[3]	33.6	34.3	38.0	39.1

[1]0.1–3.9 ha.   [2]4.0–20.1 ha.   [3]20.2 ha and over.   [4]Provisional.

Yields

In the latter part of the 19th century and the early part of this century yields averaged about 14 or 15 tonnes per hectare. By 1939 they still had reached only about 17 tonnes, but after 1960 they moved up more rapidly at about 2% per annum and have now reached about 36 tonnes, or more than double the pre-war average. Maincrop yields have risen from about 23 tonnes per hectare in 1960–1964 to 36.3 tonnes in 1982–86 while earlies have risen from 15.3 tonnes to 21.2 tonnes.

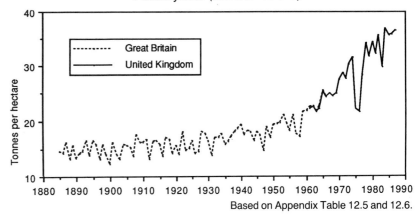

Potato yields (tonnes/hectare)

Based on Appendix Table 12.5 and 12.6.

Production

Potato production increased to over 10 million tonnes during World War II, almost twice as much as in 1938. The high level of production was maintained until 1950 after which production began to decline. By 1986 production had fallen to 6.45 million tonnes. In recent years early potatoes have accounted for about 5–6% of total production.

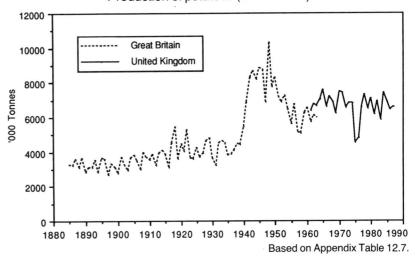

Production of potatoes ('000 tonnes)

Based on Appendix Table 12.7.

Supplies

The United Kingdom continues to import approximately 10% of its total potato requirements. Most of the raw potato imports are new potatoes. Domestic early production in recent years has accounted for about two thirds of consumption, the remainder being imported. The Channel Isles, Cyprus and Egypt are the main sources of imports. Ware potatoes are only imported if there is a short fall in home production. About 350–400 000 tonnes (raw equivalent) of processed potatoes have also been imported in recent years, mainly in dehydrated or frozen form. The Netherlands is the main supplier of processed potatoes.

Exports of potatoes have shown some increase in recent years. In 1987 exports are estimated to have totalled 142 000 tonnes, about 3% of output for human consumption.

Supplies *(continued)*

Potato supplies ('000 tonnes)

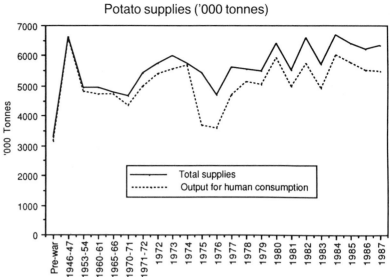

Based on Appendix Table 12.9.

Consumption

Potato consumption in total showed a major increase during World War II and the immediate post-war years, but has since then fallen. Unprocessed potato consumption declined between 1970 and 1984, but has since then again shown some recovery. The consumption of crisps as well as frozen par fries has increased dramatically since 1970, but the consumption of dehydrated potatoes has declined. Total per head potato consumption, in terms of raw equivalent, in 1986 was about 30% higher than prior to World War II.

Potato consumption (kg per head per annum)

	Pre-war	1942	1946	1950	1960	1970	1980	1985	1986
Potatoes						88.9	77.4	77.6	81.2
Crisps[1]						6.3	8.3	11.5	10.8
Frozen par fries[1]						3.4	9.9	13.4	15.7
Canned[1]							0.4	1.0	0.9
Dehydrated[1]						4.9[2]	3.3	4.1	3.8
Total[1]	86.2	102.0	127.6	109.8	101.5	103.5	99.3	107.6	112.4

[1]Weight of raw equivalent. [2]Including canned.

Based on Appendix Table 12.12.

Prices

Potato prices are dependent on availability and are therefore subject to considerable annual fluctuations. In the five years 1982–86 farm gate prices averaged almost 200% more than a decade earlier. Apart from the years when prices were abnormally high because of a shortfall in supplies (e.g. 1975 and 1976), prices have fallen continuously in real terms.

Potato prices (£ per tonne)

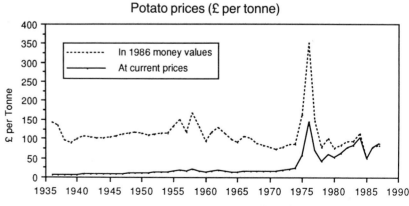

Based on Appendix Table 12.13.

CHAPTER 13

Sugar beet

Sugar beet output, valued at £211 million in 1987, accounts for about 7% of crop output and 2% of total farm output.

Production is limited by quota arrangements. Prior to entry into the EC the area was limited to 179 000 hectares which was distributed on a factory area basis. The EC regime provides for national maximum quotas (the United Kingdom's quota is 1.144 million tonnes). Any production above this level has to be exported at world sugar prices without EC export refunds, or carried forward to the next quota year. British Sugar Plc (formerly the British Sugar Corporation) is the sole purchaser of sugar beet. The tonnage of sugar beet which farmers contracted to grow in 1986 represented an area of about 205 000 hectares.

Sugar beet was introduced into the United Kingdom in the 1920s and is regarded as a useful break and cash crop. The tops and pulp can be fed to livestock, thus improving profitability. The area under beet increased rapidly in the 1930s and there was a further sharp rise during World War II. Since then there has been some further increase, the peak being reached in 1980. Virtually all of the production is in England and Wales.

There are relatively few holdings with sugar beet, and the number has fallen by over 50% during the past two decades to only 11 100 in 1987. The average beet area has risen almost two and a half times during this period.

Sugar beet yields are now double those of before World War II. Yields began to increase particularly rapidly from the late 1950s onwards. The sugar content of the beet depends on seasonal factors and ranges from about 16–18%.

The United Kingdom remains a major importer of sugar, although self-sufficiency has risen from about 33% in 1970 to 57% in 1987. Prior to World War II about 2.2 million tonnes of raw sugar were imported; in recent years imports have amounted to only slightly over one million tonnes, mostly from Fiji, Guyana, Jamaica, Mauritius and Swaziland, all of which are dependent on the export of sugar. There are no longer any imports from Australia, Cuba or South Africa.

Per head consumption of sugar declined sharply during World War II as a result of reduced imports, in spite of an increase in home production. By 1955 consumption exceeded the pre-war level, but after 1960 it declined once more, and in recent years has been stable, at a level well below the peak reached in 1960.

The average price paid to growers by the British Sugar Corporation rose rapidly during the second half of the 1970s but has changed little since. In real terms, i.e. after allowing for inflation, prices have fallen by more than a third since 1974.

Production

Increases in the area of sugar beet grown until 1980, together with improved yields resulted in a rise in production from 497 000 tonnes in 1925 to 8 million tonnes in 1987. Production is unlikely to show any further major increase because of the quota arrangements which make any further expansion by farmers uneconomic.

Yields showed little change until after World War II, since when they have risen sharply. There was a two-fold increase in yields between the periods 1926–30 and 1980–84 which can be attributed to improvements in plant breeding and cultivation practices.

Sugar beet has been grown in this country since the mid-1920s but the production area has expanded rapidly since then. Production increased particularly rapidly during World War II when imported supplies were restricted. Since the UK entered the EC and production has been subject to quota arrangements, the area grown has fallen slightly from the 1980 peak of 213 000 hectares.

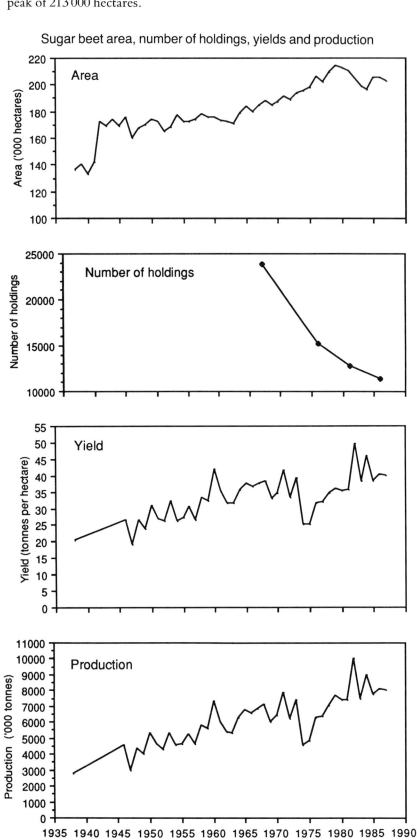

Sugar beet area, number of holdings, yields and production

Based on Appendix Tables 13.2, 13.4, 13.5.

Holdings

The number of holdings with sugar beet has fallen by over 50% during the past 20 years to only 11 100. The average area has increased from 7.6 hectares in 1967 to 18.2 hectares in 1987. By 1987 67% of the total sugar beet area was on holdings growing 20 hectares or more.

Number of holdings with sugar beet ('000)

Hectares	1967	1972	1975	1980	1985[1]	1987[1]
0.1–9.9	11.4[2]	7.2[2]	9.7	6.9	5.8	5.2
10–19.9	10.3[3]	9.3[3]	3.2	3.1	2.8	2.8
20 and over	2.0[4]	2.5[4]	2.8	3.2	2.9	3.1
Total	23.8	19.0	15.7	13.2	11.6	11.1
Average area (ha)	7.6	10.0	12.5	16.0	17.2	18.2
% of total sugar beet area on holdings growing 20 ha or more	39.4[4]	49.0[4]	55.9	63.9	65.3	67.1

[1]Provisional. [2]0.1–3.9 ha. [3]4.0–20.1 ha. [4]20.2 ha and over.

Supplies

Sugar production has increased rapidly since before the war while imports have fallen. Compared to the pre-war period, 1987 production was up three times and imports down by 46%. More than 55% of the sugar consumed is now home produced compared with about 20% pre-World War II. The International Sugar Agreement provides for a minimum import quantity which has to be imported by the European Community.

Sugar supplies ('000 tonnes)

	Pre-war	1946–47	1953–54	1960–61	1970–71	1980	1985	1986	1987[2]
Production	422	602	796	954	954	1106	1210	1318	1200
Imports	2204	1595	3305	2282	2159	1340	1303	1255	1193
Exports	349[1]	100[1]	673[1]	490[1]	213	94	354	173	282
New supply	2277[1]	2097[1]	3428[1]	2746[1]	2900	2352	2159	2400	2111
Production as % of new supply	19[1]	29[1]	23[1]	35[1]	33	47	56	55	57

[1]Author's estimate. [2]Forecast.

Based on Appendix Table 13.7.

Consumption

Sugar consumption declined sharply during World War II because of shortage of imported supplies, and it was not until the mid-1950s that consumption recovered to the pre-war level. Since then consumption has again declined. Consumption of refined sugar has shown virtually no change since 1980. In 1986 glucose, which is used for manufacturing, accounted for almost a fifth of total consumption. The National Food Survey statistics (see Chapter 9, *Food consumption*) show that sugar consumption has fallen continuously since 1960 and in 1985 was only about half that of 1965. Less sugar is being bought for use in food and drink prepared in the home while more is being consumed in the form of manufactured products.

Consumption of sugar and syrups (kg per head per annum)

	Pre-war	1942	1946	1950	1960	1970	1980[2]	1985[2]	1986[2]
Sugar, refined	41.2	28.5	34.0	36.4	47.3	44.0	37.0	37.1	37.3
Honey	0.2	0.4	0.2	0.3	0.3	0.4	0.3	0.4	0.4
Glucose	3.0	1.5	1.4	1.7	3.4	5.3	7.9	7.6	7.9
Total[1]	43.5	30.3	35.1	38.0	53.8	48.8	43.4	43.2	43.6

[1]Sugar content. [2]New series.

Prices

Sugar beet prices showed little change until World War II when the Ministry of Food increased the price in order to encourage greater production. Prices ranged between £5 and £7 per tonne during the 1950s and 1960s and it was not until the mid–1970s that they began to increase rapidly. There was some reduction in 1986 as sugar production rose to almost 1.3 million tonnes compared with 1.2 million tonnes a year earlier. There was a further small price reduction in 1987. Prices have fallen continuously in real terms since 1975 and in 1987 averaged 40% less than at the outbreak of World War II.

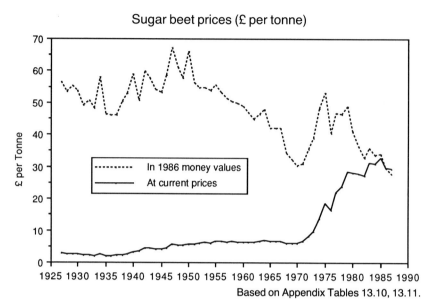

Sugar beet prices (£ per tonne)

Based on Appendix Tables 13.10, 13.11.

CHAPTER 14
Horticulture

The total farm gate value of horticultural output in 1987, at £1368 million, accounted for 11% of total agricultural output. Vegetables, the most important output, were valued at £839 million, fruit at £228 million and flowers, bulbs and nursery stock etc at £302 million.

The United Kingdom has always been a major producer of temperate fruits, primarily apples, pears and plums. The cropped area reached a peak at the beginning of the century and this level was maintained until the mid–1950s since when there have been major changes in the fortunes of the industry. Although fruit consumption has almost doubled since 1950, most of the increase has come from citrus and tropical fruit, particularly imported fruit juice.

The areas devoted to apple and pear production have fallen sharply since the early 1970s, mainly because of increased competition from imports. Not only have imports from other EC member states largely replaced produce from the southern hemisphere, but total apple imports have also risen sharply by almost 60% since the mid–1970s. Since 1950 the cropped area of dessert apples has fallen by almost half and that of culinary apples by two thirds. The plum area has fallen by about 80%. Kent and East Sussex account for almost half of the dessert apples produced in the UK and over 60% of the culinary apples.

The cropped area of soft fruit has also fallen, particularly since 1980, primarily because of increased competition from imports. Imports of fresh strawberries have risen almost seven-fold since the early 1970s and there is now also a major import trade in frozen strawberries.

Although the numerous changes in the methods of calculating fruit and vegetable yields mean that the series are not always comparable, it is evident that there have been considerable improvements in the yields of most fruits, particularly apples and pears. Much has also been done to improve the quality, and particularly the marketing, of fruit produced in this country.

Vegetable production falls into two broad categories: field crops and protected crops. Field crops include roots, onions, brassicas and legumes. Green peas for processing (primarily freezing) account for almost a quarter of the total area of field vegetables and have largely displaced fresh green and dry pea production. The area of carrots grown rose to a peak in the late 1970s, but has since then fallen sharply. There has been a similar decline in home production since the late 1970s while imports have almost doubled. Cabbage and dry bulb onion production is increasing but brussels sprouts are declining. Cauliflower production has shown some recovery, but imports have more than doubled since 1980.

Tomatoes and lettuces are the most important protected crops. Tomato producers have had to face increased competition from imports and the cropped area has fallen by about one third since 1970. This has not, however, resulted in a similar fall in production because of increased yields. The cropped area of lettuce has increased by almost 60% since the early 1970s and production has more than doubled. The increase in salad consumption has also benefited cucumber growers. Mushroom production has almost doubled since the early 1970s because of increases in both cropped area and yields.

The area of flowers and bulbs grown in the open has shown a small decline in recent years, but there has been a small rise in the area of hardy nursery stock. In England and Wales more narcissi are grown, but the tulip area has declined by over 70% during the past 10 years.

Carnations, roses, chrysanthemums and pot plants are the most important protected non-edible crops. The cropped areas of carnations and roses are declining but there has been a major rise in the production of container-grown plants and ornamental bedding plants in boxes.

Fruit

There has been a sharp reduction in the total cropped area of both orchard and soft fruit since before World War II. The total area of orchard fruit has fallen from about 107 000 hectares pre-war to only 35 000 hectares in 1986. All types of fruits are affected but particularly apples which currently account for 65% of the total area.

The area of soft fruit has declined from over 25 000 hectares pre-war to only 15 000 hectares in 1986. Strawberries remain the most important crop and currently account for about 45% of the total soft fruit area.

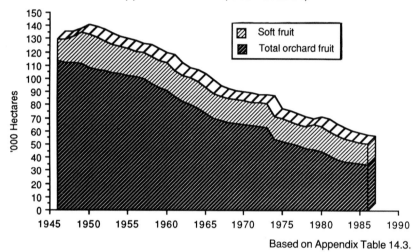

Cropped area of fruit ('000 hectares)

Based on Appendix Table 14.3.

Apple supplies

The total supply of apples has shown relatively little change since the early 1960s, but the proportion of home produced supplies has fallen from about 65% in the 1960s and the early 1970s to only about 40% in recent years. Increased imports from other EC member states have not only resulted in a reduction in imports from the Southern hemisphere but have also increased competition for British producers. Golden Delicious apples from France have, in particular, become very popular.

There has also been some reduction in the output of pears since the early 1960s, but imports have remained relatively stable. Output as a percentage of new supply has ranged from 38%–42% since 1980.

Apple supplies ('000 tonnes)

	1961–62 to 1963–64	1970–71	1980	1985	1986	1987[1]
Output	415	438	313	287	282	266
Imports	228	255	374	428	442	428
Exports	4	11	13	24	19	22
New supply	638	682	674	691	705	672
Output as % of new supply	65	64	46	42	40	40

[1]Forecast.
Note. Output is the actual quantity moved off the national farm for which revenue was received.

Based on Appendix Table 14.22.

Field vegetables

There has been a sharp reduction in the cropped area of green peas grown for market from about 2300 hectares pre-war to only 3000 hectares in 1986, while the area grown for processing (mainly for freezing) has increased from about 3000 hectares to over 46 000 hectares during the same period. The cabbage area has fallen from a post-war peak in 1948 to only 23 000 hectares in 1986. The area of cauliflowers has shown some increase since the mid–1970s, but brussels sprouts have shown a reduction. Cauliflower supplies have increased considerably since the early 1960s mainly due to more home produced supplies, although there has also been a rise in imports and supplies from the Channel Isles. Output as a percentage of total new supply has ranged between 83% and 86% since 1984, similar to the early 1960s.

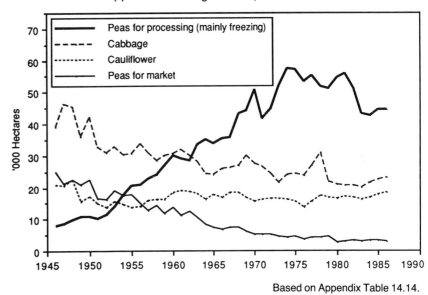

Cropped area of vegetables ('000 hectares)

Based on Appendix Table 14.14.

Cauliflower supplies ('000 tonnes)

Based on Appendix Table 14.22.

Tomatoes and protected vegetables

The cropped area of protected vegetables has varied between 2900 hectares and 3400 hectares since the early 1970s. The area of tomatoes has fallen from about 1000 hectares in 1972 to only 707 hectares in 1986, much of the reduction being due to a decline in the area of unheated glass used for tomato growing. The area of lettuce has risen from about 1030 hectares to 1606 hectares. Both the cucumber and mushroom areas have risen since the early 1970s; in the case of cucumbers most of the increase occurred in the mid–1970s.

The increase in supplies of tomatoes since the early 1960s was mainly due to increased imports, although there was also some rise in home production in the 1960s and the first half of the 1970s. Supplies from the Channel Isles have fallen from over 60 000 tonnes in the first half of the 1970s to only 12 000 tonnes in 1987. United Kingdom output as a percentage of new supply has shown little change in recent years, ranging from 32% to 34%.

Cropped area of protected vegetables (hectares)

	1972	1975	1980	1985	1986
Tomatoes	1009	984	859	704	707
Cucumbers	165	210	238	230	227
Lettuce	1029	1309	1384	1576	1606
Mushrooms	420	388	404	524	525
Others	261	209	267	322	308
Total	2884	3100	3152	3356	3373

Based on Appendix Table 14.19.

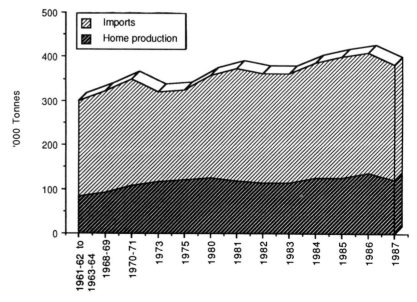

Tomato supplies ('000 tonnes)

Based on Appendix Table 14.22.

Non-edible crops

The statistics of value of output at constant 1980 prices give an indication of the changes in volume which have occurred in sales of non-edible crops. The total output has increased by about 25% during the past decade. Output of flowers grown in the open and of flower bulbs has shown virtually no change, but output of nursery stock has risen by about 52%. This increase is almost entirely due to the rapid increase in container-grown sales which have risen almost four-fold during the past decade.

Value of non-edible crop output at constant 1980 prices (£ million)

	1977	1978	1979	1980	1981	1982	1983	1984	1985	1986
Flowers in the open	15	14	13	13	14	14	14	14	14	14
Flower bulbs	5	4	4	4	4	4	4	4	5	4
Hardy nursery stock	65	66	73	76	78	78	81	86	95	99
Protected crops	79	79	83	85	89	91	88	91	83	86
Total non-edible crops	164	163	173	178	185	187	187	195	196	202

Prices

Tomato prices were affected by the shortage of supplies during World War II and have risen almost continuously since then although there have been seasonal fluctuations. After allowing for inflation, however, prices have fallen by about 50% since the late 1930s and by about 30% since 1973.

Apple and pear prices showed a sharp rise during World War II because supplies were short, but there was then little change except for variations due to seasonal conditions until the early 1970s. Dessert apple prices have increased about three-fold since the early 1970s and pear prices about two and a half times. In real terms both apple and pear prices have fallen sharply since the early 1970s. Dessert apple prices declined by 32% between 1973 and 1987 while pear prices were 45% less.

Cauliflower prices have also risen almost continuously since World War II although there have been considerable seasonal fluctuations. In real terms prices in 1987 were slightly higher than before World War II, but there has been a 20% reduction since 1973.

Tomato prices (£ per tonne)

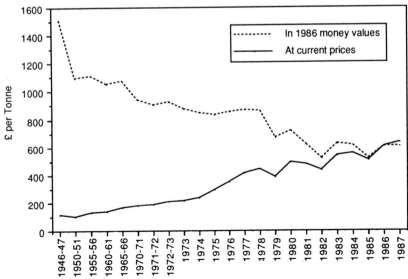

Based on Appendix Table 14.27.

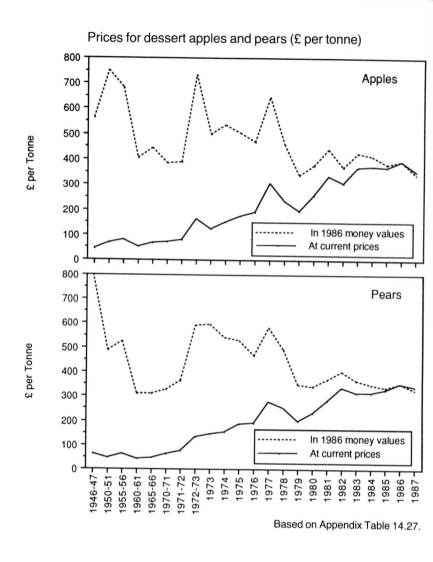

Prices for dessert apples and pears (£ per tonne)

Based on Appendix Table 14.27.

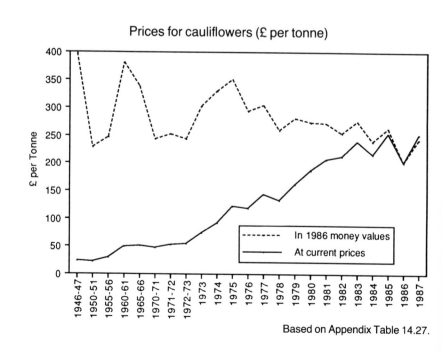

Prices for cauliflowers (£ per tonne)

Based on Appendix Table 14.27.

CHAPTER 15

Hops

Hops have traditionally been grown in the south of England and are an important ingredient for the brewing industry. The farm gate value of output in 1987 amounted to £12 million or 3% of total farm crop output. Until comparatively recently production was subject to the quotas set by the Hops Marketing Board. This no longer exists and certain of its functions have been taken over by English Hops Ltd.

The area of hops grown has fallen sharply since the mid-19th century. There was a major reduction during World War I, partly because of a labour shortage. This was followed by only a modest recovery; from the beginning of the 1930s to the first half of the 1970s there was little change but since then there has been a considerable reduction.

Unlike most agricultural crops there has been no increase in hops yields since the 1920s although there are considerable annual variations because of seasonal factors. There have also been disease problems.

Hops production is now very much less than in the past. To meet brewers' requirements for hops with a high alpha acid content, new varieties have been developed. Moreover, improvements in brewing technology mean that from a given quantity of hops, a much greater quantity of beer can now be produced.

Production in 1987 was less than half that at the end of World War II. There is some international trade but overall, production as a percentage of new supply has tended to decline in recent years.

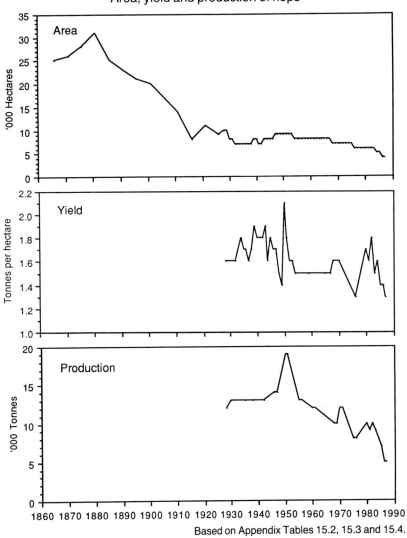

Area, yield and production of hops

Based on Appendix Tables 15.2, 15.3 and 15.4.

Area, yield and production

The area of hops in this country was at a peak in the early 1880s when over 30 000 hectares were grown. Only 8000 hectares were grown during World War I and, although there was some recovery, the area never again exceeded 11 000 hectares. The hops area has been falling since the early 1970s, and by 1987 there were only 4000 hectares.

There has not been any long term upward trend in yields, although there are considerable annual variations, depending on seasonal factors. Yields normally range from about 1.4 tonnes to 1.8 tonnes per hectare. Only about 5000 tonnes of hops were produced in 1987 compared with about 13 000 tonnes in the 1930s.

Supplies

Hops supplies have fallen sharply during the past two decades and in 1987 totalled only 6000 tonnes. Some hops are both imported and exported. The self-sufficiency percentage has fallen in recent years.

Hops supplies ('000 tonnes)

	1928	1938	1942	1946	1950	1960	1970	1980	1985	1986	1987[1]
Production	12	13	13	14	19	12	12	10	7	5	5
Imports							1	2	2	2	2
Exports							1	4	2	2	1
New supply							12	8	7	6	6
Production as % of new supply							97	126	96	86	78

[1] Forecast

Based on Appendix Table 15.4.

Prices

The prices for hops declined to low levels during the 1930s, but rose again sharply during World War II. Prices rose particularly rapidly during the second half of the 1970s and by 1980 the farm gate price was over £2 300 per tonne. The average price rose to over £3 000 in 1983 and 1984 when supplies were low. There has been a considerable reduction since then. In real terms prices have fallen continuously since the end of World War II, and by 1987 the average price in 1986 money values was 36% less than in 1980.

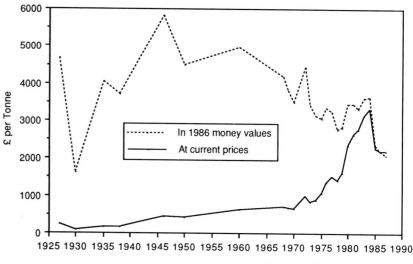

Hops prices (£ per tonne)

Based on Appendix Table 15.5.

CHAPTER 16

Fodder crops, grass and straw

There have been considerable changes in feeding practices in respect of both purchased feeds and the use of feed grown on the farm. Although much remains to be done to improve the productivity and utilization of grassland, there have been considerable achievements, particularly since World War II. The grassland itself has become more productive because of reseeding and the increased use of fertilisers, and this has enabled stocking rates to be increased. Although haymaking continues in some areas, silage is now of major importance. The feeding of turnips, swedes and mangolds, which in the past were important winter and early spring feeds, has greatly diminished.

Hay continues to be an important winter feed, particularly for cattle, but is gradually being less used. Although grass cutting and haymaking have been largely mechanised, the quantity and quality of hay produced continues to be dependent on the vagaries of the weather. Because of this hay is being replaced increasingly by silage and more intensive grazing systems.

About nine million tonnes of hay were produced annually in Great Britain during the latter part of the 19th century and the first two decades of the 20th century. Production began to decline in the 1930s in line with the general contraction of agriculture, but there was an increase during World War II because of the shortage of feed grains. Hay production began to show a longer term downward trend from the mid-1970s onwards as silage became more popular.

There are two types of silage – grass and arable, but grass silage is the most common. The great advantage of silage is that green fodder can be preserved in a pit or silo without the necessity of having to dry it. It is therefore very suitable for the British climate, particularly in years when the weather is poor. There are also major nutritional advantages and lower labour costs when silage is fed. Silage production increased rapidly from the early 1970s onwards. In 1980 almost 29 million tonnes were produced; by 1985 this had risen to over 42 million tonnes. There were further increases in 1986 and 1987, and this trend can be expected to continue.

Hay and silage production ('000 tonnes)

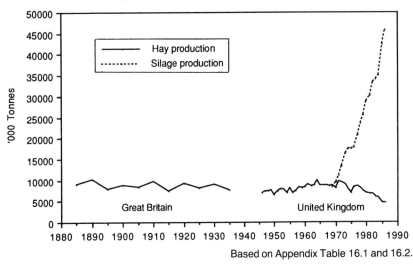

Based on Appendix Table 16.1 and 16.2.

Turnips, swedes and mangolds

Turnips, swedes and mangolds used to be a traditional feed for cattle, and to a lesser extent sheep, during the winter and early spring. This is now much less common. The disappearance of these crops has been largely due to their heavy labour costs and low profitability relative to other arable crops.

Root production for feeding stock began to decline in the 1930s with the general contraction in agricultural production, but there was a revival during World War II. The area of turnips and swedes has fallen by 70% since 1960 while the area of mangolds has fallen by 75%. There have been similar reductions in production.

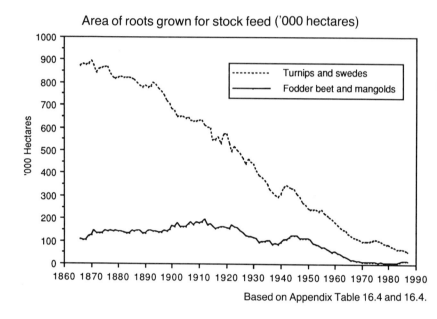

Area of roots grown for stock feed ('000 hectares)

Legend:
- - - - - Turnips and swedes
———— Fodder beet and mangolds

Based on Appendix Table 16.4 and 16.4.

Straw

Straw is produced from wheat, barley, oats, mixed corn and peas. In the past production tended to vary with the areas grown, but this is no longer necessarily the case as straw production varies according to the variety of cereals. Cereal growing areas now often have a large surplus of straw which cannot be used and is uneconomic to transport to livestock-producing areas. Considerable quantities are therefore disposed of by ploughing in or burning, despite the fact that burning has been discouraged in recent years for environmental reasons.

Production of straw for use on the farm or for sale showed a sharp reduction between the mid-1960s and about 1981 but has increased again since then. Wheat straw production increased from 1.6 million tonnes in 1981 to 3.4 million tonnes in 1986, while barley straw production rose by about 875 000 tonnes to 4.3 million tonnes during the same period.

CHAPTER 17

Beef and veal

In terms of value, the output of cattle for slaughter and calves is the second most important agricultural product (£1890 million in 1987) after milk and milk products (£2411 million). The value of output of slaughter cattle and calves in 1987 accounted for 43% of livestock output and 15% of farmers' total receipts.

Total cattle numbers have risen sharply since the middle of the 19th century. In the past cattle numbers tended to increase during periods of low crop prices when producers reduced their arable area and switched to grass. This is reflected in the cattle population statistics from 1866 to 1914 and in the 1920s. There was a further rise in cattle numbers during World War II and the post-war years. However, since 1974 there has been a reduction. The fall during the past five years reflects the deterioration in the profitability of both milk and beef as well as the imposition of EC milk quotas.

Currently about two thirds of the beef production in this country is derived from the dairy herd and about 29% from the beef herd, while imported Irish cattle account for the balance. The proportion of beef from the beef herd has fallen since the mid-1970s, and imports of Irish cattle have also become less important.

Cattle slaughterings reached a peak in 1975, but have since fallen sharply in line with the fall in the cattle population. Calf slaughterings, which consist virtually entirely of bobby calves, have been at low levels since the mid-1960s, due mainly to the development of a good export market and increased retentions for feeding. The high level of cow slaughter since 1984 has followed the decline in profitability of milk production and the imposition of EC milk quotas.

Beef and veal production, although much higher than in the first three decades of this century, has fallen sharply since 1975; there has been some recovery since 1984 because of the high level of cow slaughterings. The reduction in beef production between 1975 and 1983 has, however, been much less than the reduction in total cattle slaughterings because of increases in average carcase weights.

The United Kingdom, which in the past had been a major importer of beef, has become almost self-sufficient. In spite of this it remains a major trader. The percentage of beef supplies from home production has risen from slightly less than half in the 1930s to over 95%. The UK tends to import forequarter beef and to export hindquarter beef and cow beef.

Prior to joining the European Community, and particularly before World War II, much of the beef was imported from South America and Australasia. Currently, about half the beef imports originate in the Irish Republic, but significant quantities are also imported from other EC member states, particularly France and the Federal Republic of Germany. Although imports from the Irish Republic have fallen sharply the UK remains a significant importer of live cattle. However, most of the trade is now between the Irish Republic and Northern Ireland.

Livestock producers and meat traders have become export conscious since the UK's entry into the European Community. In 1986 about two thirds of the beef was exported to other member states and the remainder mostly to North Africa and the Middle East. Most of the live calves are exported to France and the Netherlands.

Consumers in this country eat more beef than any other kind of meat, although consumption is now much less than in the 1930s when little pork and poultry meat was eaten; poultry meat consumption is, however, soon expected to overtake beef and veal. There has again been some rise in beef consumption since 1984 because of the plentiful supplies which have been reflected in more favourable retail prices.

Prices for slaughter cattle increased sharply during World War I and the immediate post-war years, but fell again from 1922 onwards. Prices did not rise above the 1920 level until after World War II. The rapid rise in prices was partly due to the general increase as well as entry into the European Community. There has been little change since 1983. In real terms, with the exception of the period during World War I, prices declined continuously from 1900 to 1938. The fall has been about 20% in real terms since 1960 with a particularly sharp decline since 1982.

With the exception of a brief period after entry into the European Community beef producers have had the benefit of deficiency or variable premium payments since the end of war-time controls in 1954. In real terms producers' total returns have fallen by 16% since the mid-1950s.

Cattle numbers

Cattle numbers in Great Britain increased almost continuously between the mid-1860s and the early 1890s as the profitability of crop production deteriorated. There was a further rise during World War I and in the 1920s. The need to produce more food, particularly milk, resulted in a further rise in cattle numbers during the second World War and in the post-war years. Cattle numbers reached a peak in 1974. The fall since 1983 reflects a deterioration in the profitability of both milk and beef production as well as the imposition of milk quotas in 1984.

In 1922, 75% of the UK's cattle were in England and Wales, 15% were in Scotland and 10% in Northern Ireland. These proportions showed little change during the 1930s and World War II. Cattle have become relatively less important in England and Wales since the mid 1950s as this part of the United Kingdom is more suitable for profitable crop production, while in Scotland the opposite has occurred. Cattle have also become more important in Northern Ireland.

Cattle numbers (millions)

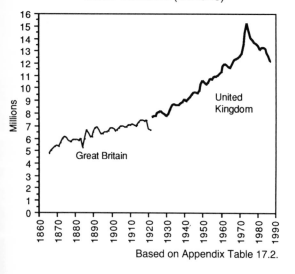

Based on Appendix Table 17.2.

Cattle numbers by country

	Cattle population			
	England and Wales (%)	Scotland (%)	Northern Ireland (%)	United Kingdom (%)
1922	74.6	15.0	10.4	100.0
1930	75.4	15.9	8.7	100.0
1938	76.6	15.0	8.4	100.0
1955	75.4	16.2	8.4	100.0
1965	73.6	17.1	9.4	100.0
1970	71.7	17.8	10.5	100.0
1980	71.1	17.7	11.2	100.0
1985	70.8	17.4	11.8	100.0
1986	71.2	17.1	11.7	100.0
1987	71.4	16.9	11.7	100.0

Based on Appendix Table 17.2.

The breeding herd

The proportion of beef type cows in the national herd reached a peak in 1975 when they accounted for 36.9% of the total. Since then there has been a downward trend; by 1986 beef cows accounted for only 29.4% of the breeding herd because of lower profits from suckler calf production. The profitability of sheep, which often competes with suckler calves, has also improved since the coming into operation of the EC sheep meat regime in late 1980.

There was a slight recovery in the proportion of beef type cows in 1987 following a three per cent reduction in dairy cow numbers between 1986 and 1987 and a two per cent rise in the beef herd.

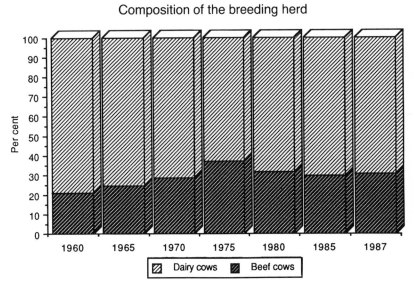

Composition of the breeding herd

Based on Appendix Table 17.3.

Production

Beef and veal production levels showed relatively little change until the outbreak of World War II, ranging between 600 000 and 700 000 tonnes per annum. There was a sharp reduction during World War II, but production began to recover from the mid-1950s, reaching a peak of 944 000 tonnes in 1963. This level was not again reached until 1970.

Beef was in short supply in 1973, but production had again recovered to 1 216 000 tonnes by 1975. Since then it has ranged between 1.0 and 1.1 million tonnes. Calf slaughterings have fallen to low levels as a considerable number are exported live and an increasing proportion are being retained for feeding. The relatively high levels of beef production in recent years have been due to an increase in the number of cows culled.

The United Kingdom, which produced less than half its beef requirements prior to World War II, has become almost self sufficient in recent years. Imports, which had totalled 600–700 000 tonnes before 1938 fell sharply during the war, particularly after 1942, when shipping became difficult. Imports did not begin to recover until the early 1950s. Since the early 1970s there has not only been a sharp reduction in imports but also a major increase in exports. Self sufficiency has ranged between 96% and 100% since 1983. In 1987 96% of new supplies came from home production.

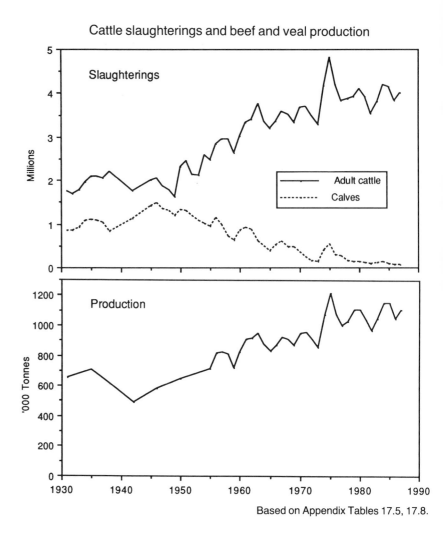

Cattle slaughterings and beef and veal production

Based on Appendix Tables 17.5, 17.8.

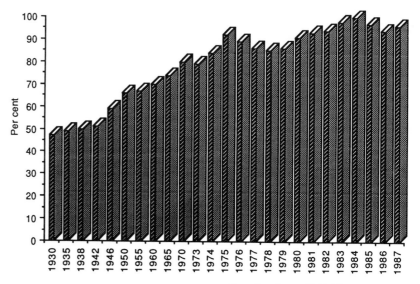

The importance of home production to overall supply[1]

Based on Appendix Tables 17.10, 17.11.

[1]Production as a proportion of new supplies i.e. home production plus imports less exports (including supplies sent to Channel Isles).

Consumption

Beef and veal consumption has fallen sharply since the beginning of this century. Consumption fell sharply during World War II due to shortage of supplies but there was some recovery in the 1950s and 1960s. Consumption has again declined since the post war peak of 1975 when per head consumption recovered to 23.6 kg. The increasing consumption of pig and poultry meat has meant that beef consumption has become relatively less important. However, in 1987 it still accounted for 28% of total meat consumption, more than any other individual meat.

Beef and veal consumption

	Kg per head per annum	As per cent of total meat consumption[1]
1905–1909	30.6	
1929	30.8	
1930	29.9	
1935	30.8	
1938	25.1	40
1942	22.1	44
1946	21.0	41
1950	21.7	40
1955	21.5	34
1960	21.8	33
1965	20.8	30
1970	22.2	31
1975	23.6	35
1980	20.9	30
1985	19.0	28
1986[2]	19.3	28
1987[3]	19.4	28

[1]Including poultry meat and offal. [2]Provisional. [3]Forecast.

Based on Appendix Table 17.15.

Prices and returns for slaughter cattle

Slaughter cattle prices in current terms almost doubled during World War I, but were very weak during the 1930s. There was again a sharp increase during World War II and this upward trend continued into the 1950s and 1960s. Prices rose particularly sharply during the 1970s and early 1980s. However, if allowance is made for the effects of inflation, real prices in 1987 were about 30% less than in 1955.

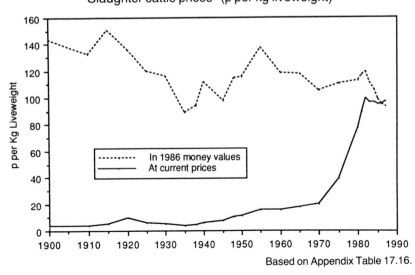

Producers' total returns for slaughter cattle[1]
(p per kg liveweight)

Based on Appendix Table 17.17.

[1]Including deficiency or variable premium payments. Certified cattle only.

Slaughter cattle prices[1] (p per kg liveweight)

Based on Appendix Table 17.16.

[1]Since 1955 includes Certified cattle only i.e. cattle meeting specified quality standards.

With the exception of a brief period after entry into the European Community, beef producers have had the benefit of deficiency or variable premium payments to supplement returns since decontrol in 1954. Total returns at current prices per kg live weight remained relatively stable until about 1970 but then rose sharply between 1970 and 1985. Since then there has been little change. Producers' total returns were fairly steady in real terms between 1955 and 1980 but have declined in recent years.

Retail prices

Retail beef prices showed virtually no change between 1939 and 1946, but then increased fairly rapidly until the mid-1950s because of the shortage of supplies. Prices again remained relatively stable from 1955 until the mid-1960s. Prices rose continuously between 1967 and 1982. Since then there has been relatively little change as supplies have been plentiful.

In real terms prices declined during World War II, then rose almost continuously until 1973. The average price in 1987, after allowing for inflation, was 23% less than in 1973. Prices have fallen continuously since 1982.

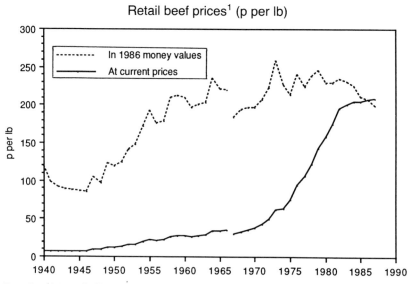

Retail beef prices[1] (p per lb)

Based on Appendix Tables 17.18, 17.19.

CHAPTER 18

Sheepmeat

The United Kingdom is the European Community's major sheepmeat producer and in 1987 produced 325 000 tonnes of sheepmeat with a farm gate value of £659 million. Sheepmeat output in 1987 accounted for 15% of the value of livestock output.

There are three main methods of producing lamb: out of season production; off grass which enables marketing to take place from May to November; and production utilising grass and forage which involves retaining the lambs after the end of the grazing season, when they are finished on forage crops. Production off grass remains the most popular method of production.

The sheep population has been rising rapidly in recent years, particularly since the introduction of the CAP for sheepmeat in 1980 which resulted in improved profitability. However, the United Kingdom has always had a large sheep population; as early as 1867, almost 29 million sheep were recorded in Great Britain. There was some reduction during World War I and the early 1920s, but by the mid-1930s the United Kingdom sheep flock had again recovered.

The emphasis on increased crop production, particularly cereals production, during World War II resulted in a sharp fall in sheep numbers. By 1966 the sheep population had recovered. Sheep numbers then showed no clear trend until 1977 when it became apparent that the CAP for sheepmeat would almost certainly be introduced. The sheep population has risen continuously since 1977.

England and Wales currently account for almost three quarters of the United Kingdom's sheep population, and Scotland for almost a quarter. There are relatively few sheep in Northern Ireland. The greatest increase in recent years has occurred in England, particularly in the lowlands.

Not only has there been an increase in sheep numbers during the past decade, but there has also been a rise in the number of holdings with sheep. This is exceptional; for all other major agricultural products the numbers of producers have been falling.

Sheep slaughterings have, as might be expected, followed the trends in the sheep population. Sheepmeat production increased by more than two thirds between 1955, the first year after decontrol, and 1987. However, in spite of this, total supplies and therefore consumption, have fallen because of reduced imports. Since 1983 domestic production has accounted for over three quarters of total new supplies compared with about half in the early 1970s. Total mutton and lamb imports have fallen by about two thirds compared with the late 1930s.

Mutton and lamb consumption per head has fallen sharply since the early 1930s. In 1987 it was slightly over half the pre-war level.

Associated with the decline in imports has been a change in the source. In 1938 New Zealand accounted for only about half of the UK's total lamb imports; Australia held about a quarter and there were also significant imports from Argentina. Currently New Zealand accounts for virtually all imports and only negligible quantities are imported from other sources. Imports from non-EC countries are currently restricted by the Voluntary Restraint Agreement, but in most years imports have been well below quota. The quotas reflect the quantities imported prior to the adoption of the CAP for sheep meat.

The sharp rise in domestic sheepmeat production during the past decade has enabled the United Kingdom to become a significant exporter of sheep meat. Exports have risen almost six fold since 1970. France is the main importer, accounting for about three quarters of the UK's exports.

Producers have, since decontrol, benefited from a system of guaranteed prices which has meant that returns from the market have been supplemented by either deficiency or variable premium payments to bring the average market price up to the guide price level. Since 1982 this applies only to Great Britain. The CAP also provided for a ewe premium which is paid to all countries.

In real terms, producers' total returns for slaughter sheep have fared better than those for most other agricultural products. After declining steadily in the period 1955–1967, returns have generally been well maintained although there were strong fluctuations in the 1970s. However, the recent trend for returns has been slightly downward. There was some recovery in 1987.

Sheep numbers

The sheep population in Great Britain showed considerable fluctuations during the second half of the 19th century, ranging from about 25 million to 30 million. Sheep numbers fell to a low of 19.7 million during World War I, but by the early 1930s the sheep population in the United Kingdom had again risen to about 27 million. There was a sharp reduction during World War II and by 1947 numbers had fallen to less than 17 million. There was no significant recovery until 1956 when profitability began to improve. The expansion continued into the mid-1960s, when the sheep population peaked at 30 million. This level was not again attained until 1979.

The sheep population has increased by almost 24% since 1980 when the CAP for sheep meat was introduced. The increases in recent years have been due primarily to the relative decline in the profitability of suckler calf production in the uplands and milk and beef production in other regions, resulting in a switch to sheepmeat production.

Sheep and lamb numbers (millions)

Based on Appendix Table 18.2.

Holdings with breeding sheep

The number of holdings with breeding sheep had been falling until the coming into operation of the EC sheep meat regime in 1980. It has since moved upwards. After falling to a low of 79 000 in 1980, numbers had risen to 85 000 by 1987. The average flock size has risen continuously from 123 ewes in 1967 to 212 in 1987. The proportion of breeding sheep in flocks of 500 and over has also risen steadily and by 1987 47% of the breeding sheep were in flocks of 500 and over.

Number of holdings with breeding sheep ('000)

No. of breeding sheep	1967	1975	1980	1985[1]	1987[1]
1–99	71.6	45.3	41.7	43.3	41.5
100–499	34.0	29.8	30.5	32.4	34.2
500 and over	4.6	5.6	6.6	7.9	9.1
Total	110.2	80.7	78.7	83.5	84.7
Average size of flock	123	164	181	191	212
% of breeding sheep in flocks of 500 and over	29.4	37.6	40.8	43.8	47.0

[1]Provisional.

Mutton and lamb production

Sheep slaughterings ranged between 10 and 11 million during the 1930s and then fell sharply during World War II. It was not until 1960 that they again recovered to over 11 million. Separate statistical series for ewe and ram and other sheep and lamb slaughterings have been available since 1960. Other sheep and lamb slaughterings increased almost continuously during the 1970s and by 1980, when the CAP for sheep meat was introduced, had risen to 12.8 million.

Sheep and lamb slaughterings and mutton and lamb production

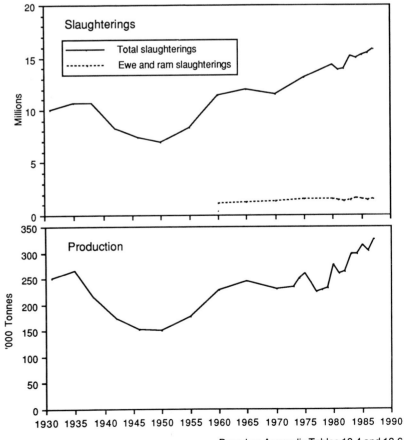

Based on Appendix Tables 18.4 and 18.6.

However, because of the large number of sheep kept for breeding, it was not until 1987 that other sheep and lamb slaughterings exceeded 14 million. Ewe and ram slaughterings have ranged between 1.3 and 1.6 million since 1980.

Mutton and lamb production has increased by nearly 14% since 1980.

Mutton and lamb supplies

In spite of the sharp rise in home production, total new supplies have fallen sharply and by 1987 amounted to only two thirds of the quantity available in the early 1970s. Not only has there been a sharp reduction in imports but also a substantial increase in exports.

The United Kingdom has traditionally been a major importer of both mutton and lamb. However, not only have mutton imports been at negligible levels in recent years but there has also been a sharp fall in lamb imports. Mutton imports have fallen from a peak of 120 000 tonnes in 1950 to only 1100 tonnes in 1987. Lamb imports in 1987, almost entirely from New Zealand, declined to only 130 000 tonnes.

An increasing proportion of bone-in and boneless cuts is, however, being imported in place of frozen carcases. The figures in the table, which are on the basis of product weight, therefore overstate the decline in meat imports. Total mutton and lamb imports amounted to 131 000 tonnes in 1987. Exports of mutton and lamb have risen sharply in recent years mainly because of the increasing demand for sheepmeat in France. Exports have risen from 11 000 tonnes in 1970 to 71 000 tonnes in 1987: there may be considerable further potential for exporting as demand for sheepmeat is still increasing in France.

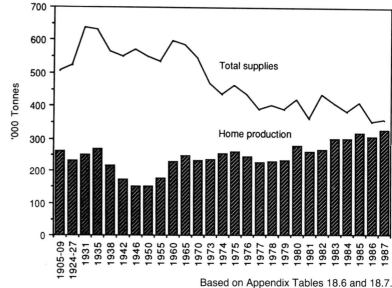

Mutton and lamb supplies ('000 tonnes)

Based on Appendix Tables 18.6 and 18.7.

Imports of mutton and lamb ('000 tonnes)

	1938	1942	1950	1960	1970	1980	1985	1986	1987
Argentina	45	70	41	31	–	–	–	–	–
Australia	97	74	65	31	32	2	5	6	5
New Zealand	187	217	275	305	296	189	151	118	124
Other countries	22	16	19	5	3	1	1	1	2
Total	351	377	400	372	331	192	157	125	131

Based on Appendix Table 18.9.

Exports of mutton and lamb ('000 tonnes)						
	1970	1975	1980	1985	1986	1987
Belgium/ Luxembourg	1	2	14	6	7	8
France	8	26	4	35	44	54
West Germany	–	3	14	3	3	3
Other countries	2	2	6	5	6	6
Total	11	33	38	49	60	71

Based on Appendix Table 18.10.

Consumption

Mutton and lamb consumption has fallen sharply since the 1930s. Consumption of home produced lamb has risen, but there has been a reduction in the quantity of imported lamb which is eaten. Consumers are increasingly purchasing the new leaner cuts. In spite of the sharp reduction in per head consumption, the United Kingdom remains the second most important consumer of sheepmeat in the EC, only exceeded by Greece which has a consumption of about 14 kg per head per annum.

Mutton and lamb consumption (kg per head per annum)									
1931	1938	1942	1950	1960	1970	1980	1985	1986	1987[1]
14.1	11.4	10.9	11.4	11.1	9.6	7.5	6.9	6.4	6.3

[1]Forecast.

Prices

Prices for slaughter sheep have risen rapidly since the early 1970s for several reasons: the general inflationary pressures during the 1970s, the decline in imports from New Zealand, and improved exports. In recent years about 20% of domestic sheepmeat production has been exported, mainly to France where prices tend to be higher than in the UK. This has helped to raise the general price level.

In real terms, however, slaughter sheep prices have fallen by 28% between 1955–56 and 1987.

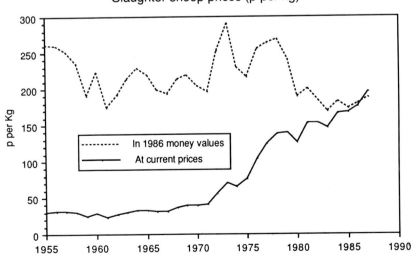

Slaughter sheep prices (p per kg)[1]

[1]Estimated dressed carcase weight.

Based on Appendix Table 18.13.

Returns

Producers' total returns (including deficiency payments or variable premiums) for slaughter sheep showed virtually no change between 1956–57 and 1967–68. There was a rapid rise in the 1970s and this continued into the 1980s.

In real terms, however, producers' total returns declined by 24% between 1955–56 and 1980. There was some recovery between 1980 and 1985. Since then there has again been a reduction.

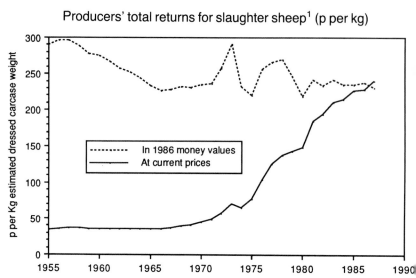

Producers' total returns for slaughter sheep[1] (p per kg)

[1]Estimated dressed carcase weight.   Based on Appendix Table 18.13.

Retail prices

Retail sheepmeat prices have increased almost continuously since the late 1930s. Home killed lamb prices increased by over 560% between 1967 and 1987. After allowing for inflation, lamb prices increased by over 40% between 1967 and 1973, but have since fallen sharply. In real terms prices declined by about 25% between 1973 and 1984; since then there has been little change.

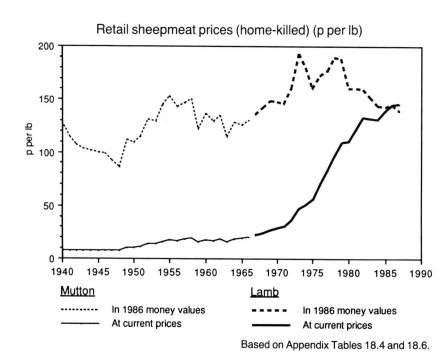

Retail sheepmeat prices (home-killed) (p per lb)

Based on Appendix Tables 18.4 and 18.6.

CHAPTER 19

Pigmeat

Pigmeat production has been increasing rapidly in recent years and in 1987 amounted to about one million tonnes in terms of fresh pigmeat equivalent, with a farm gate value of £951 million. In 1987 it accounted for 22% of the total value of livestock output. Pigmeat production is currently only slightly less in quantity than beef.

During the past 30 years there have been major changes in production techniques and in the structure of the industry. The economics of pig farming are particularly complex as feed accounts for approximately 70% of the cost of production. Also pigmeat is used for the production of bacon and ham, fresh pork and numerous manufactured products. Each is virtually a separate market and often requires different weights and qualities of pig.

In 1866 there were only 2.5 million pigs in Great Britain and it was not until the early 1930s that the population began to exceed 3 million. Since pigmeat production is in the main based on cereals and imported concentrates which were in short supply during World War II, the pig population fell sharply; the June 1943 census recorded only 1.8 million pigs on farms in the United Kingdom. It was not until 1951 that the pig population again exceeded 3 million. Numbers reached a peak of nine million in 1973, then declined to about eight million, the result of deteriorating profitability. In contrast with the policies for beef and sheep meat, there is little government or EC financial support for pig production.

Historically, most of the pigs in the United Kingdom were in England and this continues unchanged. In 1987 England accounted for 86% of the United Kingdom's pig population. The Scottish pig population has never been above the 700 000 level recorded in the 1970s. Pig numbers in Northern Ireland rose to a peak of 1.3 million in 1965, but since 1980 have not exceeded 600 000.

The number of holdings with pigs has fallen sharply and there has been a major increase in the average size of herd. In 1967 there were 78 400 holdings with breeding pigs in the United Kingdom, with an average herd size of 10; by 1987 there were only 15 700 holdings with an average of 52 breeding pigs. In 1987 85% of the breeding pigs were in herds of 50 and over.

A particularly interesting feature since the mid-1950s has been the development of the multi-purpose pig, which can be used for bacon, fresh pork or manufacturing products. In 1987, 27% of the pigs were used partly for bacon compared with only 7% in 1960. Bacon and ham consumption has fallen sharply since the end of post-war rationing from 11.2 kg per head per annum in 1955 to only 8.0 kg in 1987. Despite the decline in consumption, the result of changed eating habits, domestic production of bacon and ham has been relatively well maintained. Imports have fallen sharply; Denmark remains the main source, but shipments from the Netherlands have risen rapidly in recent years.

Pork consumption (including pork used for manufacturing) has increased dramatically since World War II and has since the mid-1970s exceeded bacon consumption. Little pork is imported and since 1982 the United Kingdom has become a net exporter, mostly in the form of sow meat to the Federal Republic of Germany.

As with other livestock enterprises, pig producers benefited from a system of guaranteed prices and deficiency payments until 1972 when the United Kingdom became a member of the European Community. The guaranteed price for pigmeat was linked to a feed price formula as well as to a forecast of slaughterings. This meant that producers' returns varied with feed costs and at least partly explains the rapid rise in the pig population in the late 1960s and early 1970s.

Since 1973, following the UK's joining of the EC, pig producers have had to rely on returns from the market, and the cost of feed has been crucial in determining profitability. After allowing for inflation, slaughter pig prices have fallen by about 30% since 1972 while barley prices in 1986 were down by only about 3%. The Cambridge University Pig Management Scheme results show that, whereas in 1970–72 pig producers' margins averaged £14.50 per £100 output, in 1980–86 the average was only £7.10, with margins ranging from −£5.70 in 1983 to +£10.40 in 1985. Profitability is extremely volatile.

Pig numbers

The pig population began to expand in the 1930s, but there was a major reduction in numbers during World War II and the national pig herd did not begin to recover until after 1951. Expansion was then rapid. Pig numbers reached a peak of 9 million in 1973, but since 1980 have ranged between 7.8 and 8.2 million. This stability is due to the fact that the industry now consists in the main of specialist pig producers who have invested heavily in buildings and equipment and must maintain production to minimise overheads. They cannot afford to cut back even during periods of low profitability.

Pig numbers (million)

1866	1900	1910	1920	1930	1938	1942	1950	1960	1970	1980	1985	1986	1987
2.5[1]	2.4[1]	2.4[1]	2.1[1]	2.7	4.4	2.1	3.0	5.7	8.1	7.8	7.9	7.9	7.9

[1]Great Britain.

Based on Appendix Table 19.2.

Holdings with breeding pigs

The number of holdings with pigs has fallen dramatically. In 1987 there were only 15 700 holdings with breeding pigs in the United Kingdom compared with 78 000 in 1967. Most of the breeding pigs are in England. Of the 16 626 herds in 1986, 11 270 were in England, 1184 in Wales, 569 in Scotland and 3603 in Northern Ireland. In England most of the breeding sows are to be found in the Eastern and Northern regions, where the average herd sizes are over 70 sows.

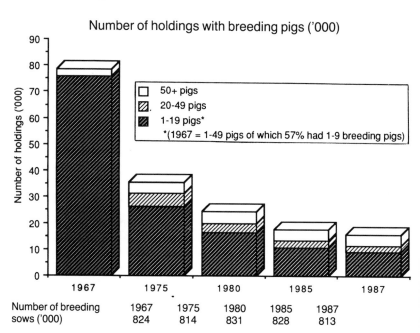

Number of holdings with breeding pigs ('000)

Legend:
- 50+ pigs
- 20-49 pigs
- 1-19 pigs*
- *(1967 = 1-49 pigs of which 57% had 1-9 breeding pigs)

Number of breeding sows ('000)	1967	1975	1980	1985	1987
	824	814	831	828	813

Pig slaughterings and pigmeat production

Pig slaughterings have followed the trends in pig numbers. There has been surprisingly little change in the average weight of pigs produced during the past 30 years, but there has been a major increase in sow productivity. Slaughterings began to increase in the 1930s, fell sharply during World War II, then recovered. There was a temporary reduction in the mid-1970s, but until 1983 there was an almost continuous upward trend. Since 1984 slaughterings have ranged between 15 and 16 million a year.

Until the mid-1950s bacon and ham production was of greater importance than pork. Bacon and ham production was comparatively well maintained during World War II and rose to a peak of about 250 000 tonnes in 1970. Since 1980 production has ranged between 200 000 and 212 000 tonnes per annum.

Pork production was at negligible levels during World War II, but has since risen sharply. After declining in 1984, production resumed its upward trend to reach a record level of 791 000 tonnes in 1987.

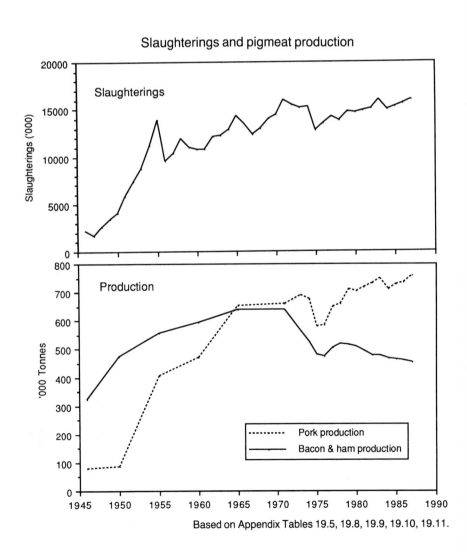

Slaughterings and pigmeat production

Based on Appendix Tables 19.5, 19.8, 19.9, 19.10, 19.11.

Use of slaughter pigs

The proportion of pigs used wholly for bacon has fallen sharply since 1960, while the proportion of pigs used in part for bacon is currently well over 25%. The increasing proportion of 'other pigs' slaughtered since 1970 reflects the increasing production of fresh pork and manufactured products.

Use of slaughter pigs (%)

	1960	1970	1975	1980	1985	1986	1987
Wholly for bacon	30.3	21.4	17.7	14.0	11.2	11.1	9.5
Partly for bacon	7.2	24.6	29.0	27.7	26.8	26.2	26.8
Others[1]	62.5	54.0	53.3	58.3	62.0	62.7	62.0
Total	100.0	100.0	100.0	100.0	100.0	100.0	100.0

[1]Mainly fresh pork and manufactured products.

Based on Appendix table 19.5

Bacon and ham supplies

Although the United Kingdom's self-sufficiency in bacon and ham has increased from about a third in the late 1930s to 44% in 1987, total supplies have fallen. They reached a peak of almost 640 000 tonnes in the early 1970s, but have since fallen to only slightly over 450 000 tonnes in 1987. Domestic production has fallen from a peak of about 270 000 tonnes in the early 1970s to 197 000 tonnes in 1987. Imports were at a peak in the 1960s, but in 1987 totalled only 63% of the quantity imported in 1960. The Netherlands has in recent years increased its share of the import market at the expense of Denmark.

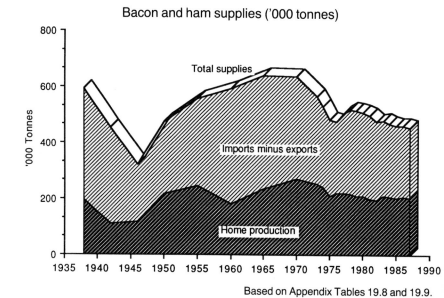

Bacon and ham supplies ('000 tonnes)

Based on Appendix Tables 19.8 and 19.9.

Pork supplies

In the 1930s the United Kingdom produced about 80% of its pork requirements. Little pork was produced because of the shortage of feed during World War II. Since then there has been a rapid increase. The UK has been virtually self-sufficient in pork since 1960 and has been a net exporter since 1982. Total pork production rose to a peak of 791 000 tonnes in 1987; imports amounted to 46 000 tonnes and exports to 51 000 tonnes.

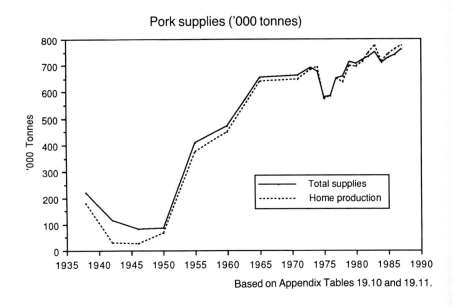

Pork supplies ('000 tonnes)

Based on Appendix Tables 19.10 and 19.11.

Consumption

Pork consumption, which had been relatively unimportant before 1939, fell even further to a negligible level during the war. Consumption has risen rapidly since the 1960s as pork has become increasingly good value. Efforts to breed lean pigs have been particularly successful and pork is now consumed throughout the year. Virtually all of it is produced in the United Kingdom.

Bacon and ham consumption has fallen sharply since before the war, but was surprisingly well maintained during World War II because of the large quantity of bacon imported from Canada. The decline in consumption of bacon for breakfast accounts for this decrease although consumption levels have remained relatively stable since 1982.

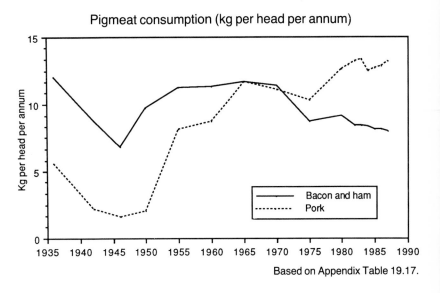

Pigmeat consumption (kg per head per annum)

Based on Appendix Table 19.17.

Prices and returns

Total returns to the producer (p per kg d.w.)[1]

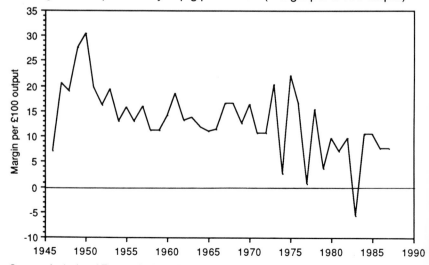

Based on Appendix Table 19.18.

[1]Excluding sows and boars.

Before 1973, the year in which the United Kingdom joined the European Community, pig producers received a deficiency payment in addition to their return from the market. The guaranteed price for pigs varied with the price of feed as well as forecast of slaughterings. Total returns ranged between 24p and 29p per kg dead weight from 1955–56 to 1970–71.

Slaughter pig prices began to rise rapidly from 1973 onwards reaching a peak of almost 108p in 1984. Plentiful supplies then resulted in a weak market and by 1987 the Average All Pigs Price had again fallen to 98.3p per kg dead weight.

In real terms producers' returns have fallen continuously since decontrol in the mid–1950s and by 1987 were 62% less than in 1955–56. This would not have been possible without greatly improved technical efficiency in pig production.

Profitability

The profitability of pig production is volatile and varies from year to year depending primarily on the relationship between feed costs and the return received for the pigs. Cambridge University Pig Management Scheme costings are available since 1946 and show that the margin per £100 output has ranged from £30.4 in 1950 to minus £5.70 in 1983. During the last decade margins have tended to be well below those achieved in the 1950s and 1960s; since 1980 they have ranged from £10.5 to minus £5.70 per £100 output.

There has been a spectacular improvement in the efficiency of pig production since the 1950s. The number of pigs weaned per sow and per gilt has risen almost continuously from only 10.8 in 1946 to 21.0 in 1987. The quantity of feed per weaner produced has fallen from 135 kg to only 79 kg. Feeding efficiency has also greatly improved. The average feed conversion ratio of the pigs in the Cambridge University Scheme has fallen from 4.95 in 1946 to 2.77 in 1987. This is in spite of the fact that the average weight of pig sold has only fallen from 88 kg to 82 kg during the past 41 years.

Changes in the profitability of pig production (margin per £100 output)

Source: *Agricultural Economics Unit, Department of Land Economy, University of Cambridge.*

Retail prices

Retail prices for bacon are not only influenced by what is paid for slaughter pigs in the United Kingdom, but also by the prices of foreign bacon, particularly from Denmark. Bacon prices, after remaining relatively stable during World War II, increased in the early 1950s. Although showing some fluctuations, they remained relatively stable until the early 1970s. There was then a rapid increase in price. In real terms retail bacon prices increased by almost 30% between 1972 and 1973 when the United Kingdom joined the European Community. Since then prices have again fallen sharply and by 1987 the real average price was 30% less than in 1973.

Retail pork prices also increased in the early 1950s and then showed relatively little change until the early 1970s. Prices increased by almost 150% between 1973 and 1982. There was a further sharp rise in 1984. In real terms pork prices have fallen almost continuously since 1973. The average real price in 1987 was 34% less than in 1973 and this has led to a considerable increase in consumption.

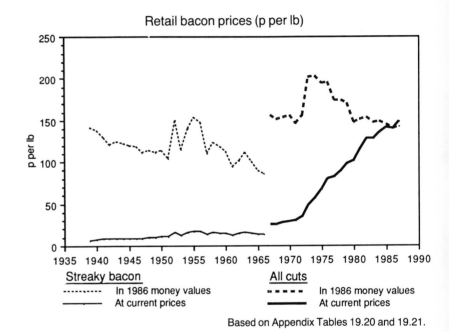

Retail bacon prices (p per lb)

Based on Appendix Tables 19.20 and 19.21.

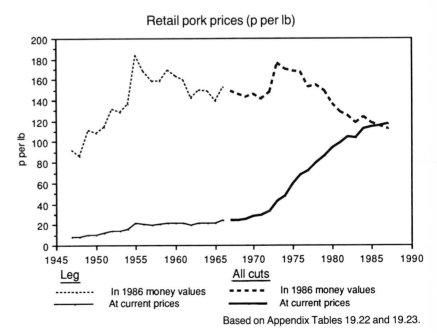

Retail pork prices (p per lb)

Based on Appendix Tables 19.22 and 19.23.

CHAPTER 20

Poultry meat

Poultry meat production has increased dramatically since World War II and in 1987 amounted to 1.01 million tonnes, only 7% less than beef and veal production. The farm gate value of poultry meat was estimated at £785 million in 1987, accounting for 18% of the value of livestock output.

Not only has the increase in poultry meat production and consumption been dramatic, but there have also been major changes in production techniques which have reduced the costs in real terms to the benefit of consumers. Chicken is no longer a luxury product but is bought as a staple item of diet by most sections of the community. Turkeys were in the past eaten only at Christmas, now there is a demand for them all the year round and especially at Easter. The bulk of poultry sold today is oven-ready either frozen or chilled, but there is still a considerable demand for the fresh product.

Given the short time required to produce poultry meat, it is more difficult to trace the history of the industry statistically than is the case for other sectors. It now only takes about 10 weeks to produce a broiler, so the June census results are not necessarily an accurate reflection of production trends. Moreover, it is only since 1960 that there have been separate statistics for laying and table fowls.

Whatever the pitfalls in evaluating the census results for poultry there can, however, be no doubt that there has been an enormous increase in production. The slaughter and production statistics, which have also been subject to periodic revision, give a more accurate picture of developments. In 1987, 526 million fowls, 8.1 million ducks and 31.9 million turkeys were slaughtered.

Unlike egg production, which continues to take place on about 42 000 agricultural holdings, the production of poultry meat has become very specialised. In June 1987 there were only 2000 agricultural holdings producing broilers with an average flock size of about 33 000. Of the 2000 holdings 69% are located in England and Wales, 14% in Scotland and 17% in Northern Ireland.

Notwithstanding the rapid increase in poultry meat production, there has also been a significant rise in imports in the past 10 years. In 1987 the United Kingdom imported 82 000 tonnes of poultry meat of which 38 000 tonnes were of French origin. Imports from the Netherlands amounted to 32 000 tonnes. The United Kingdom has also become an exporter of poultry meat; in 1987 exports amounted to 48 000 tonnes, of which 11 000 tonnes were sent to the Federal Republic of Germany and 8000 tonnes to the Irish Republic. In 1987 domestic production accounted for 96% of the total available on the United Kingdom market.

Consumption of poultry meat increased to a record level of about 18.0 kg per head in 1987 compared with only 2.3 kg pre-World War II. Poultry meat is increasingly being eaten in forms other than whole birds, for example, chicken and turkey pieces and rolled joints. There is also evidence that poultry meat is no longer eaten because it is good value, but rather because it fits in well with modern theories on diet and health. Consumers are also increasingly prepared to pay for 'better quality', demanding chilled and fresh rather than frozen poultry meat. Historically producers have not had the benefit of government price support, nor do they receive any support in the European Community.

Broiler prices increased by only 8% between 1980 and 1987. In real terms prices have fallen by 29% since 1980. Retail prices have also been relatively stable in recent years; so that prices after allowing for inflation also declined by 29% between 1970 and 1987.

Poultry numbers

The table fowl population on farms, as shown by the annual June census, has risen rapidly from only 16.3 million in 1960 to 70.6 million in 1987. Turkey numbers have also risen sharply, from only three million in 1960 to almost eight million in 1985.

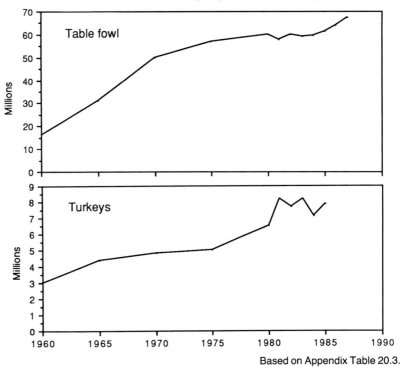

Table fowl and turkey population (millions)

Based on Appendix Table 20.3.

Holdings with broilers

Since it first began, broiler production has been a large scale enterprise run by relatively few farmers. In 1967 there were 3700 broiler producers in the United Kingdom with an average flock size of 9800 birds. In 1987 there were only 2000 producers with an average flock size of about 33 000. In 1987 almost 56% of the birds were in flocks of 100 000 and over.

Number of holdings with broilers ('000)

	1967	1972	1980	1985[1]	1987[1]
No. of broilers					
1–9999	2.8	1.7	1.4	1.0	1.0
10 000–99 999	} 0.9	0.6	0.7	0.8	0.8
100 000 and over		0.1	0.1	0.2	0.2
Total	3.7	2.4	2.2	2.0	2.0
Average flock size ('000)	9.8	23.4	26.5	31.0	33.0
% broilers in flocks of 100 000 and over		59.9	56.7	54.3	55.9

[1]Provisional.

Slaughterings and meat production

The number of poultry slaughtered has increased almost 12-fold since before World War II. In 1987, 526 million fowls, 32 million turkeys, 8.1 million ducks and 200 000 geese were slaughtered.

Poultry meat production amounted to 978 000 tonnes in 1987 compared with only 81 000 tonnes pre-World War II.

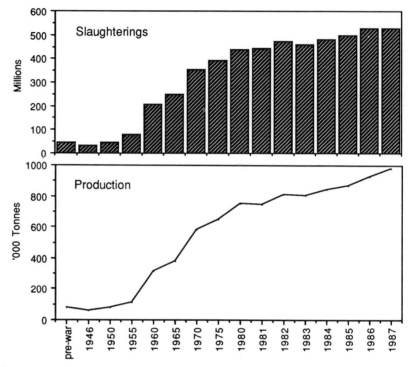

Slaughterings of fowl and poultry meat production[1]

[1] Including turkeys, ducks and geese.

Based on Appendix Table 20.5.

Supplies

The United Kingdom produced about 80% of its poultry meat requirements in the late-1930s. In spite of the ten-fold increase in supplies which has occurred since then, domestic production currently accounts for about 96% of the total supply coming onto the market. There has been some increase in imports, particularly from France and the Netherlands in recent years, but exports from the UK have also risen. Net imports in 1987 only amounted to 44 000 tonnes.

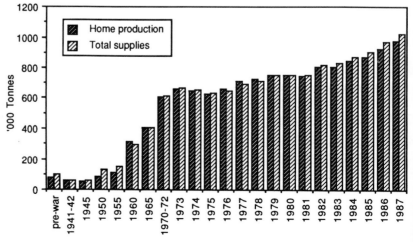

Poultry meat supplies ('000 tonnes)

Based on Appendix Tables 20.6 and 20.7.

Consumption

Poultry meat consumption has increased dramatically from only 2.3 kg per head per annum pre-World War II to about 18.0 kg in 1987. Most of the increased consumption is in the form of broilers and turkeys. There has been some increase in duck consumption since the beginning of the 1980s, but little goose meat is consumed.

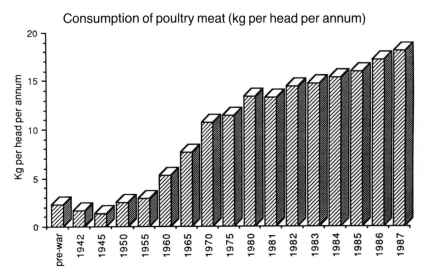

Consumption of poultry meat (kg per head per annum)

Based on Appendix Table 20.10.

Prices

Wholesale poultry meat prices showed relatively little change between 1950 and 1970. Pre-World War II, poultry meat was considered a luxury, but since the late 1960s it has become an increasingly popular low-priced meat. Price reductions in real terms have been made possible by improved economic efficiency. Nevertheless producers' profit margins have often been very slender; broiler prices have fallen by 40% in real terms since 1970. Retail poultry meat prices have increased much less rapidly than most other meats and in 1987 were only 300% higher than in 1967. This compares with increases of 600% for beef and 565% for home-killed lamb. After allowing for inflation, retail poultry meat prices declined by 29% between 1970 and 1987. There was little change in the retail price of beef or lamb in real terms during this period.

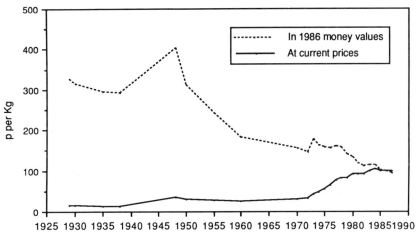

Wholesale poultry meat prices (p per kg)

Based on Appendix Table 20.11.

CHAPTER 21

Milk and milk products

In 1987 milk and milk products, at £2411 million, accounted for 20% of farmers' total receipts, making this commodity group the most important in agriculture in the United Kingdom.

For more than a century until 1984 the steady expansion of milk production had been a major feature in the changing pattern of British farming. This expansion was the combined result of an increase in the number of cows and rising yields. Within one generation, from 1946 to 1978, the output of milk for human consumption (liquid or manufactured) doubled.

From 1960 to 1983 the number of dairy cows remained stable at around 3.2 million, but yields continued to rise at an average annual rate of 1.6%, reaching a peak of 5055 litres per cow in 1982–83. In 1984 the EC quota system came into effect; since then there has been a perceptible reduction in cow numbers. Yields fell substantially in 1984 but have since shown some recovery.

There are a number of reasons why milk yields have increased. Herd management has been greatly improved, particularly in feeding practices and in disease control. Not only have the yields of the various breeds been increased by selection but many producers have given up other breeds in favour of the higher yielding Friesians. In recorded herds, Friesians yield 10–15% more than the formerly much-favoured Dairy Shorthorns, which have now almost disappeared.

The post-war expansion of the dairy herd brought with it a transformation of the size structure of herds. The number of holdings on which dairy cows are kept has fallen from 132 000 in 1967 to 50 000 in 1987, and this decline is continuing. In the same period the average size of herd has risen from 24 to 61 cows. Today nearly half of the United Kingdom's milk production comes from herds of 100 cows or more. This development has enabled farmers to make substantial savings in the labour cost per cow and per litre. Farm buildings have been modernised and efficient systems of mechanical milking have displaced hand milking.

Producers have seized opportunities to enlarge their dairy enterprises as the most effective way of countering falling real prices for milk. Economies of scale have resulted in lower real costs of production per litre. In this way profit margins in most years have been fairly well maintained, though in recent years the financial strains on dairy farmers have become more severe.

The utilisation of the milk supplied by British farms has undergone a profound change. The expansion of production has not been accompanied by a corresponding increase in liquid milk consumption. Indeed utilisation for liquid milk and cream has declined by about 18% since 1975. Consequently there has been a rapid increase in the quantity of milk which is used for the production of butter, cheese and other manufactured products. In 1978, for the first time milk destined for manufacture exceeded the amount used for liquid consumption. The proportions are now about 53% and 47% respectively; in 1955 they were 23% and 77%.

The change in the pattern of domestic supplies has greatly affected the United Kingdom's trading situation in dairy products. Net imports of butter have fallen from 493 000 tonnes in 1975 to 111 000 tonnes in 1986.

The supply-demand balance for British dairy products has meanwhile been affected by a substantial swing in consumption patterns away from butter and towards margarine. Since 1980, consumption of margarine has exceeded that of butter by a steadily increasing margin.

Production

Milk output for human consumption has more than doubled since pre-war days. Although farmers were encouraged to increase production during World War II, it was not until after the war when feed became easier to obtain that production began to rise significantly. By the mid-1950s output had risen to 10 500 million litres, almost 50% more than pre-war. The major increase, however, has occurred since the United Kingdom's entry into the EC. Output reached a peak of 16 590 million litres in 1983, 28% more than in 1971–72. There has been some reduction since then, primarily due to the imposition of EC milk quotas. Output for human consumption totalled only 14 798 million litres in 1987; this sharp reduction was due to poor seasonal conditions, lower yields and to a fall in cow numbers. The sharp rise in milk production since the mid-1950s has been due almost entirely to increased yields. The output per cow has risen from 3412 litres in 1955–59 to 4913 litres in 1985–87. Dairy cow numbers showed little change between the early 1960s and 1984. Since then there has been some reduction because of the introduction of EC milk quotas. Profitability has also declined in real terms.

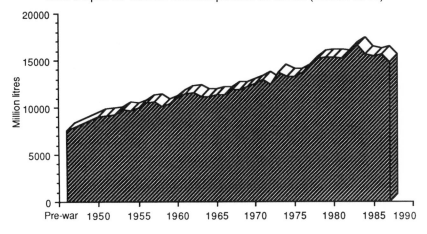

Milk output for human consumption in all forms (million litres)

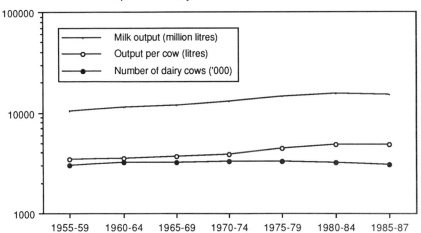

Milk production, yields and cow numbers

Holdings and herd size

The total number of holdings with dairy cows has fallen sharply from about 188 000 in 1960 to 52 262 in 1986 in spite of little change in the size of the national herd. The average size of herd has therefore increased from only 16.8 head in 1960 to 60.3 in 1986. The number of dairy cows in small and medium sized herds has fallen while those in large herds has increased. In 1960 32% of the total dairy cow population were in herds with 1–19 cows, 45% in herds of 20–49 cows and 23% in herds with more than 50 cows. By 1986 79% of the cows were in herds of 50 or more.

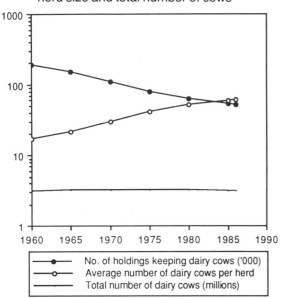

Number of holdings with dairy cows, herd size and total number of cows

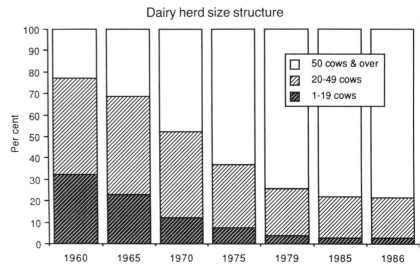

Dairy herd size structure

Prices

Although the average net prices per litre received by producers for milk have increased more than five-fold since 1960, after allowing for inflation, returns have fallen by almost 35%. There has been a reduction of about 16% since 1980.

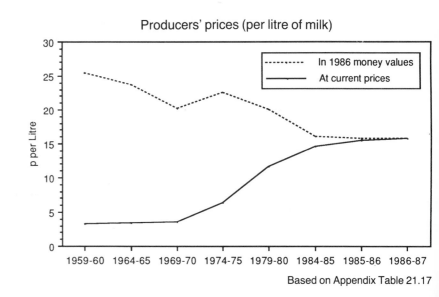

Producers' prices (per litre of milk)

Based on Appendix Table 21.17

Value of output

In raising yields per cow, producers have not entirely succeeded in offsetting the fall in real milk prices. The real value of output per cow has fallen, though there was some recovery in the 1970s.

Increases in the prices paid for feed, labour, machinery and other inputs compared to the price received for milk have resulted in a prolonged fall in the real net margin per cow. Many producers have been unable to withstand the squeeze and have gone out of milk production. The remaining farmers have almost always had to increase the number of cows in the herd. This has often meant purchasing or leasing more land.

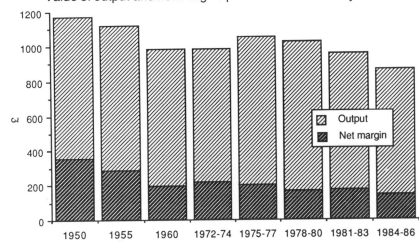

Value of output and net margins per cow in 1986 money values

Milk

Milk utilisation (million litres)

Based on Appendix Table 21.6.

Since 1950 there have been considerable changes in the quantities of milk used for different purposes. The use of milk for liquid consumption and for cream peaked at 9000 million litres in 1975 but has since fallen to only about 7400 million litres.

The amount of milk used for butter production has risen from only 436 million litres in 1950 to 5294 million litres in 1983, but has fallen to only 3766 million litres in 1987. The use of milk for cheese making has also increased, from 496 million litres in 1950 to almost 2620 million litres in 1987. There have also been increases in the quantities of milk used for other purposes, particularly milk powder. The proportion of sales used for liquid milk or cream has fallen by a half between 1950 and 1987.

Butter

Butter supplies fell sharply during World War II and did not regain the pre-war level of about 530 000 tonnes until the mid-1970s. Since then supplies have fallen again because of reduced consumption. Both the quantity and the proportion of butter produced in the UK, however, has increased sharply, from only about 9% both pre-war and in 1975 to about 65% in 1986. In 1987 stocks were sharply reduced and exports increased which meant that statistically the United Kingdom was a net exporter of butter. The consumption of butter was in fact very similar to 1986.

Prior to World War II Australia and New Zealand were the major suppliers. New Zealand continues to be an important source of imports, while the remainder comes from other EC member states, particularly Denmark, the Irish Republic and the Netherlands.

Percentage of home production and imports

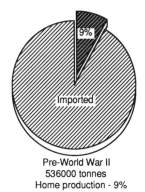

Pre-World War II
536000 tonnes
Home production - 9%

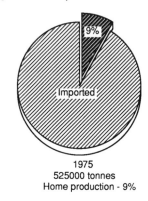

1975
525000 tonnes
Home production - 9%

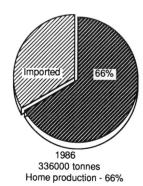

1986
336000 tonnes
Home production - 66%

Based on Appendix Table 21.7.

Cheese

There has been a considerable increase in cheese consumption. Supplies have risen from 190 000 tonnes prior to World War II to over 390 000 tonnes in 1987. Most of the rise has occurred since 1970. Home production has increased from only 46 000 tonnes pre-war to over 260 000 tonnes in 1987. The United Kingdom now produces about 65% of its cheese requirements compared with only about a quarter in the late 1930s. Pre-war most of the cheese was imported from Canada and New Zealand, now the main sources are Belgium, the Irish Republic, the Federal Republic of Germany and the Netherlands.

Percentage of home production and imports.

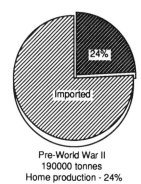

Pre-World War II
190000 tonnes
Home production - 24%

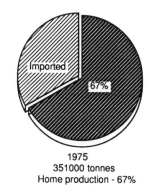

1975
351000 tonnes
Home production - 67%

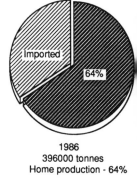

1986
396000 tonnes
Home production - 64%

Based on Appendix Table 21.9.

CHAPTER 22

Eggs

The value of egg output rose to a peak of £554 million in 1984, but by 1987 had fallen to only £506 million, mainly because of a sharp fall in egg prices. There was virtually no change in the level of supplies during this period.

As in the case of poultry meat, there are difficulties in compiling long term statistical series. Many of the series have been subject to changes in methodology and there have been numerous revisions. This is not surprising as the industry has undergone a multitude of changes. Nevertheless, the statistics featured give a good indication of both longer and shorter term developments.

The fowl population has risen at least three-fold during the past century, but the number of laying fowls has fallen quite sharply since 1970.

Although there has been a major reduction in the number of agricultural holdings producing eggs, there are still many farms with laying fowls. In 1987 there were 42 100 egg producers compared with only 15 700 holdings with breeding pigs and 2000 broiler producers. The average number of laying fowls per holding has increased more than three-fold during the past twenty years and in 1987 68% of the laying fowls were in flocks of 20 000 birds or more. In 1986 England accounted for 65% of the holdings producing eggs, Wales 14%, Scotland 13% and Northern Ireland 8%.

In common with agriculture generally, large increases in productivity have been due to genetic research and changes in management. Egg yields have risen by 75% since pre-World War II. There has been a 19% increase in yields since 1970.

There was a major increase in egg production between the end of World War II and 1970, but since then production has fallen by 8% in spite of continuing improvements in yield per bird and efficiency of management. This is not surprising as producers' prices for eggs have fallen by over 50% in real terms since 1970.

Historically, the United Kingdom was a major importer of eggs. At the beginning of the 20th century, domestic production accounted for only 32% of total supplies, but by the outbreak of World War II this had risen to 61%. This country has been virtually self-sufficient since the beginning of the 1970s, although some eggs continue to be imported, mainly from France and the Netherlands. During the 1930s eggs were also imported from Australia, China, the USSR and South Africa. Imports of egg products have fallen to a negligible level. Exports have never been significant in quantity.

Of particular concern to the industry is the fall in egg consumption, primarily due to the fact that fewer cooked breakfasts are now eaten. Consumption per head is estimated to have fallen by about 20% since 1970. Consumption, however, appears to have shown greater stability since about 1981.

Number of fowls

The total number of fowls in Great Britain rose between the mid 1880s and the mid-1920s. Figures for the United Kingdom since 1929 show a further major rise until the mid 1960s.

Numbers of laying fowls have been separately enumerated since 1966 and rose to a peak in 1970, since when there has been a sharp decline. Because of further changes in statistical methodology, the laying fowl figures are not entirely comparable until the period since 1980; numbers have fallen by 16% since that year.

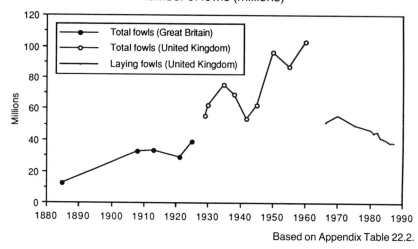

Number of fowls (millions)

Based on Appendix Table 22.2.

Holdings

Although the figures are not entirely comparable, the number of holdings with laying fowls has fallen from about 188 000 in 1967 to only 42 100 in 1987, while the average flock size has increased from 275 to 900 birds. In 1986 there were 28 917 holdings producing eggs in England, 6193 in Wales, 5782 in Scotland and 3707 in Northern Ireland.

Number of holdings with laying flocks ('000)

	1967	1975	1980	1985[2]	1987[2]
Number of laying fowls					
1–4999	186.1[1]	82.0	57.5	45.2	40.9
5000–19 999	} 1.8	1.6	1.2	0.9	0.8
20 000 and over		0.4	0.4	0.4	0.4
Total	187.9	84.1	59.2	46.5	42.1
Average size of flock	275	587	770	848	900
% of total in laying flocks of 20 000 and over		47.1	60.0	65.7	68.1

[1]Of which 179 000 holdings had less than 1000 laying fowls. [2]Provisional.

Yields

Egg yields have increased sharply since the end of World War II as a result of genetic improvements and changes in management. By 1987 the average egg yield per bird had increased to 261 eggs per annum compared with only 149 eggs pre–World War II.

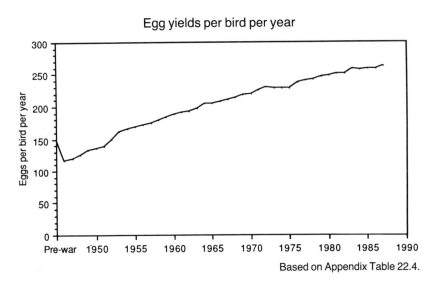

Egg yields per bird per year

Based on Appendix Table 22.4.

Output and supplies

Egg output for human consumption, which had fallen sharply during World War II due to a shortage of feed, increased rapidly in the 1950s and 1960s reaching a peak of 1158 million dozen in 1970–71. Since then output has fallen by almost 10%. Total supplies have followed a similar trend. The United Kingdom has been virtually self-sufficient since the beginning of the 1970s, although there is a small foreign trade in both directions.

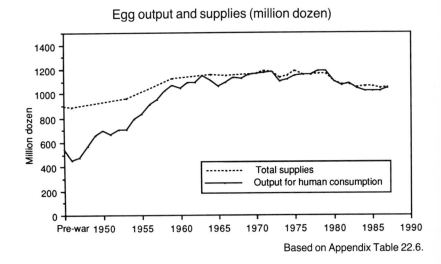

Egg output and supplies (million dozen)

Based on Appendix Table 22.6.

Consumption

Egg consumption was surprisingly well maintained during World War II although about a third of the total was in the form of mainly imported egg products. Egg consumption, particularly fresh eggs, showed a sharp recovery after derationing and by 1970 the total had risen to the equivalent of 275 eggs per head per year. Since then there has been a substantial fall, but the most recent figures show more stability.

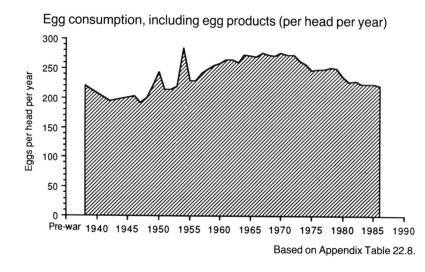

Egg consumption, including egg products (per head per year)

Based on Appendix Table 22.8.

Producer prices

Egg producers benefited from guaranteed price arrangements administered by the Egg Marketing Board until 1970–71. Since then returns have been dependent on market conditions. Egg prices can be very sensitive to fluctuations in supply and demand and have ranged between 32p and 45p per dozen since 1980. Prices were unusually high in 1984 when there was a reduction in output during two consecutive years.

In real terms prices have fallen almost continuously since the early 1970s and by 1987 the average price had declined by over 50% compared with 1970.

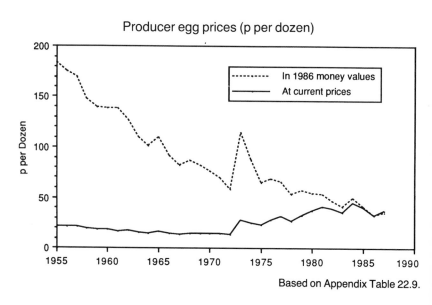

Producer egg prices (p per dozen)

Based on Appendix Table 22.9.

CHAPTER 23

Wool

The value of output of clip wool in 1987 is estimated at £44 million. If this is added to the value of output of slaughter sheep and lambs, sheep producers' total output was £703 million in 1987. This represents 9% of the total value of output of livestock and livestock products.

Sheep can adapt themselves to a wide range of environments. In the UK there are about 50 recognised breeds suited to different varieties of climate, soil, herbage and terrain.

British sheep produce mostly coarse quality wool which is ideally suited for carpets, tweeds and knitting yarns. British flocks may be roughly classified into three main groups: short-wool and down; long wool and lustre; and mountain and hill.

Hill and lowland sheep production is complementary. Flocks on hill and upland grazing (comprising three quarters of the land mass of the United Kingdom) provide lambs for fattening in the lowlands and cross-bred ewes to produce future lambs for slaughter. Meat production is more important in the lowlands, but the hill producer can derive as much as a third of his income from wool.

All the clip wool produced has to be marketed through the producer-operated British Wool Marketing Board. The Board, which came into operation in 1959, collects, grades and stores the wool and then sells to the trade at auction, paying farmers on the basis of grade.

The total sheep population and the ewe flock have both risen sharply since 1979 when it became obvious that an EC sheepmeat regime would be introduced. Although this did not affect wool producers' returns directly as wool is an industrial and not an agricultural product in the European Community, the introduction of the regime was undoubtedly of major benefit to the industry as a whole.

The increase in ewe numbers since 1979 has led to a rise in wool production. In 1987, at 61 000 tonnes, it was 18% higher than before World War II. Clip wool and skin wool, which are the product of slaughtered sheep, have both shown major rises.

The United Kingdom is still a major importer of wool, though much less is now imported than before World War II. Total available supply fell sharply following the introduction of man-made fibres, but this trend has been reversed now that wool has regained some of its former popularity.

Historically the United Kingdom has been an exporter of wool and exports appear to have risen in recent years. It is difficult to quantify this trade as some imported wool is almost certainly re-exported.

Wool is not an agricultural product under the CAP. The annual guaranteed price fixed by the Government helps to provide producers with a stable income.

Unlike most other agricultural products, there has been only a relatively slow increase in the average price paid to producers; current prices only doubled between 1955–56 and 1987–88 compared with an almost seven-fold increase in producers' total returns for lamb. This was due not only to the relatively slow rise in the guaranteed price for wool, but also the sharp rise in the British Wool Marketing Board's costs since the mid-1970s as a result of inflation and the high interest rates required to finance storing of wool.

In real terms, clip wool prices are now only about one quarter of their 1955 level – a more severe fall than for any other agricultural product.

Production

Ewe numbers declined sharply during World War II but began to rise again from 1951 until the second half of the 1960s when the ewe population began to fall. Numbers ranged between about 10.5 million and 11.2 million between 1970 and 1977, after which they began to increase sharply as the profitability of lamb production improved. Ewe numbers have risen by 21% since the introduction of the EC sheepmeat regime in 1980. The number of registered wool producers increased by 34% between 1950 when the British Wool Marketing Scheme was introduced, and 1960–61. After a 33% reduction between 1960–61 and 1979–80 there has again been an increase to 97 200.

Clip wool production, which had fallen during World War II, began to recover from the mid-1950s onwards, although there was a temporary decline in the second half of the 1960s. It has risen continuously since the mid-1970s.

Skin wool production has increased by 30% since 1980 in line with the increase in sheep slaughterings.

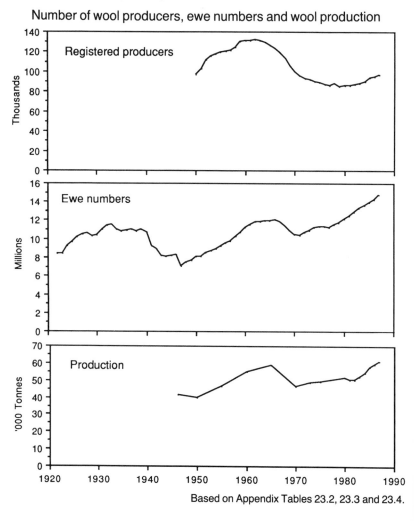

Number of wool producers, ewe numbers and wool production

Based on Appendix Tables 23.2, 23.3 and 23.4.

Supplies

Wool production has increased almost continuously since 1970. Imports declined sharply during World War II and after a temporary recovery again fell sharply as man-made fibres became increasingly popular. There has been some recovery in imports since 1982 but exports, which include re-exports, have also risen. The United Kingdom continues to be a major importer of wool.

Wool supplies

	Production			Imports[2]	Exports[2]	New supply	Production as % of new supply
	Total	Clip	Skin				
1925	40	31	9	342			
Pre-war	52	35	17	400	13	439	12
1946	42	28	14	215	5[3]	252[2]	17
1955	46	32	15	328	16[3]	358[2]	13
1960	55	37	19	293	19	329	17
1970	46	32	14	206	25	227	20
1980	52	39	13	96	31	117	44
1985	58	41	17	145	45	158	37
1986	59	42	17	145[4]	74[4]	131[4]	45
1987[5]	61	44	17	152[4]	73[4]	140[4]	44

[1]Greasy weight.   [2]Greasy weight from 1981 onwards therefore not comparable with earlier years.   [3]Estimated.   [4]Provisional.   [5]Forecast.

Prices

The prices paid to producers for clip wool, including stabilisation payments, showed relatively little change between 1952–53 and 1975–76, ranging from about 41 p to 49 p per kg during the whole of the period. Prices have risen considerably since then, but it was not until 1985–86 that the average price exceeded 100 p. Since then there has been another reduction. In real terms prices have fallen continuously since 1960–61.

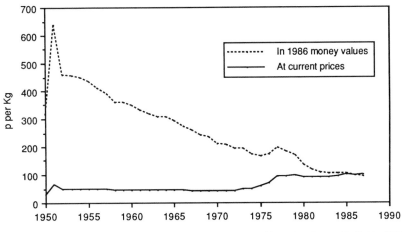

Producer prices for clip wool (p per kg)

Based on Appendix Table 23.8.

CHAPTER 24

Forestry

Although the area of woodland on agricultural holdings has increased, farm woodland has no great significance as far as the forestry industry as a whole is concerned. The aim of this section is not to produce a detailed picture of forestry, but rather to highlight some of the background and to trace developments on the farm.

Estimates of total forest area are available since before World War I and statistics relating to Forestry Commission activities are available from 1920 onwards. There is not much information on the private sector prior to 1970, but woodland on agricultural holdings has been recorded as part of the June census since 1968. Censuses of woodlands and trees carried out by the Forestry Commission in 1947, 1965 and 1982 give details of forest areas by forest type, ownership, species and age structure and have been used to make national estimates.

National estimates based on censuses indicate that forestry has become increasingly important in Great Britain during the past 40 years. In 1947 there were only 1.80 million hectares of forest in the UK accounting for 6.7% of the total land area; by 1965 this had risen to 1.75 million hectares (7.8% of the land area). Estimates based on the 1980 census indicate that there were then 2.12 million hectares accounting for 9.4% of the total land area. Since then there have been further increases, but in 1986 the United Kingdom still produced only 12% of its total timber requirements.

Most of the increase during the past decade has been in the private sector. The area of productive woodland owned by the Forestry Commission has risen by only 6% during the past decade, whereas the area of private productive woodland has increased by as much as 41%. Since 1982 the new area planted each year by the private sector has exceeded the new area planted by the Forestry Commission.

The area of woodland on agricultural holdings in the United Kingdom has been rising continuously since 1968, the rise being particularly marked since 1984, although estimates made in 1982 suggest that forestry still occupies less than 2% of the total agricultural area. If mountain and upland areas are excluded there are probably not more than 26 000 holdings with a total woodland area of 150 000 hectares in Great Britain, mostly in the south east of England.

The 1980 woodlands and trees census showed that broadleaved trees accounted for 46% of the total standing volume of timber, the most important species being oak, beech, sycamore, ash and birch. Pine trees accounted for 34% of the conifers, and spruce 41%.

Although the economics of timber production on farms is complex, there will almost certainly be further expansion in view of the surpluses of many agricultural products and reduced profitability in real terms. The farmer's main problem is to decide whether it is worthwhile investing in timber which will take many years to mature, a time during which he will see little or no return on his capital. Financial assistance is available, the nature of which is currently changing. Planning grants are available but other changes such as the removal of forestry operations from the tax system and a Farm Woodland Scheme have recently been announced.

Area

The total area of forest in the United Kingdom (including unproductive woodland) is estimated to have risen from about 1.25 million hectares in 1937–38 to 2.33 million hectares in 1986–87. Much of this increase has occurred since the early 1970s. There is relatively little woodland on farms and the available census results need to be interpreted with caution.

Although the latest estimates of private productive woodland are not entirely comparable with those before 1982–83, there can be no doubt that private woodland has increased rapidly in recent years. In 1986–87 private woodland accounted for 57% of the total area of productive woodland compared with 50% in 1976–77.

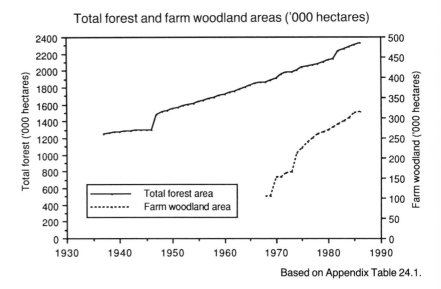

Total forest and farm woodland areas ('000 hectares)

Based on Appendix Table 24.1.

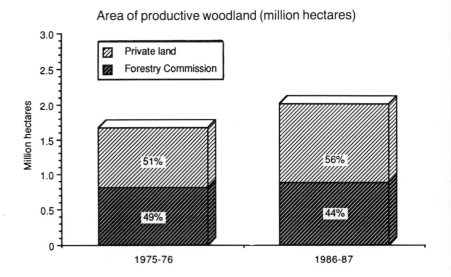

Area of productive woodland (million hectares)

New plantings

The area of newly planted private woodlands also now exceeds the area planted by the Forestry Commission, but in 1986–87 about 99% of it was grant aided by the Commission. Almost 90% of the newly planted area was in Scotland and consisted mostly of conifers. Scotland accounts for 48% of the productive woodland area, England 41% and Wales 11%.

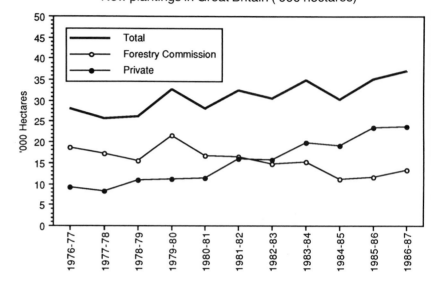

New plantings in Great Britain ('000 hectares)

Usage

The production of timber in the United Kingdom, although relatively small in total, has increased by over 60% during the past 16 years. Imports of timber and timber products have been comparatively stable, except for a drop in the mid-1970s and a slight rise in 1986, reflecting economic trends. Total use of timber has been increasing gradually since 1980. In 1986 home-produced timber accounted for 12% of apparent consumption compared with 8% in 1970.

Apparent consumption of wood[1] and wood products[2] (million m^3)

	1970	1975	1980	1985	1986
UK production	3.2	3.2	3.9	4.7	5.2
Imports	40.3	30.9	34.7	37.5	40.6
Apparent consumption[1]	42.3	33.1	36.3	39.9	43.0
Production as % of apparent consumption	7.6	10.2	10.7	11.8	12.1

[1]Imports plus production of roundwood timber less exports.   [2]Raw material equivalent.

CHAPTER 25

Purchased feeding stuffs

Purchased feed is the largest single item of farmers' expenditure. In 1987 it totalled £2667 million and accounted for 29% of farmers' total spending. Most of the expenditure is on compound feeds which totalled £1810 million. Of this, £579 million was spent on cattle compounds, £396 million on pig compounds and £666 million on poultry compounds. Expenditure on straights, (feeds which have not been mixed but may have been processed) which in 1987 accounted for 26% of the total feed bill, amounted to £683 million.

Farmers' purchases of compounds reached a peak of over 12 million tonnes in 1983, but since then purchases of cattle compounds have fallen. This is the result of attempts to reduce costs and contain continuing increases in milk yields following the introduction of EC milk quotas and a fall in profitability.

Purchases of pig compound feeds have remained almost constant during the past 20 years in spite of increased pigmeat production. This is partly due to improvement in the pigs' ability to convert feed efficiently, as well as to more grinding and mixing on the farm associated with the increased use of home grown cereals.

Farmers' purchases of poultry compound feeds, which are used for both egg and poultry meat production, have also shown remarkably little change since the late 1960s in spite of the increase in poultry meat production. This is partly due to lower egg production since the beginning of the 1970s and partly to the improved utilisation of feed in all poultry systems.

The raw material content of compound feeds has changed dramatically since the United Kingdom's entry into the European Community. Cereal usage has fallen sharply, although there has recently been some recovery. Maize and oats consumption has declined and more wheat is being used instead of barley.

Protein feeds, particularly oil cakes and meal, have risen in popularity due partly to the greater availability of rape seed and maize gluten. The use of milk and whey products and hay and grass meal has fallen.

Other raw materials reached a peak usage in 1982, when 778 000 tonnes of manioc went into the manufacture of compounds. Since then manioc has become less economic partly due to the imposition of a quota which has restricted supplies, and in 1986 only 60 000 tonnes were used. The recovery in cereal usage since 1983 is partly associated with the reduction in the use of manioc.

In spite of the very large increase in cereal production, the United Kingdom is still a major importer of animal feed; imports amounted to £612 million in 1986. As might be expected, feed cereal imports have fallen sharply in the face of rising production; maize and maize meal imports have been most affected. Imports of oil cakes and meals have risen as, unlike cereals, they are not subject to import levies.

There has been a five-fold rise in soya bean meal imports since 1964 and significant increases in the imports of sunflower cakes and meals and, more importantly, rape seed meal. On the other hand, imports of groundnut cakes and meals have fallen to negligible levels. Fish meal imports continue at a significant level but in 1986 were only half the quantity imported 20 years earlier.

Purchases

Overall, compound feed purchases increased by 26% between 1967–69 and 1983, but have declined since. Purchases of straights have risen continuously since 1967–69 and there has also been a greater use of home-grown grain for feeding livestock.

Purchases of cattle compounds increased by 64% between 1967–69 and 1983 but have fallen sharply since, with some recovery in 1986. Pig and poultry compound purchases have remained remarkably stable over the past 20 years, ranging between 2.2 and 2.4 million tonnes for pig compounds and 3.2 and 3.6 million tonnes for poultry compounds. This has been made possible by better utilisation of feed through genetic improvement.

Farmers' purchases of compounds (million tonnes)

Compounds	1967-69	1975	1980	1983	1985	1986
Cattle	3.3	4.0	4.5	5.4	4.1	4.5
Calf	0.4	0.4	0.4	0.5	0.4	0.4
Pig	2.2	2.4	2.2	2.3	2.1	2.2
Poultry	3.6	3.2	3.5	3.5	3.2	3.5
Other	0.2	0.1	0.4	0.4	0.5	0.6
Total	9.6	10.1	11.1	12.1	10.4	11.2

Based on Appendix Table 25.3.

Farmers' purchases of feed (million tonnes)

	1967–1969	1975	1980	1983	1985	1986
Compounds	9.6	10.1	11.1	12.1	10.4	11.2
Straights	3.7	3.9	3.9	4.2	5.1	5.2
Total concentrates	13.3	14.0	15.0	16.3	15.5	16.3
Non concentrates	0.4	0.4	0.7	0.7	0.8	0.7
All purchased feed	13.7	14.5	15.7	17.0	16.3	17.1

Based on Appendix Table 25.3.

Composition

The importance of wheat as a concentrate feed has increased dramatically. To some extent this has been at the expense of barley, but maize has been most affected. Whereas in 1980 maize accounted for 14% of total cereal usage, by 1986 this had fallen to 1.5%. Wheat has become more economic to use as EC production has increased and the compounding industry has improved its ability to use wheat instead of maize. Also the price of maize to the UK livestock producer has risen sharply, mainly because of the EC import levy system under which imports from the United States were curtailed.

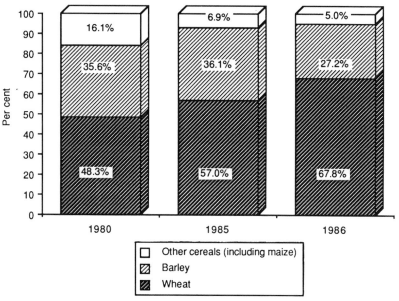

Composition of cereal content of concentrated feed

Based on Appendix Table 25.5.

Prices

Feed wheat and barley meal prices showed very little change until 1973, the beginning of the transition period after the United Kingdom's entry into the European Community. Since 1973 feed wheat prices have risen by 175% at current prices but after allowing for inflation there has, in fact, been a 36% reduction, most of it since 1983. Barley meal prices have also fallen sharply in real terms since the mid-1970s.

Maize meal prices have risen particularly rapidly since entry into the European Community, but there has been some reduction in real terms since 1980.

Fish meal prices depend on the availability of supplies. The sharp fall in supplies since 1970 has resulted in a rapid increase in prices although prices have been falling in real terms since 1977.

Straights feed price indices (1986 = 100)

	1955	1960	1965	1970	1975	1980	1983	1986	1987
Feed wheat									
At current prices	20	18	19	22	48	89	115	100	107
In 1986 money values	178	139	126	118	138	131	132	100	102
Barley meal									
At current prices	17	16	17	19	44	76	94	100	100
In 1986 money values	152	121	112	102	125	112	109	100	96
Maize meal									
At current prices	17	14	15	19	38	78	94	100	106
In 1986 money values	144	106	97	99	108	114	108	100	102
White fish meal									
At current prices	20	18	22	28	42	78	95	100	98
In 1986 money values	172	136	143	148	119	114	109	100	94

Based on Appendix Tables 25.7–25.10.

Compound feed prices have been affected by an increase in on-farm grinding and mixing and strong competition between suppliers. As a result, prices have risen less sharply than straights since 1975. Although compound prices have risen almost five-fold since the mid-1950s, after allowing for inflation there was, in fact, a 46% reduction between 1955 and 1986. Prices have also fallen in real terms since the United Kingdom's entry into the European Community in 1973.

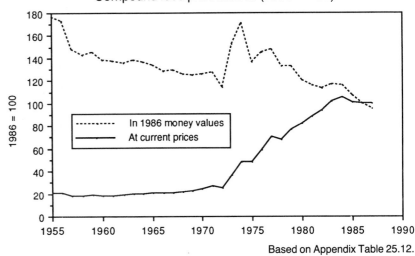

Compound feed price indices (1986 = 100)

Based on Appendix Table 25.12.

CHAPTER 26

Seeds

Seeds feature both as an intermediate output and an input in the Ministry of Agriculture's Departmental Net Income Calculation. Sales are included as an output but may subsequently be repurchased; if this is the case they will reappear as an item of expenditure.

In terms of farmers' output seeds were valued at £132 million in 1987 while seed purchases were valued at £282 million. Of that, £21 million was spent on grass and clover seed, £46 million on roots and fodder crops, £130 million on cereals and £24 million on seed potatoes. Vegetable and other horticultural seeds accounted for a further £61 million.

About 17 000 hectares of herbage and legume seeds were grown in the United Kingdom in 1987 compared with a peak of 22 600 tonnes in 1975–76. Seed production reached a peak of 19 000 tonnes in 1984 and in 1987 amounted to 15 000 tonnes. Virtually all of the seed is now certified.

The United Kingdom is also a major importer of seed, though there has been some decline in recent years. Imports in 1986–87 amounted to 12 200 tonnes and accounted for 47% of total supply. Exports of herbage and legume seeds in 1986–87 totalled 2 400 tonnes.

Prices

Seasonal conditions determine the availability of supplies, therefore seed prices can vary considerably from year to year. Prices were very high in 1976 and 1977, partly because of a shortfall in potato production which resulted in a shortage of seed potatoes. In 1984 there was again a sharp rise due to the shortage of potatoes.

Apart from the years of abnormally high prices, seed selling prices have fallen almost continuously in real terms since the early 1970s.

The purchase prices of seed tend to be slightly more stable than selling prices as supplies are supplemented by imports, but the longer term price trends have been similar.

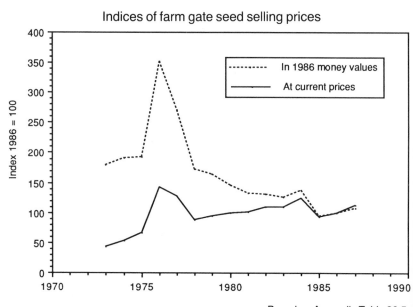

Indices of farm gate seed selling prices

Based on Appendix Table 26.5.

CHAPTER 27

Fertilisers and lime

Producers' expenditure on fertilisers and lime in 1987, at £737 million, accounted for 11% of total expenditure. It reached a peak of £954 million in 1984, but by 1987 had fallen to £737 million, primarily because of a reduction in fertiliser prices between 1985 and 1987. There was a sharp reduction in purchases of fertilisers between 1984 and 1985, but there has since been a recovery.

Fertilisers and lime were subsidised during World War II, and this remained the case for fertilisers until 1975 and for lime until 1977. The objective was to encourage their greater use to raise yields and thus increase agricultural production.

Fertilisers are purchased either as compounds or straights. Expenditure on nitrogen accounts for almost all the expenditure on straights; in 1986 money values it increased by over 50% between 1972 and 1986. In terms of nutrient nitrogen, purchases doubled between 1976 and 1984; there was a reduction in 1985, but since then there has again been some recovery.

Purchases of compounds have risen since the mid-1970s, but to a lesser extent than straights and since 1984 there has been a slight reduction. The proportion of nitrogen applied in compound form has fallen considerably during the past decade.

That there was a reduction in fertiliser usage in 1985 is also borne out by the ADAS, Rothamsted Experimental Station and Fertilisers Manufacturers' Association *Survey of Fertiliser Practice*. The latest survey results show that almost all crops were receiving less nitrogen in 1985 than in 1984. Lime usage has also fallen, in respect of both tillage and grass. The 1986 statistics show little change.

There are several factors, apart from the general decline in farming profitability, which have contributed to the reduction in fertilisers and lime use. The principal reasons are the reduction in numbers of cattle which followed the introduction of milk quotas and the reduced profitability of cereal production.

Fertiliser prices, net of subsidy, remained virtually unchanged between the outbreak of World War II and the early 1950s but increased more than five times after the mid-1950s. After allowing for inflation, there has, however, been a reduction of about a third in price.

Expenditure

Expenditure on fertilisers and lime rose to a peak of £954 million in 1984. It has fallen since then because of reduced usage and lower prices between 1985 and 1987.

Expenditure on fertilisers and lime (£ million)

	1937 –38	1942 –43	1950 –51	1960 –61	1972	1975	1980	1984	1985	1986	1987[2]
Straights					63	99	224	402	372	322	293
Compounds					124	200	380	478	462	426	377
Other					5	9	17	23	26	24	25
Total fertilisers					191	309	621	903	859	773	695
Lime					11	16	28	47	38	39	40
Total fertilisers and lime[1]	8	24	51	120	203	325	651	954	901	815	737

[1] Including VAT from 1973 onwards. [2] Forecast.

Purchases and prices

The statistics of fertiliser expenditure at constant prices are a good indication of changes in the quantities purchased.

The index of fertiliser expenditure at constant prices and the index of fertiliser prices in 1986 money values show the strong relationship between purchases and prices. Purchases of fertilisers declined between 1970 and 1975, a period during which real fertiliser prices increased by almost 25%. There was then an almost 50% rise in purchases between 1975 and 1984, at a time when there was a major reduction in real prices. Purchases have shown only a modest recovery since 1985, in spite of a 13% reduction in real fertiliser prices, because of the depressed state of agriculture.

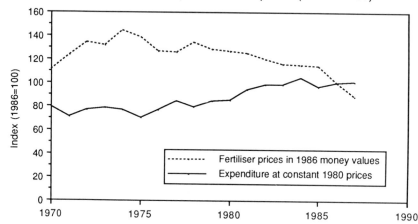

Indices of fertiliser expenditure and prices (1986 = 100)

Purchases of inorganic fertilisers

Purchases of nitrogen have risen sharply during the past decade, peaking in 1984 followed by some reduction. Phosphate purchases have almost halved during the past decade. Purchases of compounds also reached a peak in 1984, then fell, though there was also some recovery in 1987.

Purchases of inorganic fertilisers (1976 = 100)

	1976	1980	1984	1985	1986	1987[3]
Straights[1]						
Nitrogen	100	127	205	180	190	195
Phosphate	100	88	55	55	55	55
Potash	100	100	145	100	209	136
Compounds[2]	100	106	117	110	112	114

[1]In terms of nutrients.   [2]In terms of product weight.   [3]Forecast.

Nitrogen usage

The use of nitrogen on all crops and grass increased by about 80% between 1970 and 1986. In the case of tillage its use rose by as much as 81% between 1975 and 1986, the greatest increase being for winter cereals. Nitrogen use on permanent grass increased by 36%.

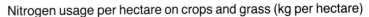

Nitrogen usage per hectare on crops and grass (kg per hectare)

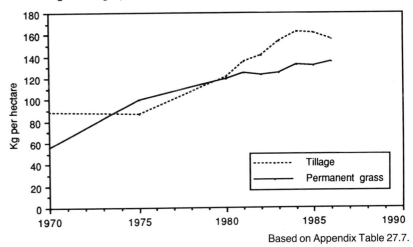

Based on Appendix Table 27.7.

Lime usage

The withdrawal of the lime subsidy in 1977 does not appear to have affected the percentage of the tillage area receiving lime, but it does appear to have had a temporary effect on usage on grassland. The use of lime on both tillage and grassland seems to be in line with the general reduction in fertiliser use since 1984. Unfortunately there are no comparable figures after 1985.

Percentage of crop area receiving lime

	1975	1981	1984	1985
All tillage	7.2	8.4	9.0	7.5
All grass	5.6	4.1	6.0	3.5
All crops and grass	5.5	6.2	7.5	5.5

Based on Appendix Table 27.8.

Fertiliser and soil improver prices

Fertiliser and soil improver prices showed relatively little change during World War II and the post-war years and it was not until the early 1950s that prices began to increase significantly. There was a particularly sharp rise during the 1970s and prices continued to rise until 1985. In real terms prices have been falling since 1974. In 1987 the real price of fertilisers was about 35% less than in 1938. The price indices are calculated so as to take into account changes in fertiliser manufacturing practices.

Indices of fertiliser and soil improver prices[1]

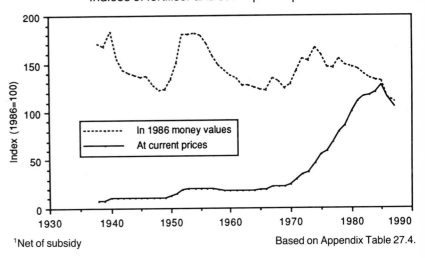

[1]Net of subsidy

Based on Appendix Table 27.4.

CHAPTER 28

Machinery expenses

Expenditure on machinery (other than capital expenditure and depreciation) in 1987 totalled £997 million accounting for 15% of gross input. In the Ministry of Agriculture's Departmental Net Income Calculation, which aims to measure the economic prosperity of the national farm, machinery expenses are estimated under three headings: repair of machinery and farm cars, fuel and oil, and other machinery expenses. Separate estimates are made of depreciation, and net product and farming income are calculated after allowing for this.

Repairs

Expenditure on machinery and farm car repairs in 1987 totalled £534 million. Of this £443 million was spent on machinery repairs, £38 million on farm car repairs and £54 million on replacement tyres and tubes.

The price index for the maintenance and repair of plants has risen more than five-fold since 1970. It rose 314% between 1970 and 1980 and a further 45% by 1987. In real terms, i.e. after allowing for inflation, there has been relatively little change, in fact, there has been some reduction since 1978.

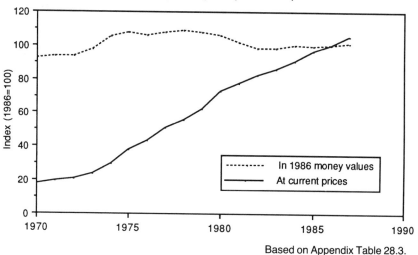

Maintenance and repair of plant purchase price indices

Based on Appendix Table 28.3.

Fuel and oil

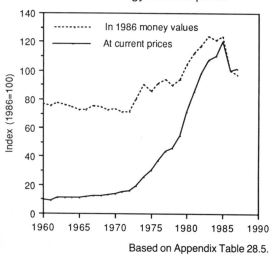

Indices of energy and fuel prices

Based on Appendix Table 28.5.

Expenditure on fuel and oil reached a peak of £475 million in 1985, but by 1987 this had fallen to only £364 million due primarily to a reduction in the price of fuel oil. Of this £364 million, £113 million was spent on petrol, £185 million on gas and diesel for agricultural production and £10 million on gas and diesel for horticultural purposes. Lubricating oil accounted for a further £21 million.

The index of energy and lubricant purchase prices shows that prices increased almost 14-fold between 1955 and 1985 followed by a 16% reduction between 1985 and 1987. After allowing for inflation, energy and lubricant prices have risen by 25% since the mid-1950s. Between 1973 and 1987 real prices of lubricant increased by 14%, fuel oil for heating by 45% and motor fuel 32%.

CHAPTER 29

Farm maintenance and depreciation

The annual cost of farm maintenance was estimated at £308 million in 1987. Expenditure is calculated separately for landlords and occupiers. Occupiers' expenses were estimated at £245 million and landlords' at £63 million.

Depreciation in the Ministry of Agriculture's Departmental Net Income Calculation consists of two major components: plant, machinery and vehicles; and buildings and works. Total depreciation in 1987 is estimated at £1486 million of which £841 million was for machinery depreciation, £86 million for farm car depreciation and £558 million for buildings and works depreciation.

Replacement costs and therefore purchase price indices are central to the calculation of depreciation. The overall index of machinery and equipment prices has shown a price rise in real terms.

Maintenance of buildings

The purchase price index for maintaining and repairing buildings has risen continuously since 1970 and by 1987 had increased over seven-fold. There has also been a continuous rise in prices after allowing for inflation; the increase was 33% between 1970 and 1987.

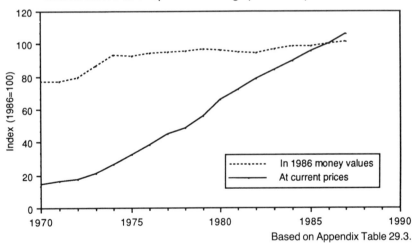

Maintenance and repair of buildings purchase price indices

Based on Appendix Table 29.3.

Purchase prices

Prices for machinery and plant for cultivation increased almost five-fold between 1970 and 1987, most of the increase occurring during the second half of the 1970s. Prices have risen by 35% since 1980 though this is in fact a fall of 11% if inflation is taken into account. In spite of this there has been a reduction in investment in new machinery as farming incomes have fallen in real terms.

Prices for machinery and plant for harvesting have increased more than seven-fold since 1970, partly no doubt due to the increasing sophistication of the machinery. Prices have risen by as much as 56% since 1980. After allowing for inflation prices have still increased by 35% since 1970; there has been relatively little change since 1978.

Tractor prices have risen almost eight-fold since 1970, also partly due to technical improvements. There has been a 51% increase since 1980. After allowing for inflation prices have tended to decline since 1978, a trend which has been exacerbated as farmers have become increasingly reluctant to purchase new tractors.

The overall index of machinery and other equipment purchase prices shows a rise of about 550% since 1970, most of the rise having occurred in the 1970s. In real terms prices increased by 18% between 1970 and 1987.

Farm building prices increased more than seven-fold between 1970 and 1987, most of the increase occurring prior to 1982. Since then costs have risen by a further 35%. In real terms, building costs have increased by 22% since 1970.

The costs of engineering and soil improvement operations increased by over 700% between 1970 and 1987, again with most of the rise occurring before 1982. After allowing for inflation costs rose by 50% between 1970 and 1987.

Machinery and other equipment purchase price indices

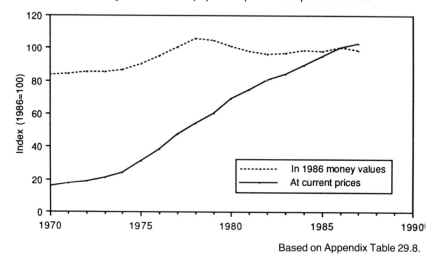

Based on Appendix Table 29.8.

Farm building, engineering and soil improvement purchase price indices

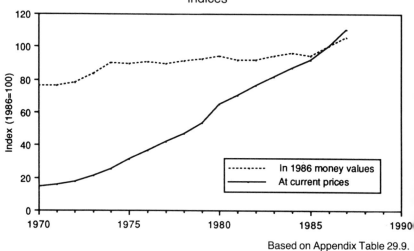

Based on Appendix Table 29.9.

CHAPTER 30

Commercial interest

Agriculture's interest charges can be divided into two groups: those arising from the purchase of land and interest on commercial debt. Capital for the former is often borrowed from the Agricultural Mortgage Corporation, and to a lesser extent from the banks.

Interest charges in MAFF's Departmental Net Income Calculation are defined as interest on commercial debt only. The most important component of the overall bill is interest on bank borrowings. The other components of the interest bill are charges for instalment credit and Agricultural Mortgage Corporation credit as well as other credit which includes loans from the Department of Agriculture for Northern Ireland loans fund, Agricultural Credit Corporation charges, leasing charges and borrowings from private sources. An estimate of the "interest received by farmers on capital held on short term" is deducted.

In 1987 farmers' commercial interest charges amounted to £646 million. Of this £605 million was for bank advances to agriculture, £29 million for instalment credit, £6 million for Agricultural Mortgage Corporation loans and £47 million for other credit. Interest on deposits, which is deducted, was estimated at £41 million.

Total bank advances to agriculture have risen rapidly in recent years as farming income has tended to fall in real terms. However, bank interest charges to farmers declined between 1985 and 1987 because of lower interest rates.

Not only has there been a rise in bank advances but more money is also being borrowed from sources other than the banks.

Interest charges

In 1980, 91% of farmers' interest charges were paid to the banks; by 1987 this had fallen to 88%. In 1972 the proportion was only 84% due to loans from the Agriculture Mortgage Corporation being relatively more important. Instalment credit in 1987 accounted for 4% of total interest charges compared with 8% in 1971.

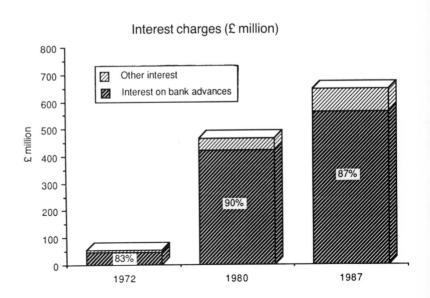

Interest charges (£ million)

Total bank advances to agriculture

Total bank advances to agriculture for farming purposes and for buildings and works have increased more than ten-fold since 1971 and in 1987 were forecast at £5962 million. The rise was particularly rapid beween 1980 and 1984. There has also been a major increase in advances after allowing for inflation; bank advances in real terms in 1987 were at £5724 million, almost double the amount borrowed in 1972.

Since the mid-1970s rates of interest have been much higher than in previous years. Estimated rates of interest averaged 13.4% in 1985–87 compared with 6.5% in 1960–62. They show wide variations, ranging from 8.0% in 1972 to 18.7% in 1980. Rates were lowest in 1977 and 1978; the 1987 level of 12.1% was the lowest since 1984.

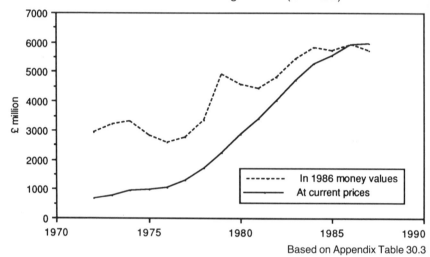

Total bank advances to agriculture (£ million)

Based on Appendix Table 30.3

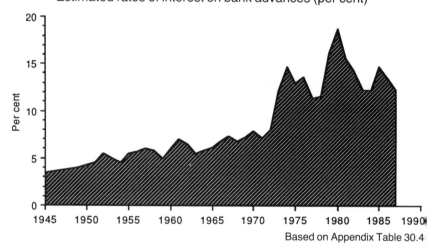

Estimated rates of interest on bank advances (per cent)

Based on Appendix Table 30.4

CHAPTER 31

Rent

The rent bill for the United Kingdom in the MAFF Departmental Net Income Calculation is calculated for tenanted land and relates to England, Wales and Scotland only. Virtually all the agricultural land in Northern Ireland is owner occupied. In England and Wales the estimates of average rents are derived from information obtained from annual rent enquiries and in Scotland from regular field surveys.

Deductions are made to take account of:
- the estimated benefit value of farm houses and cottages attributable to domestic use
- current expenses incurred by landlords for repairs and maintenance, insurance, management costs and statutory charges
- landlords' share of the depreciation on buildings and works as estimated from the investment data.

The total rent paid on all tenanted land in 1987 is estimated at £417 million. Deductions made for benefit value of farm houses (£49 million), land-owners' current expenses (£124 million), and landlords' depreciation (£78 million), resulted in a net rent bill of £167 million.

There are considerable statistical problems in trying to compare the number of rented and owned holdings over longer periods because of changes in the definitions of agricultural holdings. The number of rented holdings in England and Wales appears to have shown little change during the late 19th century, but some reduction appears to have occurred after World War I. There seems also to have been some reduction between 1950 and 1960. The number of rented or mainly rented holdings in Great Britain also appears to have fallen since 1971 with some increase since 1980 in the number of owned or mainly owned holdings.

In England and Wales the area rented declined by about a third between 1887 and 1960 while the area owned has risen by 235%. This comparison needs to be treated with caution mainly because of variations in the total area covered in the various MAFF rent enquiries.

More recent information for Great Britain suggests that there has been a further reduction in the area rented since 1970 while there has been some increase in the area owned. In 1986, 39% of the total area of crops and grass was rented and 61% owned.

Rents have risen rapidly since the early 1970s and there have also been rises after allowing for inflation, particularly in England. In England the proportion of farms with rent changes has averaged 35.8% since 1977, compared with 29.6% in Wales and 18.4% in Scotland. The proportion of farms with rent changes has fallen slightly since 1982.

Rented holdings

The proportion of holdings which are rented or mainly rented has declined continuously since the early 1970s. In 1971 40% of the holdings in Great Britain were wholly or mainly rented; by 1986 this proportion had fallen to 29%.

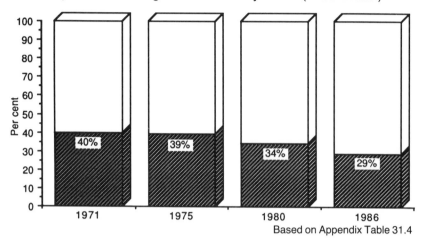

Proportion of holdings rented or mainly rented (Great Britain)

Based on Appendix Table 31.4

Area rented and owned

Until about 1960 only areas of crops and grass were recorded in the official statistics. Rough grazing (with numerous changes in definition) was then added and finally from 1970 onwards the total land area of the farm was recorded. It is therefore not possible to measure the changes in the proportion of land areas owned and rented.

However, the statistics for the 1880s and 1890s suggest that then about 85% of the area of crops and grass was rented. This percentage appears to have increased from about 1900 to the outbreak of World War I. There was then a decline, probably because more owner-occupied land was brought into cultivation during and after the war.

The statistics since 1970, which relate to the total area of the holdings, show that there has been some decline in land rented from about 43% in 1970 to 39% in 1986.

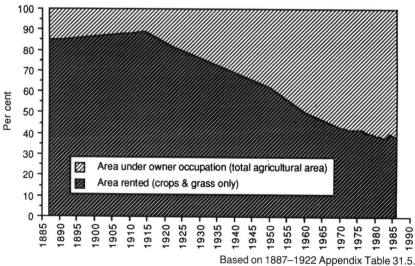

Percentage of area rented and owned (Great Britain)

Based on 1887–1922 Appendix Table 31.5.
1970–1986 Appendix Table 31.6.

Rents

Rents per hectare in Great Britain increased seven-fold between 1970 and 1987; since 1980 they have almost doubled.

Rents per hectare have also risen in real terms, most of the increase occurring since 1980. After allowing for inflation, rents per hectare in Great Britain went up by 32% between 1970 and 1986.

It might be expected that there would be some relationship between the levels of agricultural prices and changes in rent in real terms. This does not seem to have occurred during the past two decades. Agricultural price levels increased by almost 25% between 1970 and 1976 while the rent index declined by 14%. Since then there has been a reduction of 40% in real agricultural prices while rents increased by over 50% in real terms.

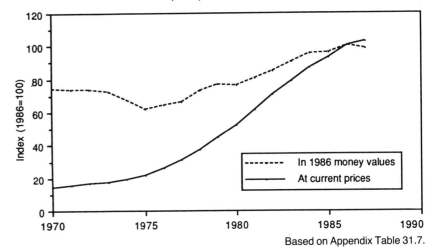

Indices of rents paid per hectare in Great Britain

Based on Appendix Table 31.7.

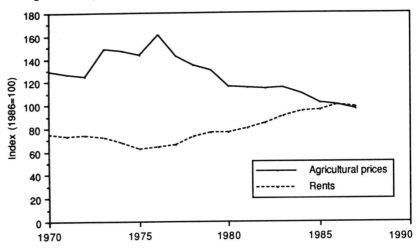

Agricultural product prices and rent indices (In 1986 money values)

CHAPTER 32

Miscellaneous expenses

Veterinary services

In the Ministry of Agriculture, Fisheries and Food's Departmental Net Income Calculation, farmers' miscellaneous expenses cover a wide range of items, particularly pesticides, veterinary expenses and medicines and electricity.

In 1987 these miscellaneous expenses totalled £1 283 million. Of this £151 million was spent on veterinary expenses and medicines, £285 million on pesticides, £136 million on electricity, £93 million on horticultural containers and £416 million on overheads such as drainage and water rates, general rates and insurance, professional fees and telephones.

Farmers' expenditure on veterinary services in 1987 amounted to £151 million. Expenditure in real terms has shown remarkably little change since the early 1970s.

The price of veterinary services, which includes practitioners' charges as well as veterinary products, has increased by about 470% since 1970. Most of the rise has occurred since 1978, partly reflecting the greater sophistication of veterinary products. After allowing for inflation, prices have risen only 3% since 1978.

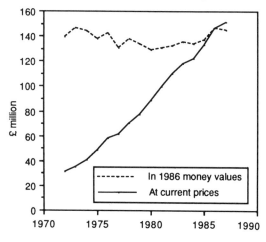

Expenditure on veterinary services and medicines (£ million)

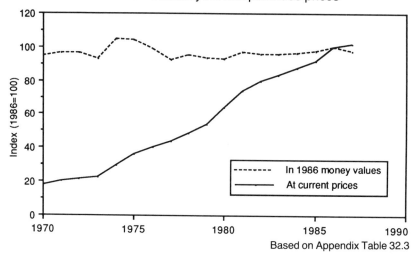

Indices of veterinary service purchase prices

Based on Appendix Table 32.3

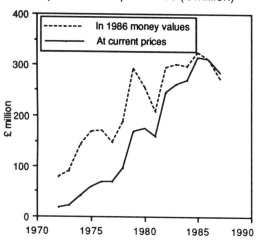

Expenditure on pesticides (£ million)

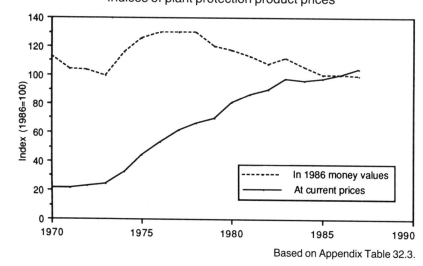

Indices of plant protection product prices

Based on Appendix Table 32.3.

Pesticides

In 1987 farmers spent £285 million on pesticides, slightly less than a year earlier, despite a 4% rise in prices. In real terms expenditure on pesticides has increased by 250% since 1972.

The purchase price of pesticides has risen almost five-fold since 1970, most of the rise occurring in the 1970s. Since 1980 there has been an increase of about 30%. After allowing for inflation, prices have been falling almost continuously since 1978, the index in real terms being 23% less in 1987 than in 1978.

Power and fuel

Farmers spent £154 million on power and fuel in 1987. In terms of 1986 money values expenditure increased by 26% between 1972 and 1981; since then there has been a 10% reduction.

Electricity purchase prices have risen by 315% since 1973. After allowing for inflation prices increased by 17% between 1973 and 1981 and have since fallen again by 18%.

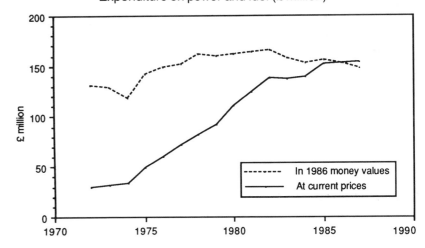

Expenditure on power and fuel (£ million)

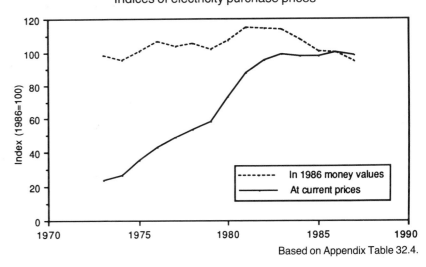

Indices of electricity purchase prices

Based on Appendix Table 32.4.

Sundry equipment

Farmers' expenditure on sundry equipment totalled £105 million in 1987. In 1986 money values expenditure was at a peak in 1974; since then there has been some reduction, although there has been little change during the past few years.

Materials and small tool prices have risen almost six-fold since 1970. After allowing for inflation, prices reached a peak in 1978 but have since then fallen by eight per cent.

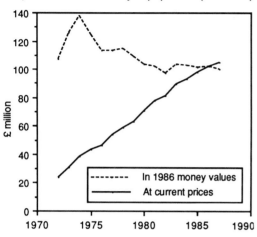

Expenditure on sundry equipment (£ million)

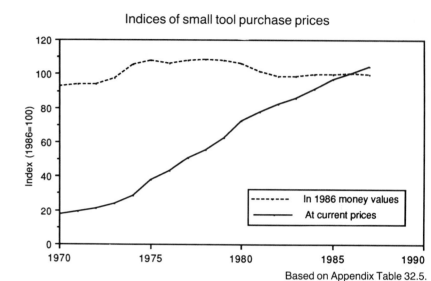

Indices of small tool purchase prices

Based on Appendix Table 32.5.

General expenses

The index of 'general expenses' purchase prices has shown a more than seven-fold rise since 1970; prices increased particularly rapidly from 1978 onwards; there was a rise of 23% between 1984 and 1987. In real terms prices have risen by 36% since 1970; there was an increase of seven per cent between 1985 and 1987.

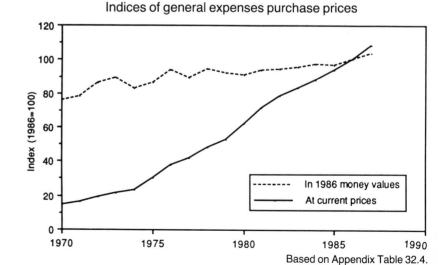

Indices of general expenses purchase prices

Based on Appendix Table 32.4.

Appendices

Appendix 1: Agriculture in the national economy

Table 1.1. Agriculture's contribution to gross domestic product[1]

	UK GDP	Agriculture forestry fishing GDP	% of UK GDP	Agriculture GDP	% of UK GDP
1964	29 255	996	3.4		
1965	31 733	1027	3.2		
1966	33 500	1061	3.2		
1967	35 095	1106	3.2		
1968	37 742	1113	2.9		
1969	40 494	1171	2.9		
1970	44 537	1241	2.9	1126	2.5
1971	49 680	1373	2.8	1234	2.5
1972	56 450	1582	2.8	1436	2.5
1973	65 714	2006	3.1	1770	2.7
1974	74 467	2099	2.8	1864	2.5
1975	94 487	2507	2.7	2392	2.5
1976	110 800	3225	2.9	2947	2.7
1977	128 975	3353	2.6	3159	2.4
1978	148 099	3590	2.4	3417	2.3
1979	172 118	3922	2.3	3743	2.2
1980	199 715	4303	2.2	4158	2.1
1981	218 954	4837	2.2	4612	2.1
1982	238 836	5530	2.3	5271	2.2
1983	260 402	5365	2.1	5068	2.0
1984	279 686	6222	2.2	5903	2.1
1985	306 361	5627	1.8	5268	1.7
1986	326 049	5902	1.8	5628	1.8
1987[2]				5614	1.7

[1]Income based. [2]Forecast.
Source. Central Statistical Office: *United Kingdom National Accounts.*
HMSO: *Annual Review of Agriculture.*

Table 1.2. Indices of gross domestic product at constant factor cost (1980 = 100)[1]

	Agriculture, forestry, fishing	UK Gross Domestic Product
1965	71.4	76.8
1966	71.7	78.2
1967	74.0	79.5
1968	74.0	82.9
1969	73.8	84.6
1970	78.3	86.0
1971	82.4	87.3
1972	85.1	90.0
1973	87.8	95.2
1974	88.8	93.8
1975	81.9	92.0
1976	75.3	93.9
1977	85.1	96.6
1978	91.5	99.9
1979	90.1	102.9
1980	100.0	100.0
1981	102.6	98.4
1982	111.2	100.1
1983	105.2	103.3
1984	124.5	106.7
1985	118.8	110.7
1986	118.8	114.0

[1]Output based. The series has been carried back before 1975 by splicing with constant price series using earlier base years.
Source. Central Statistical Office: *United Kingdom National Accounts.*

Table 1.3. Agriculture's share of gross fixed capital formation

	Buildings and works (£ million)	Plant vehicles and machinery (£ million)	Total	% of Gross national fixed capital formation
1948	21	66	87	6.3
1949	23	64	87	5.7
1950	22	65	87	5.3
1951	22	69	91	4.9
1952	20	73	93	4.5
1953	23	67	90	3.9
1954	24	72	96	3.8
1955	26	78	104	3.8
1956	27	67	94	3.1
1957	25	81	106	3.2
1958	29	97	126	3.7
1959	38	102	140	3.8
1960	45	96	141	3.5
1961	54	103	157	3.5
1962	58	94	152	3.3
1963	63	111	174	3.6
1964	65	118	183	3.2
1965	67	117	184	2.9
1966	65	107	172	2.8
1967	75	111	186	2.7
1968	89	138	227	2.9
1969	96	127	223	2.7
1970	117	133	250	2.7
1971	133	152	285	2.8
1972	159	165	324	2.9
1973	209	209	418	3.2
1974	252	263	515	3.1
1975	240	325	565	2.8
1976	226	408	634	2.6
1977	251	519	770	2.8
1978	331	560	891	2.9
1979	397	601	998	2.7
1980	557	507	1064	2.6
1981	506	464	970	2.3
1982	610	596	1206	2.7
1983	638	721	1359	2.8
1984	684	681	1365	2.5
1985	515	708	1223	2.0
1986	440	593	1033	1.6
1987[1]	380	530	910	

[1]Forecast.
Source. Central Statistical Office: *United Kingdom National Accounts.*

Table 1.4. Manpower engaged in agriculture as a proportion of manpower engaged in all occupations

	Engaged in agriculture ('000)	% of total
1970	750	3.0
1971	716	3.0
1972	709	2.9
1973	704	2.8
1974	678	2.8
1975	662	2.8
1976	682	2.8
1977	672	2.8
1978	678	2.7
1979	660	2.6
1980	650	2.6
1981	637	2.7
1982	632	2.7
1983	624	2.7
1984	618	2.6
1985	616	2.6
1986	606	2.5
1987	593	2.4

Source. HMSO: *Annual Review of Agriculture.*

Table 1.5. Imports of food, feed and beverages (1986 = 100)

	Imports (£ million)	Import volume index (1986 = 100)	Import price index (1986 = 100)
1964–65 to 1965–66	1755[1]	73.5[1]	19.5[1]
1970–71	2079[1]	74.2[1]	22.7[1]
1971–72	2236[1]	74.2[1]	24.4[1]
1972–73	2401[1]	75.5[1]	25.8[1]
1973–74	3205[1]	76.3[1]	34.4[1]
1974	3990	70.2	45.7
1975	4480	72.2	50.9
1976	5215	76.1	57.3
1977	6332	76.2	68.5
1978	6289	73.1	71.9
1979	6816	76.1	74.2
1980	6519	81.2	75.1
1981	6921	80.6	78.4
1982	7583	87.5	83.6
1983	8237	87.0	90.0
1984	9401	89.0	100.8
1985	9823	90.6	103.5
1986	10 475	100.0	100.0
1987	10 659	101.6	99.5

[1]Including alcoholic beverages.
Source. Based on HMSO: *Annual Review of Agriculture.*

Table 1.6. Exports of food, feed and beverages

	Exports (£ million)	Export volume index (1986 = 100)	Export price index (1986 = 100)
1964–65 to 1965–66[1]	305[2]	25.2[2]	20.9[2]
1970–71	484[2]	35.8[2]	23.3[2]
1971–72	567[2]	39.2[2]	24.6[2]
1972–73	636[2]	41.0[2]	26.4[2]
1973–74	853[2]	49.1[2]	29.5[2]
1974	1048	51.4	35.2
1975	1366	56.1	41.6
1976	1620	58.3	49.6
1977	2139	62.7	55.2
1978	2725	73.3	59.6
1979	2697	67.7	67.8
1980	3055	71.3	72.4
1981	3391	74.6	77.0
1982	3651	74.7	83.7
1983	3938	78.4	88.5
1984	4457	85.0	92.8
1985	4731	87.6	96.7
1986	5368	100.0	100.0
1987	5575	100.9	98.3

[1]Average. [2]Including alcoholic beverages.
Source. Based on HMSO: *Annual Review of Agriculture*.

Table 1.7. Expenditure on food as a proportion of total consumers' expenditure

	Expenditure on food[1] (£ million)	Expenditure on food as % of total consumer expenditure
1967–69[2]	6602	24.1
1974	11 339	21.9
1975	13 875	21.8
1976	16 210	21.7
1977	18 574	21.6
1978	20 602	20.8
1979	23 530	19.9
1980	26 353	19.2
1981	27 787	18.3
1982	29 386	17.6
1983	31 431	17.2
1984	33 120	16.9
1985	34 832	16.3
1986	37 726	16.1

[1]Including caterers' expenditure on foods. [2]Average.
Source. HMSO: *Annual Review of Agriculture*.

Table 1.8. Self-sufficiency in food at current prices

	Home production as % of indigenous type food consumed	Home production as % of all food consumed
1964–65	64.1	50.9
1965–66	64.9	51.4
1970–71	66.9	53.2
New series		
1973	62.2	49.8
1974	57.9	46.3
1975	63.4	51.4
1976	64.3	51.2
1977	62.5	48.1
1978	67.8	53.2
1979	67.5	52.9
1980	74.3	59.7
1981	76.9	62.0
1982	77.4	62.5
New series		
1983	77.7	61.2
1984	82.6	62.9
1985	76.5	57.8
1986	74.3	56.7
1987[1]	73.0	57.0

[1]Forecast.
Source. HMSO: *Annual Review of Agriculture*.

121

Appendix 2: British agriculture in the European Community

Table 2.1. Members states' contributions to the European Community's own resources (million ECUs)

	1973[1]	1978	1980	1986
United Kingdom	403	1844	3168	4825
Belgium	337	776	951	1448
Denmark	51	275	346	791
Fed. Rep. of Germany	1332	3738	4610	8730
Greece				632
Spain				2321
France	1136	2315	2992	6885
Ireland	13	69	139	344
Italy	872	1735	1929	4718
Luxembourg	8	14	20	66
Netherlands	433	1238	1273	2232
Portugal				279
Total own resources	4584	12004	15428	33271

Table 2.2. United Kingdom's contribution to the European Community's own resources, 1986 (million ECUs)

Customs duties	1862
Agricultural levies	285
Sugar and isoglucose levies	77
VAT	2601
Total	4825

[1]In terms of European Units of Account (EUA)
Source. Annual Reports: *Court of Auditors Official Journal.*

Table 2.3. FEOGA guarantee and guidance expenditure by member states (million ECUs)

Guarantee section	1973	1982	1983	1984	1985	1986
United Kingdom	155	1286	1693	2134	1915	2000
Belgium	210	536	617	702	916	976
Denmark	346	559	681	879	834	1071
Fed. Rep. of Germany	791	2030	3076	3323	3625	4398
Greece	–	685	1007	961	1197	1412
Spain	–	–	–	–	–	271
France	1195	2869	3635	3513	4634	5453
Ireland	87	501	616	893	1169	1215
Italy	545	2509	2872	3994	3452	3063
Luxembourg	6	3	5	4	5	2
Netherlands	594	1425	1717	1964	2091	2294
Portugal	–	–	–	–	–	31
Community	–	5	1	6	6	6
EC10	3928	12406	15920	18372	19843	21891
EC12	–	–	–	–	–	22193
Guidance Section						
United Kingdom	20	71	157	135	124	104
Belgium	12	14	16	17	20	16
Denmark	5	21	21	20	26	23
Fed. Rep. of Germany	46	97	113	93	91	104
Greece	–	30	85	110	138	140
Spain	–	–	–	–	–	87
France	36	196	187	191	161	209
Ireland	7	91	101	73	82	79
Italy	49	235	232	182	236	154
Luxembourg	--	2	2	4	1	2
Netherlands	13	28	29	20	20	22
Portugal	–	–	–	–	–	33
Community	–	–	–	–	–	–
EC10	188	783	944	845	898	852
EC12	–	–	–	–	–	972

Note: The guarantee section of FEOGA finances expenditure arising from the common agricultural market and prices policy and accounts for about 95% of CAP expenditure. The guidance section finances the structures policy.
Source. *The Agricultural Situation in the Community 1987.*

Table 2.4. Land use, 1986

	Total land area ('000 ha)	Used for agriculture ('000 ha)	Agriculture as % of total
United Kingdom	24414	18612[1]	76.2[1]
Belgium	3052	1412	46.3
Denmark	4308	2823	65.5
Fed. Rep. of Germany	24869	12000	48.3
Greece	13196	5741	43.5
Spain	50477	27213	53.9
France	54909	31418	57.2
Ireland	7028	5676	80.8
Italy	30128	17445	57.9
Luxembourg	259	128	49.4
Netherlands	3729	2025	54.3
Portugal	9207	4532	49.2
EC12	225575	129023	57.2
EC10	165891	97279	58.6

[1]Including rough grazing.
Source. Based on *The Agricultural Situation in the Community 1987.*

Table 2.5. Average size of holding (hectares)

	1975	1985
United Kingdom	64.3	69.4
Belgium	13.9	16.7
Denmark	22.6	31.0
Fed. Rep. of Germany	13.8	16.9
Greece	4.3[1]	5.7
Spain		15.3
France	24.3	29.2
Ireland	22.3	22.7
Italy	7.5	8.0
Luxembourg	23.5	31.5
Netherlands	14.4	16.7
Portugal		8.9
EC12		16.5
EC10		17.4

[1]Estimated.   Source. Based on *The Agricultural Situation in the Community 1987*.

Table 2.6. Employment in agriculture, 1986

	Employment ('000)	Share of total working population (%)
United Kingdom	619	2.6
Belgium	103	2.9
Denmark	178	6.8
Fed. Rep. of Germany	1345	5.3
Greece	1026	28.5
Spain	1742	16.1
France	1536	7.3
Ireland	168	15.8
Italy	2242	10.9
Luxembourg	7	4.0
Netherlands	248	4.8
Portugal	890	21.9
EC12	10 104	8.3
EC10	7472	7.0

Source. Based on *The Agricultural Situation in the Community 1987*.

Table 2.7. Proportion of paid and self-employed agricultural workers, 1985 (per cent)

	Paid	Self-employed	Total
United Kingdom	52.4	47.6	100.0
Belgium	8.5	91.5	100.0
Denmark	37.5	62.5	100.0
Fed. Rep. of Germany	23.1	76.9	100.0
Greece	4.0	96.0	100.0
Spain	29.0	71.0	100.0
France	14.1	85.9	100.0
Ireland	13.1	86.9	100.0
Italy	36.2	63.8	100.0
Luxembourg	14.4	85.6	100.0
Netherlands	31.5	68.5	100.0
Portugal			
EC10	24.6	75.4	100.0

Source. Based on *The Agricultural Situation in the Community 1987*.

Table 2.8. Share of agriculture in gross domestic product, 1986 (per cent)

United Kingdom	1.8
Belgium	2.5
Denmark	5.0
Fed. Rep. of Germany	1.8
Greece	16.6
Spain	6.1
France	3.7
Ireland	10.2
Italy	5.0
Luxembourg	2.6
Netherlands	4.2
Portugal	6.5
EC12	3.5
EC10	3.4

Source. Based on *The Agricultural Situation in the Community 1987*.

Table 2.9. Trends in volume of final agricultural production (1980 = 100)[1]

	1973	1980	1982	1983	1984	1985	1986	1986/1973
United Kingdom	91.6	100.0	107.0	105.4	113.8	109.8	109.6	+19.7%
Belgium	100.0	100.0	104.8	103.2	108.8	110.1	115.0	+15.0%
Denmark	84.5	100.0	108.7	105.5	117.6	117.9	116.3	+37.6%
Fed. Rep. of Germany	89.9	100.0	107.9	105.0	108.1	104.4	108.7	+20.9%
Greece	83.4	100.0	102.8	97.4	102.7	103.8	107.4	+28.8%
Spain	77.5	100.0		100.4	107.6	110.3		
France		100.0	108.9	106.1	109.4	110.8	111.2	
Ireland	86.7	100.0	106.0	109.4	118.7	116.8	114.4	+31.9%
Italy		100.0	97.8	104.2	101.1	101.4	103.0	
Luxembourg	108.2	100.0	117.2	111.2	113.5	111.0	114.8	+6.1%
Netherlands	76.6	100.0	109.0	111.2	115.3	116.3	121.9	+59.1%
Portugal		100.0						

[1]At constant 1980 prices in terms of ECUs.
Source. Based on *The Agricultural Situation in the Community*.

Table 2.10. Trends in agriculture's gross value added (1980 = 100)[1]

	1973	1980	1982	1983	1984	1985	1986	1986/1973
United Kingdom	77.9	100.0	111.7	104.9	125.6	118.7	118.2	+51.7%
Belgium	104.9	100.0	110.2	107.1	117.1	116.2	122.0	+16.3%
Denmark	88.0	100.0	121.3	111.2	142.1	141.1	138.6	+57.5%
Fed. Rep. of Germany	99.6	100.0	121.9	115.5	123.8	113.7	125.7	+26.2%
Greece	86.9	100.0	102.0	93.9	100.0	100.0	105.7	+21.6%
Spain	80.6	100.0		96.5	106.3	109.3		
France		100.0	115.5	110.2	114.9	116.6	116.0	
Ireland	91.4	100.0	106.6	108.3	125.3	120.7	110.0	+20.4%
Italy		100.0	97.8	106.1	101.7	102.0	103.6	
Luxembourg	110.1	100.0	131.8	113.8	119.6	112.7	117.9	+7.1%
Netherlands	80.4	100.0	122.5	124.9	131.4	127.8	140.1	+74.3%
Portugal		100.0						

[1]At constant 1980 prices in terms of ECUs.
Source. Based on *The Agricultural Situation in the Community*.

Table 2.11. The relationship between producer cost prices and input prices (1980 = 100)[1]

	1973	1980	1982	1983	1984	1985	1986
United Kingdom	119.8	100.0	100.3	97.4	94.6	92.1	94.9
Belgium	109.3	100.0	96.7	99.0	94.0	94.6	95.2
Denmark	112.0	100.0	95.8	94.1	91.3	92.0	95.3
Fed. Rep. of Germany	112.5	100.0	97.1	92.5	91.8	92.0	93.6
Greece	112.3	100.0	106.9	101.8	105.1	106.2	102.7
Spain	109.2	100.0	98.1	91.6	88.5	87.9	
France		100.0	98.0	96.4	92.0	91.4	95.0
Ireland	131.3	100.0	99.4	100.7	96.0	91.6	97.4
Italy		100.0	94.2	93.6	91.5	94.7	99.6
Luxembourg	119.2	100.0	101.1	98.4	94.4	102.6	104.4
Netherlands	114.0	100.0	99.4	97.2	97.1	99.7	101.5
Portugal		100.0					

[1]At current prices in terms of ECUs.

Note. Increases in the ratios signify favourable movements and vice versa.

Source. Based on *The Agricultural Situation in the Community.*

Table 2.12. Share of household consumption expenditure devoted to food as proportion of total expenditure, 1984 (per cent)[1]

United Kingdom	19.9
Belgium	21.9
Denmark	24.7
Fed. Rep. of Germany	17.8
Greece	41.3
Spain	27.1
France	21.2
Ireland	44.6
Italy	29.0
Luxembourg	21.3
Netherlands	19.8
Portugal	36.5
EC12	21.9
EC10	21.3

[1]Food, beverages and tobacco.

Source. Based on *The Agricultural Situation in the Community 1987.*

Table 2.13. Share of agriculture in gross fixed capital formation, 1985 (per cent)

United Kingdom	1.6
Belgium	2.2
Denmark	4.6
Fed. Rep. of Germany	2.6
Greece	2.1
Spain	
France	3.1
Ireland	7.5
Italy	8.1
Luxembourg	3.0
Netherlands	4.7
Portugal	3.7
EC12	
EC10	3.7

Source. Based on *The Agricultural Situation in the Community 1987.*

Table 2.14. United Kingdom trade in food and agricultural products with EC and non EC countries (per cent)

	Imports			Exports		
	EC	Non EC	Total	EC	Non EC	Total
1973	29.9	70.1	100.0	40.3	59.7	100.0
1974	31.2	68.8	100.0	37.5	62.5	100.0
1975	36.5	63.5	100.0	42.6	57.4	100.0
1984	49.5	50.5	100.0	51.8	48.2	100.0
1985	51.6	48.4	100.0	52.6	47.4	100.0
1986	51.6	48.4	100.0	59.8	40.2	100.0

Source. Based on *The Agricultural Situation in the Community.*

Table 2.15. Production of common wheat ('000 tonnes)

	1973	1985	1986
United Kingdom	5002	12 026	13 845
UK as % EC12	11.4	18.4	21.3
UK as % EC10	12.6	20.0	22.9
Belgium	1015	1187	1292
Denmark	542	1972	2171
Fed. Rep. of Germany	7134	9799	10 269
Greece	1361	1013	1259
Spain	3806	4958	4038
France	17 407	28 092	25 548
Ireland	229	495	424
Italy	6212	4665	4678
Luxembourg	34	28	30
Netherlands	725	851	940
Portugal	496	368	434
EC12	43 963	65 454	64 932
EC10	39 661	60 129	60 460

Source. Based on *The Agricultural Situation in the Community 1987.*

Table 2.16. Production of barley ('000 tonnes)

	1973	1985	1986
United Kingdom	9007	9740	10010
UK as % EC12	22.6	18.9	21.4
UK as % EC10	25.5	23.9	25.4
Belgium	718	685	790
Denmark	5432	5251	5134
Fed. Rep. of Germany	6622	9690	9377
Greece	850	606	680
Spain	4402	10698	7331
France	10948	11440	10063
Ireland	904	1494	1428
Italy	450	1630	1660
Luxembourg	58	61	65
Netherlands	383	197	262
Portugal	57	65	84
EC12	39830	51558	46884
EC10	35371	40795	39469

Source. Based on *The Agricultural Situation in the Community 1987*.

Table 2.17. Production of cereals in total ('000 tonnes)[1]

	1973	1985	1986
United Kingdom	15304	22471	24402
UK as % EC12	12.6	14.0	15.9
UK as % EC10	14.0	16.2	17.9
Belgium	2114	2065	2253
Denmark	6633	7956	7968
Fed. Rep. of Germany	21177	25914	25612
Greece	3261	4428	5446
Spain	11256	20514	15799
France	42984	55687	49654
Ireland	1295	2095	1954
Italy	14719	16939	17851
Luxembourg	139	132	125
Netherlands	1359	1129	1265
Portugal	1295	1234	1437
EC12	121538	160564	153765
EC10	108987	138816	136530

[1]Excluding rice.
Source. Based on *The Agricultural Situation in the Community 1987*.

Table 2.18. Production of sugar ('000 tonnes)[1]

	1973–74	1986–87	1987–88[2]
United Kingdom	963	1318	1200
UK as % EC12	9.2	9.4	9.2
UK as % EC10	10.0	10.1	10.0
Belgium	718	938	800
Denmark	338	499	350
Fed. Rep. of Germany	2258	3192	2635
Greece	146	287	195
Spain	751	1020	989
France	3259	3715	3960
Ireland	177	186	220
Italy	1037	1719	1700
Luxembourg	–	–	–
Netherlands	766	1218	950
Portugal	7	4	2
EC12	10422	14096	13001
EC10	9662	13072	12010

[1]In terms of white sugar value.   [2]Forecast.
Source. Based on *The Agricultural Situation in the Community 1987*.

Table 2.19. Sugar quotas ('000 tonnes)[1]

	A sugar[2]	B sugar[3]		A sugar[2]	B sugar[3]
United Kingdom	1040	104			
UK as % EC12	–	–	UK as % EC10	10.9	4.6
Belgium	680	146	France[4]	2996	806
Denmark	328	97	Ireland	182	18
Fed. Rep. of Germany	1990	612	Italy	1320	248
			Luxembourg	–	–
Greece	290	29	Netherlands	690	182
Spain	–	–	Portugal	–	–
EC12	–	–	EC10	9516	2242

[1]White sugar.   [2]'A' sugar is a quota on the level of production eligible for EC market support and is subject to a maximum production levy of two per cent of the intervention price.   [3]'B' sugar is a quota on the level of production eligible for EC market support and is subject to a maximum levy of 39.5% of the intervention price, depending on the level of surplus production in the Community market.   [4]Including French overseas departments.
Source. Based on *The Agricultural Situation in the Community 1987*.

Table 2.20. Oilseed rape production ('000 tonnes)

	1973	1985	1986
United Kingdom	31	895	970
UK as % EC12	2.9	23.9	26.3
UK as % EC10	2.9	24.0	26.4
Belgium	2	6	8
Denmark	92	544	613
Fed. Rep. of Germany	222	803	969
Spain	0	12	12
France	660	1419	1046
Ireland	0	14	6
Italy	10	13	44
Luxembourg	--	1	2
Netherlands	41	31	20
EC12	1058	3737	3682
EC10	1058	3725	3669

-- Negligible.
Source. Based on *The Agricultural Situation in the Community 1987*.

125

Table 2.21. Estimated area of fruit ('000 hectares)

	1973	1985	1986
United Kingdom	70	50	49
UK as % EC12	2.6	1.8	1.8
UK as % EC10	4.7	2.9	2.9
Belgium	17	11	11
Denmark	12	9	8
Fed. Rep. of Germany	85	54	54
Greece	134	163	164
Spain	993	967	969
France	325	243	241
Ireland	3	2	2
Italy	820	950	950
Luxembourg	--	--	--
Netherlands	36	25	24
Portugal	240	246	245
EC12	2737	2720	2717
EC10	1504	1703	1699

-- Negligible.   Source. Based on *The Agricultural Situation in the Community 1987.*

Table 2.22. Estimated apple production ('000 tonnes)

	1973	1985	1986
United Kingdom	449	301	312
UK as % EC12	5.2	4.0	3.8
UK as % EC10	6.0	4.8	4.2
Belgium	238	216	262
Denmark	80	45	57
Fed. Rep. of Germany	1980	1383	2115
Greece	274	267	306
Spain	928	1004	828
France	1911	1793	1875
Ireland	12	9	8
Italy	2002	2014	1990
Luxembourg	9	6	7
Netherlands	550	300	445
Portugal	142	95	76
EC12	8573	7433	8281
EC10	7503	6334	7377

Source. Based on *The Agricultural Situation in the Community 1987.*

Table 2.23. Estimated pear production ('000 tonnes)

	1973	1985	1986
United Kingdom	44	53	50
UK as % EC12	1.4	2.0	1.9
UK as % EC10	1.7	2.8	2.3
Belgium	30	78	81
Denmark	7	4	4
Fed. Rep. of Germany	403	324	474
Greece	130	139	129
Spain	471	595	361
France	456	417	340
Ireland	0	0	0
Italy	1529	806	980
Luxembourg	--	--	--
Netherlands	65	107	103
Portugal	59	57	50
EC12	3194	2578	2569
EC10	2664	1926	2158

-- Negligible.   Source. Based on *The Agricultural Situation in the Community 1987.*

Table 2.24. Estimated area of fresh vegetables ('000 tonnes)

	1973	1985	1986
United Kingdom	180	172	172
UK as % EC12	9.2	8.8	8.7
UK as % EC10	12.9	12.5	12.2
Belgium	55	50	53
Denmark	11	19	20
Fed. Rep. of Germany	62	55	54
Greece	143	151	140
Spain	447	472	460
France	326	327	323
Ireland	7	7	8
Italy	545	521	497
Luxembourg	--	--	--
Netherlands	63	77	77
Portugal	118	94	94
EC12	1957	1946	1966
EC10	1392	1379	1413

-- Negligible.   Source. Based on *The Agricultural Situation in the Community 1987.*

Table 2.25. Estimated cauliflower production ('000 tonnes)

	1973	1985	1986
United Kingdom	346	356	360
UK as % EC12	18.0	18.6	17.8
UK as % EC10	20.1	21.3	20.3
Belgium	32	62	71
Denmark	9	11	12
Fed. Rep. of Germany	83	79	86
Greece	41	50	53
Spain	179	222	235
France	428	526	553
Ireland	10	14	12
Italy	717	528	565
Luxembourg	0	0	0
Netherlands	59	49	62
Portugal	19	18	18
EC12	1923	1915	2027
EC10	1725	1675	1774

Source. Based on *The Agricultural Situation in the Community 1987.*

Table 2.26. Estimated tomato production ('000 tonnes)

	1973	1985	1986
United Kingdom	120	116	125
UK as % EC12	1.4	0.9	1.2
UK as % EC10	2.1	1.2	1.6
Belgium	120	160	174
Denmark	20	17	17
Fed. Rep. of Germany	32	23	26
Greece	1266	2238	1699
Spain	2028	2429	2243
France	569	930	716
Ireland	24	14	12
Italy	3151	5934	4516
Luxembourg	--	--	--
Netherlands	363	525	547
Portugal	1075	885	706
EC12	8770	13271	10781
EC10	5666	9957	7832

-- Negligible.
Source. Based on *The Agricultural Situation in the Community 1987.*

Table 2.27. Potato production ('000 tonnes)

	1973	1985	1986
United Kingdom	6608	6892	6380
UK as % EC12		16.1	16.1
UK as % EC10	16.2	19.3	19.0
Belgium	1418	1805	1673
Denmark	761	1073	1129
Fed. Rep. of Germany	13676	7905	7390
Greece	787	1009	939
Spain		5781	4857
France	7336	6856	6021
Ireland	1332	686	619
Italy	2947	2397	2547
Luxembourg	57	29	25
Netherlands	5771	7150	6854
Portugal		1249	1114
EC12		42832	39549
EC10	40693	35802	33578

Source. Based on *The Agricultural Situation in the Community 1987.*

Table 2.28. Hops production (tonnes)

	1973	1985	1986
United Kingdom	10400	7050	5071
UK as % EC12		14.9	11.7
UK as % EC10	20.1	16.2	12.3
Belgium	1900	1230	1016
Fed. Rep. of Germany	37100	34000	33989
Greece		10	–
Spain		3248	2004
France	2400	1257	1087
Ireland		87	14
Portugal		376	329
EC12		47258	43510
EC10	51800	43634	41177

Source. Based on *The Agricultural Situation in the Community 1987.*

Table 2.29. Beef and veal production ('000 tonnes)[1]

	1973	1985	1986
United Kingdom	858	1146	1045
UK as % EC12			13.0
UK as % EC10	15.3	15.4	13.9
Belgium	259	317	316
Denmark	183	237	242
Fed. Rep. of Germany	1240	1576	1670
Greece		82	82
Spain		401	435
France	1460	1893	1910
Ireland	208	449	511
Italy	1073	1201	1176
Luxembourg	8	9	10
Netherlands	308	571	539
Portugal			104
EC12			8041
EC10	5597	7421	7501

[1]Net production.
Source. Based on *The Agricultural Situation in the Community 1987.*

Table 2.30. Pigmeat production ('000 tonnes)[1]

	1973	1985	1986
United Kingdom	977	966	989
UK as % EC12		8.3	8.2
UK as % EC10	11.8	9.2	9.2
Belgium/ Luxembourg	589	717	749
Denmark	769	1083	1144
Fed. Rep. of Germany	2652	3243	3335
Greece	96	147	153
Spain		1157	1162
France	1577	1662	1677
Ireland	145	139	127
Italy	689	1187	1172
Netherlands	813	1368	1444
Portugal			171
EC12		11669	12123
EC10	8307	10512	10790

[1]Net production.
Source. Based on *The Agricultural Situation in the Community 1987.*

Table 2.31. Sheepmeat production ('000 tonnes)[1]

	1973	1985	1986
United Kingdom	254	304	291
UK as % EC12			34.2
UK as % EC10	40.4	40.9	41.4
Belgium/			
Luxembourg	3	4	6
Denmark	1	1	1
Fed. Rep. of			
Germany	12	24	23
Greece	120	122	106
Spain		133	134
France	136	172	162
Ireland	41	50	47
Italy	46	48	49
Netherlands	16	18	17
Portugal			13
EC12			850
EC10	629	743	703

[1]Gross production.
Source. Based on *The Agricultural Situation in the Community 1987*.

Table 2.32. Poultry meat production ('000 tonnes)[1]

	1973	1985	1986
United Kingdom	663	876	920
UK as % EC12		16.3	16.9
UK as % EC10	20.5	20.0	20.3
Belgium/			
Luxembourg	111	131	134
Denmark	90	115	116
Fed. Rep. of			
Germany	281	357	377
Greece	105	155	145
Spain		815	759
France	791	1277	1327
Ireland	41	55	62
Italy	796	998	1009
Netherlands	352	425	442
Portugal		155	155
EC12		5358	5446
EC10	3230	4388	4532

[1]Gross internal production.
Source. Based on *The Agricultural Situation in the Community 1987*.

Table 2.33. Production of milk from dairy herds ('000 tonnes)

	1973	1985	1986
United Kingdom	14 316	16 077	16 149
UK as % EC12		13.9	
UK as % EC10	15.6	14.8	14.7
Belgium	3611	3796	3918
Denmark	4729	5099	5111
Fed. Rep. of			
Germany	21 266	25 674	26 349
Greece	646	660	700
Spain		6375	
France	24 850	27 790	28 000
Ireland	3566	5823	5607
Italy	9350	10 946	10 660
Luxembourg	239	301	299
Netherlands	9354	12 550	12 695
Portugal		1058	
EC12		116 079	
EC10	91 927	108 646	109 488

Source. Based on *The Agricultural Situation in the Community 1987*.

Table 2.34. Butter production ('000 tonnes)[1]

	1973	1985	1986
United Kingdom	95	203	222
UK as % EC12			
UK as % EC10	5.7	9.9	10.3
Belgium	67	83	80
Denmark	146	110	112
Fed. Rep. of			
Germany	510	515	566
Greece		2	2
Spain		17	29
France	523	586	619
Ireland	84	160	154
Italy	74	78	81
Luxembourg	8	8	8
Netherlands	169	263	292
Portugal			
EC12			
EC10	1678	2055	2164

[1]Including butter oil manufactured from cream (butter equivalent). Production in dairies.
Source. Based on *The Agricultural Situation in the Community 1987*.

Table 2.35. Production of cheese ('000 tonnes)

	1973	1985	1986
United Kingdom	182	256	257
UK as % EC12			6.2
UK as % EC10		6.6	6.8
Belgium	38	41	
Denmark	127	256	254
Fed. Rep. of			
Germany	563	913	923
Greece		125	
Spain		154	
France	859	1283	1279
Ireland	39	79	
Italy	434	590	
Luxembourg	1	3	3
Netherlands	328	530	546
Portugal			
EC12			
EC10			

Source. Based on *The Agricultural Situation in the Community 1987.*

Table 2.36. Estimated egg production in shell ('000 tonnes)[1]

	1973	1985	1986
United Kingdom	864	774	772
UK as % EC12		15.8	15.6
UK as % EC10	22.7	18.6	18.7
Belgium/			
Luxembourg	241	176	184
Denmark	73	80	81
Fed. Rep. of			
Germany	896	765	743
Greece	104	122	123
Spain		683	723
France	720	907	909
Ireland	37	37	36
Italy	601	628	628
Netherlands	275	663	654
Portugal		78	80
EC12		4913	4933
EC10	3811	4152	4130

[1]Usable production of total eggs.
Source. Based on *The Agricultural Situation in the Community 1987.*

Table 2.37. Industrial production of compound feeds ('000 tonnes)

	1973	1985	1986
United Kingdom	11 228	10 457	11 192
UK as % EC12	17.2	11.1	11.6
UK as % EC10	19.2	13.1	13.6
Belgium	5053	5021	5078
Denmark	2705	4326	4535
Fed. Rep. of			
Germany	11 039	16 669	16 478
Spain	5280	11 690	11 411
France	10 981	14 721	15 366
Ireland	1225	2000	2387
Italy	6201	10 600	10 970
Netherlands	10 078	16 217	16 533
Portugal	1527	2578	2925
EC12[1]	65 317	94 279	96 875
EC10[1]	58 510	80 011	82 539

[1]Excluding Greece and Luxembourg.
Source. Based on *The Agricultural Situation in the Community 1987.*

Appendix 3: Farm structure and land use

Table 3.1. Land area used by agriculture ('000 hectares)

	1929	1938	1942	1950	1955	1960	1965	1970	1975	1980	1981	1982	1983	1984	1985	1986	1987
Total area of United Kingdom	24 400	24 400	24 400	24 400	24 400	24 400	24 410	24 410	24 105	24 088	24 089	24 088	24 088	24 088	24 085	24 085	24 085
Area of agricultural land[1]							19 621	19 124	18 978	18 953	18 808	18 783	18 735	18 720	18 703	18 676	18 652
% agricultural land							80.4	78.3	78.7	78.7	78.7	78.0	77.8	77.7	77.7	77.5	77.4
Crops and grass – total	13 172	12 851	12 626	12 597	12 587	12 489	12 408	12 143	12 028	12 136	12 085	12 083	12 078	12 095	12 080	12 088	12 116
arable	5783	5244	7081	7428	7099	7305	7496	7199	6954	6996	6982	6986	6970	6990	7061	7010	7008
grass over 5 years	7389	7607	5547	5167	5476	5184	4912	4944	5074	5140	5103	5097	5107	5105	5019	5077	5108
Rough grazing including common			8683	6921	6829	7406	7216	6692	6555	6333	6235	6198	6139	6107	6088	6045	5989
Woodland on farms								153	225	271	277	285	292	299	312	316	} 547
All other land								135	170	213	211	217	226	219	223	227	

[1]There have been some minor changes in the definition of total area of the UK
Source *Annual Abstract of Statistics*   MAFF: *Agricultural Statistics, United Kingdom*

Table 3.2. Relation of crops and grass to total land area ('000 hectares)

	England and Wales			Scotland			Great Britain		
	Total land area	Crops and grass	Per cent	Total land area	Crops and grass	Per cent	Total land area	Crops and grass	Per cent
1866	15 105[1]	9924	65.7	7948[1]	1683	21.2	23 053	11 607	50.3
1876	15 103[1]	10 892	72.1	7890[1]	1877	23.8	22 993	12 769	55.5
1886	15 103[1]	11 225	74.3	7878[1]	1964	24.9	22 981	13 189	57.4
1896	15 102[1]	11 196	74.1	7872[1]	1982	25.2	22 974	13 178	57.4
1906	15 027	11 086	73.8	7718	1971	25.6	22 745	13 057	57.4
1916	15 030	10 957	72.9	7718	1933	25.0	22 748	12 890	56.7
1926	15 029	10 391	69.1	7718	1899	24.6	22 747	12 290	54.0
1936	15 028	10 062	67.0	7717	1858	24.1	22 745	11 920	52.4
1946	15 027	9841	65.5	7717	1789	23.2	22 744	11 630	51.1
1956	15 028	9910	65.9	7717	1777	23.0	22 745	11 687	51.4
1966	15 027	9845	65.5	7718	1744	22.6	22 746	11 589	51.0

[1]Includes inland waterways.
Source. MAFF: *A Century of Agricultural Statistics 1866–1966.*

Table 3.3. Changes in the balance of tillage and grassland (%)

Great Britain

	Tillage	Temporary grass	Arable land	Permanent grass	Total crops and grass[1]
1866–75	45.5	13.6	59.1	40.9	100.0
1886–95	36.2	14.4	50.7	49.3	100.0
1906–15	32.5	13.1	45.6	54.4	100.0
1926–35	29.9	13.0	42.8	57.2	100.0
1946–55	41.2	18.1	59.3	40.6	100.0
1956–65	37.8	21.4	59.2	40.8	100.0

United Kingdom

	Crops and fallow	Grasses < 5 years[2]	Arable land	Grasses 5 years and over[3]	Total crops and grass[1]
1929	29.9	14.0	43.9	56.1	100.0
1938	28.2	12.6	40.8	59.2	100.0
1942	43.7	12.4	56.1	43.9	100.0
1950	41.2	17.8	59.0	41.0	100.0
1955	36.7	19.7	56.4	43.5	100.0
1960	36.5	22.0	58.5	41.5	100.0
1965	39.0	21.3	60.4	39.6	100.0
1970	40.3	18.9	59.3	40.7	100.0
1975	40.0	17.8	57.8	42.2	100.0
1980	41.4	16.2	57.6	42.3	100.0
1985	43.5	14.9	58.5	41.5	100.0
1986	43.7	14.3	58.0	42.0	100.0
1987	43.8	14.0	57.8	42.0	100.0

[1]Excluding rough grazing, woodland and other land on agricultural holdings. [2]Temporary prior to 1975. [3]Permanent prior to 1975.

Table 3.4. Number of holdings by crops and grass area: England and Wales ('000 acres)

	5 or less	Over 5–20	Over 20–50	Over 50–100	Over 100–300	Over 300–500	Over 500–1000	Over 1000	Total[1]
				Holding size (acres)					
1875	–	333.6	–	54.5	65.8	11.7	4.0	0.5	470.0
1885	136.4	126.7	73.5	54.9	67.0	11.8	4.2	0.6	475.1
1895	97.8	126.7	74.8	56.8	68.3	11.5	4.0	0.5	440.5
1905	91.6	198.3	–	127.5	–	15.2	–	–	432.6
1915	90.6	120.6	78.4	59.7	69.7	14.3	–	–	433.4
1925	75.3	110.4	79.1	60.9	67.3	12.7	–	–	405.7
1935	67.2	96.9	75.1	62.3	66.3	8.9	2.7	0.3	379.7

	Under 5	5–19¾	20–49¾	50–99¾	100–299¾	300–499¾	500–999¾	1000 and over	Total[1]
1944	67.7	88.5	68.8	60.3	65.4	8.9	2.9	0.4	362.9
1951	80.9	90.8	68.2	60.0	64.7	9.1	3.1	0.5	377.2
1955	79.6	87.1	66.2	59.6	64.0	9.4	3.2	0.5	369.6
1960	71.8	77.7	61.4	57.6	62.6	9.6	3.6	0.7	344.9
1966	63.5	70.0	52.7	51.8	58.4	10.3	4.5	0.9	312.2
1969	24.9	← 97.0 →		47.7	56.1	10.5	← 6.1 →		242.3

[1]Excluding rough grazing holdings.
Note: 5 acres = 2.02 hectares
      20 acres = 8.09 hectares
      50 acres = 20.23 hectares
      100 acres = 40.47 hectares
      300 acres = 121.41 hectares
      500 acres = 202.35 hectares
      1000 acres = 404.69 hectares
Source. MAFF: *A Century of Agricultural Statistics 1866–1966.*
            Agricultural Statistics, United Kingdom.

Table 3.5. Holdings by crops and grass area: Scotland ('000 acres)

	5 or less	Over 5–30	Over 30–50	Over 50–100	Over 100–300	Over 300–500	Over 500–1000	Over 1000	Total
				Holding size (acres)					
1875	–	56.3	–	9.9	11.8	2.0	0.7	0.1	80.8
1885	21.5	22.1[2]	10.7[3]	9.8	12.5	2.0	0.6	0.1	79.4
1895	20.2	23.1[2]	10.8[3]	9.8	13.0	2.1	0.6	0.1	79.6
1905	18.7	← 34.7 →		← 23.1 →		←	2.7	→	79.1
1915	18.2	27.2	5.9	10.1	13.1	←	2.6	→	77.1
1925	17.0	27.2	6.3	10.2	13.0	←	2.5	→	76.2
1935	15.6	27.0	6.5	10.2	12.6	←	2.4	→	74.3
1945	17.5	27.2	6.5	10.1	12.3	←	2.1	→	75.7
1950	17.4	26.6	6.4	10.0	12.3	←	2.2	→	74.8
1955	16.9	25.6	6.2	9.9	12.2	←	2.2	→	73.0
1960	14.0	19.7	4.8	8.6	11.6	←	2.7	→	61.3
1966[1]	10.8	17.5	4.1	7.6	11.5	2.2	0.8	0.1	54.6

[1]Up to 4¾ acres, 5 to 29¾ acres etc.   [2]Over 5 to 20 acres.   [3]Over 20 to 50 acres.
Note: 5 acres = 2.02 hectares
      20 acres = 8.09 hectares
      50 acres = 20.23 hectares
      100 acres = 40.47 hectares
      300 acres = 121.41 hectares
      500 acres = 202.35 hectares
      1000 acres = 404.69 hectares
Source. MAFF: *A Century of Agricultural Statistics 1866–1966.*

Table 3.6. Number of holdings by size ('000)

Holding size (hectares)	Under 2	2–4.9	5–9.9	10–19.9	20–29.9	30–39.9	40–49.9	50–99.9	100–199.9	200–299.9	300–499.9	500–699.9	700 and over	Total
England														
1977	13.5	17.2	19.3	22.3	17.2	12.7	10.7	28.5	16.8	4.7	2.8	0.7	0.6	167.1
1980	10.6	12.8	17.7	21.7	16.4	12.4	10.4	28.0	16.7	4.7	2.9	0.8	0.6	155.7
1985	11.0	14.1	17.7	20.9	15.1	11.9	9.9	27.1	16.8	4.9	2.9	0.8	0.6	153.8
1986	11.6	15.0	17.8	20.8	14.9	11.7	9.7	26.9	16.8	4.9	3.0	0.8	0.7	154.7
Wales														
1977	0.7	2.6	4.0	5.2	4.3	3.2	2.7	6.0	2.4	0.5	0.3	0.1	0.1	32.0
1980	0.5	1.4	3.6	5.1	3.9	3.2	2.5	6.0	2.4	0.5	0.2	0.1	0.1	29.5
1985	0.8	1.9	3.7	4.9	3.6	3.0	2.4	6.0	2.5	0.5	0.3	0.1	0.1	29.8
1986	0.9	2.1	3.8	4.8	3.6	2.9	2.4	6.0	2.6	0.5	0.3	0.1	0.1	29.9
Scotland														
1977	1.3	2.4	2.3	2.9	2.4	2.1	2.0	6.4	4.7	1.5	1.1	0.5	1.2	30.9
1980	1.5	2.6	2.4	2.9	2.4	2.1	1.9	6.4	4.7	1.6	1.2	0.5	1.2	31.4
1985	1.6	2.8	2.6	3.0	2.3	1.9	1.8	6.2	4.7	1.6	1.1	0.5	1.2	31.3
1986	1.7	2.9	2.6	3.0	2.3	1.9	1.8	6.2	4.7	1.6	1.1	0.5	1.2	31.5
Northern Ireland														
1977	1.3	5.9	12.1	16.2	8.2	4.0	2.1	2.7	0.6	0.1	←	0.1	→	53.3
1980	1.3	5.9	11.6	15.5	8.0	4.0	2.1	2.9	0.6	0.1	←	0.1	→	52.2
1985	0.5	1.2	9.5	14.6	7.7	4.0	2.2	3.1	0.6	0.1	←	0.1	→	43.5
1986	0.6	1.5	9.5	14.4	7.6	3.9	2.2	3.1	0.7	0.1	←	0.1	→	43.6
United Kingdom														
1970	31.8[1]	55.6[2]		91.1[3]		61.9[4]		31.4[5]	36.4[6]		12.9[7]	7.4[8]		328.7
1975	20.5[1]	41.3[2]		80.9[3]		56.4[4]		29.7[5]	35.5[6]		13.2[7]	8.2[8]		285.7
1977	16.9	28.0	37.7	46.7	32.2	22.1	17.4	43.7	24.5	6.7	←	7.4	→	283.3
1980	13.9	22.8	35.4	45.2	30.8	21.6	17.0	43.2	24.5	6.9	←	7.6	→	268.8
1985	13.9	20.1	33.4	43.4	28.8	20.8	16.2	42.4	24.7	7.1	←	7.7	→	258.5
1986	14.8	21.5	33.7	43.0	28.4	20.5	16.1	42.2	24.8	7.1	←	7.7	→	260.0

[1]Under 2 ha. [2]2–5.9. [3]6–19.9. [4]20–39.9. [5]40–59.9. [6]60–119.9. [7]120–199.9. [8]200 and over.

Source. MAFF: *Agricultural Statistics, United Kingdom.*

Table 3.7. Proportion of holdings by size: United Kingdom (per cent)

	Holding size (hectares)								
	Under 2 (per cent)	2–5.9 (per cent)	6–19.9 (per cent)	20–39.9 (per cent)	40–59.9 (per cent)	60–119.9 (per cent)	120–199.9 (per cent)	200 and over (per cent)	Total
1962	19.0	20.3	24.8	15.7	7.7	8.6	2.6	1.2	100.0
1965	18.5	19.9	24.7	16.1	7.8	8.9	2.9	1.3	100.0
1970	9.7	16.9	27.7	18.8	9.6	11.1	3.9	2.3	100.0
1975	7.2	14.5	28.3	19.7	10.4	12.4	4.6	2.9	100.0
Number of holdings 1975 ('000)	20.5	41.3	80.9	56.4	29.7	35.5	13.2	8.2	285.7

	Holding size (hectares)											
	Under 2 (per cent)	2–4.9 (per cent)	5–9.9 (per cent)	10–19.9 (per cent)	20–29.9 (per cent)	30–39.9 (per cent)	40–49.9 (per cent)	50–99.9 (per cent)	100–199.9 (per cent)	200–299.9 (per cent)	300 and over (per cent)	Total
1979	5.9	10.5	13.3	16.2	11.1	7.8	6.1	15.4	8.7	2.4	2.7	100.0
1980	5.2	8.5	13.2	16.8	11.5	8.0	6.3	16.1	9.1	2.6	2.8	100.0
1981	5.2	7.4	12.8	17.1	11.7	8.2	6.4	16.4	9.4	2.6	2.9	100.0
1982	5.4	7.6	12.8	16.9	11.5	8.1	6.4	16.4	9.4	2.6	2.9	100.0
1983	5.7	8.1	12.8	16.7	11.3	8.0	6.3	16.3	9.4	2.7	2.9	100.0
1984	5.1	7.3	13.0	17.0	11.4	8.1	6.3	16.5	9.4	2.8	2.9	100.0
1985	5.4	7.8	12.9	16.8	11.1	8.0	6.3	16.4	9.6	2.7	3.0	100.0
1986	5.7	8.3	13.0	16.5	10.9	7.9	6.2	16.2	9.5	2.7	3.0	100.0
Number of holdings 1986 ('000)	14.8	21.5	33.7	43.0	28.4	20.5	16.1	42.2	24.8	7.1	7.7	259.8

Note. There have been changes in the definition of agricultural holdings which primarily affect small holdings. The percentage distributions for the different years are therefore not entirely comparable, but the trends are correct.

Source. Based on MAFF: *Agricultural Statistics, United Kingdom.*

Table 3.8. Area of crops and grass by holding size 1875–1966: England and Wales (million acres)

	5 or less	Over 5–10	Over 20–50	Over 50–100	Over 100–300	Over 300–500	Over 500–1000	Over 1000	Total
				Holding size (acres)					
1875	–	4.2	–	4.0	11.2	4.4	2.6	0.6	26.8
1885	0.3	1.4	2.5	4.0	11.5	4.5	2.7	0.7	27.7
1895	0.3	1.4	2.5	4.2	11.7	4.3	2.6	0.7	27.7
1915	0.3	1.4	2.6	4.3	11.8	–	6.6	–	27.1

	Under 5	5–19¾	20–49¾	50–99¾	100–299¾	300–499¾	500–999¾	1000 and over	Total
				Holding size (acres)					
1944	0.2	0.9	2.3	4.3	10.8	3.3	1.9	0.6	24.3
1951	0.2	0.9	2.3	4.3	10.7	3.4	2.0	0.7	24.5
1955	← 1.1 →		← 6.5 →		← 14.1 →		2.1	0.8	24.5
1960	0.2	0.8	2.0	4.1	10.4	← 5.9 →		0.9	24.4
1966	0.2	0.7	1.8	3.7	9.8	3.9	2.9	1.4	24.3

Source. MAFF: *A Century of Agricultural Statistics 1866–1966.*

Table 3.9. Area of crops and grass by holding size: Scotland (million acres)

	5 or less	Over 5–30	Over 30–50	Over 50–100	Over 100–300	Over 300–500	Over 500–1000	Over 1000	Total
				Holding size (acres)					
1875	–	0.7	–	0.7	2.0	0.7	0.4	0.1	4.6
1885	0.1	0.2[2]	0.4[3]	0.7	2.1	0.8	0.4	0.1	4.8
1895	0.1	0.2[2]	0.4[3]	0.7	2.2	0.8	0.4	0.1	4.9
1908	0.1	← 0.6 →		← 3.0 →		←	1.2	→	4.9
1925	0.1	0.4	0.3	0.8	2.2	←	1.1	→	4.7
1945	0.1	0.4	0.3	0.7	2.1	←	0.9	→	4.4
1962[1]	- -	0.2	0.2	0.6	2.0	0.8	0.4	0.1	4.3
1966[1]	- -	0.2	0.2	0.6	2.0	0.8	0.5	0.1	4.4

[1] Up to 4¾ acres, 5 to 29¾ acres etc.   [2] Over 5 to 20 acres.   [3] Over 20 to 50 acres.
Source. MAFF: *A Century of Agricultural Statistics 1866–1966.*

Table 3.10. Total area of holdings by size ('000 hectares)

Size of holding (hectares)	Under 2	2–4.9	5–9.9	10–19.9	20–29.9	30–39.9	40–49.9	50–99.9	100–199.9	200–299.9	300 and over	Total
England												
1977	13	59	139	324	426	441	478	2022	2316	1124	2123	9467
1980	11	41	131	316	405	431	461	1988	2304	1139	2215	9442
1985	12	46	130	302	374	414	439	1924	2323	1177	2278	9419
1986	12	49	131	300	368	407	434	1911	2325	1173	2302	9413
1986 per cent	0.1	0.5	1.4	3.2	3.9	4.3	4.6	20.3	24.7	12.5	24.4	100.0
Wales												
1977	1	9	29	76	106	113	119	418	315	104	212	1501
1980	1	5	27	73	97	110	113	414	326	116	208	1491
1985	1	6	28	70	90	104	107	417	342	124	206	1495
1986	1	7	28	69	89	102	107	418	344	121	212	1498
1986 per cent	0.1	0.5	1.9	4.6	5.9	6.8	7.1	27.9	23.0	8.1	14.1	100.0
Scotland												
1977	1	8	16	43	61	73	88	460	651	363	3805	5569
1980	2	8	17	43	60	72	86	462	658	376	3794	5579
1985	2	9	18	43	57	67	80	451	657	387	3623	5396
1986	2	10	19	43	57	67	79	448	659	386	3606	5375
1986 per cent	- -	0.2	0.3	0.8	1.1	1.2	1.5	8.3	12.3	7.2	67.1	100.0

continued overleaf

Table 3.10 continued

Size of holding (hectares)	Under 2	2–4.9	5–9.9	10–19.9	20–29.9	30–39.9	40–49.9	50–99.9	100–199.9	200–299.9	300 and over	Total
Northern Ireland												
1977	1	23	88	231	199	138	90	178	77	22	41	1089
1980	1	23	86	222	194	137	94	189	81	23	43	1093
1985	- -	4	73	211	187	137	96	202	85	26	40	1061
1986	1	5	73	206	185	136	96	205	87	27	38	1058
1986 per cent	- -	0.5	6.9	19.5	17.5	12.8	9.1	19.4	8.2	2.5	3.6	100.0
United Kingdom												
1977	17	99	273	674	791	765	775	3078	3359	1614	6181	17 626
1980	14	78	261	652	758	750	755	3053	3369	1654	6260	17 605
1985	15	66	249	625	708	721	723	2994	3407	1715	6147	17 371
1986	16	71	250	618	699	711	716	2982	3416	1706	6158	17 344
1986 per cent	0.1	0.4	1.4	3.6	4.0	4.1	4.1	17.2	19.8	9.8	35.5	100.0

- - Negligible.

Source. MAFF: *Agricultural Statistics, United Kingdom.*

Table 3.11. Number of holdings by size of business in standard man days and British Size Units ('000)

Smd[1]	1967	1970	1972	1973	1974			
26–275	157.3	130.1	128.5	115.7	115.4			
275–599	91.8	79.6	72.3	69.3	66.5			
600–1199	58.2	55.9	55.1	55.3	55.0			
1200 +	33.3	35.4	37.5	39.5	41.1			
Total holdings	340.6	301.0	293.4	279.7	278.0			
Average, 275 and over	944	993	1042	1082	1114			

Smd (New series)[1]	1975	1978	1980	1981	1982	1983	1984	1985
Under 250	126.2	121.1	122.3	122.4	121.9	124.0	123.4	127.9
250–499	56.4	51.2	47.7	46.4	45.6	44.6	43.8	42.0
500–999	45.4	44.5	43.9	43.6	43.9	43.5	42.0	40.5
1000 +	28.3	29.2	30.0	29.9	30.9	31.1	30.3	29.8
Total	256.8	246.0	243.8	242.3	242.3	243.3	239.4	240.3
Average, 250 and over	857	898	909	906	915	913	909	928

BSU[2]	1984	1987
Under 4.0	102.7	110.2
4.0–15.9	68.8	64.6
16.0–39.9	51.7	50.0
40.0 +	29.0	29.5
Total	252.1	254.3
Average, 4 BSU and over	29.0	30.0

[1]Standard man days (smd) is a measure of the labour needed to farm the crops and livestock on a holding. From 1978 onwards the figures are not directly comparable with earlier statistics as the standard man days were revised. [2]British Size Units (BSU) measure the financial potential of the farm in terms of the margins which might be expected from its crops and stock. 1 BSU = 2000 ECU of standardised gross margins at average 1978–80 values. 4 BSU is judged to be the minimum for a full-time farm.

Source. HMSO: *Annual Review of Agriculture.*

Table 3.12. Number of full-time farm businesses by farm type and size group, 1986

	England	Wales	Scotland	Northern Ireland	United Kingdom
Dairying					
Small	7611	2629	187	4139	14 566
Medium	13 234	2749	1425	2009	19 417
Large	5567	593	1149	–	7309
All sizes	26 412	5971	2761	6148	41 292
Hill and upland					
(LFA) livestock					
Small	4412	5071	5166	3400	18 049
Medium	2947	3003	3141	240	9331
Large	826	486	861	–	2173
All sizes	8185	8560	9168	3640	29 553
Lowland livestock					
Small	9610	1403	353	1139	12 505
Medium	3265	406	437	111	4219
Large	963	92	187	–	1242
All sizes	13 838	1901	977	1250	17 966
Cropping					
Small	10 578	221	861	609	12 269
Medium	11 880	154	1720	177	13 931
Large	14018	69	1703	–	15790
All sizes	36 476	444	4284	786	41 990
Pigs and poultry					
Small	2510	108	–	–	2618
Medium	1837	53	–	–	1890
Large	1344	26	–	–	1370
All sizes	5691	187	–	–	5878
Horticulture					
Small	3454	73	–	–	3527
Medium	1157	11	–	–	1168
Large	640	4	–	–	644
All sizes	5251	88	–	–	5339
Total holdings					
4 BSU and over					
Small	38 175	9505	6567	9287	63 534
Medium	34 320	6376	1720	2537	44 953
Large	23 358	1270	8903	–	33 531
All sizes	95 853	17 151	17 190	11 824	142 018

Note. British Size Units (BSU) measure the financial potential of the farm in terms of margins which might be expected from its crops and stock. The margins used are standard gross margins at average 1978–80 values. A threshold of 4 BSU is judged to be the minimum for full-time farms.
Farms are defined as: Small, 4 to under 16 BSU; medium, 16 to under 40 BSU; large, 40 BSU and over. One BSU equals 2000 European Currency Units of standard gross margins at average 1978–80 values.
Source. *Farm Incomes in the United Kingdom 1987.*

Table 3.13. Area by tenure: Great Britain 1887–1960

	Rented		Owner-occupied		Total	
	Area (million ha)	per cent	Area (million ha)	per cent	Area (million ha)	per cent
1887[1]	11.2	85	2.0	15	13.2	100
1891[1]	11.3	85	2.0	15	13.3	100
1908[1]	11.4	88	1.6	12	13.0	100
1910[1]	11.4	88	1.6	12	13.0	100
1914[1]	11.5	89	1.4	11	12.9	100
1922[1]	10.2	82	2.2	18	12.4	100
1950[2]	8.3	62	5.0	38	13.3	100
1960[3]	6.7	50	6.6	37	13.3	100

[1]Area of crops and grass.   [2]Area of crops and grass and rough grazing.   [3]Total area of farms in 1961, for England and Wales 1960 and Scotland 1961.
Source. MAFF: *A Century of Agricultural Statistics 1866–1966.*

Table 3.14. Area by tenure: Great Britain 1970–86[1]

	Rented		Owned		Total	
	Area (million ha)	per cent	Area (million ha)	per cent	Area (million ha)	per cent
1970	7.7	43	10.3	57	18.0	100
1971	7.6	43	10.3	57	18.0	100
1972	7.5	42	10.4	58	17.9	100
1973	7.5	42	10.4	58	17.9	100
1974	7.5	42	10.4	58	17.9	100
1975	7.5	42	10.4	58	17.9	100
1976	7.5	42	10.4	58	17.9	100
1977	7.2	41	10.4	59	17.6	100
1978	7.1	40	10.6	60	17.7	100
1979	7.0	40	10.7	60	17.7	100
1980	6.9	39	10.8	61	17.7	100
1981	6.8	39	10.8	61	17.6	100
1982	6.7	38	10.8	62	17.5	100
1983	6.6	38	10.9	62	17.5	100
1984	6.5	38	9.8	60	16.3	100
1985	6.4	40	10.0	61	16.3	100
1986	6.3	39	10.0	61	16.3	100

[1]Virtually no land is rented in Northern Ireland.
Source. MAFF: *Agricultural Statistics of the United Kingdom.*

Table 3.15. Number of full-time farm businesses by farm type and tenure, 1986

	England	Wales	Scotland	Northern Ireland	United Kingdom
Dairying					
Tenanted	6821	1092	829	–	8742
Owner occupied	11249	3444	1932	6148	22773
Mixed	8342	1435	–	–	9777
All tenures	26412	5971	2761	6148	41292
Hill and upland (LFA) livestock					
Tenanted	2142	1236	3679	–	7057
Owner occupied	3742	5284	5489	3640	18155
Mixed	2301	2040	–	–	4341
All tenures	8185	8560	9168	3640	29553
Lowland livestock					
Tenanted	2515	380	332	–	3227
Owner occupied	7883	1058	645	1250	10836
Mixed	3440	463	–	–	3903
All tenures	13838	1901	977	1250	17966
Cropping					
Tenanted	9193	84	1732	–	11009
Owner occupied	14266	252	2552	786	17856
Mixed	13017	108	–	–	13125
All tenures	36476	444	4284	786	41990
Pigs and poultry					
Tenanted	573	14	–	–	587
Owner occupied	4046	141	–	–	4187
Mixed	1072	32	–	–	1104
All tenures	5691	187	–	–	5878
Horticulture					
Tenanted	682	7	–	–	689
Owner occupied	3366	65	–	–	3431
Mixed	1203	16	–	–	1219
All tenures	5251	88	–	–	5339
Total holdings 4 BSU and over					
Tenanted	21926	2813	6572	–	31311
Owner occupied	44552	10244	10618	11824	77238
Mixed	29375	4094	–	–	33469
All tenures	95853	17151	17190	11824	142018

Note. British Size Units (BSU) measure the financial potential of the farm in terms of margins which might be expected from its crops and stock. The margins used are standard gross margins at average 1978–80 values. A threshold of 4 BSU is judged to be the minimum for full-time farms.
Farms are defined as: Small, 4 to under 16 BSU; medium, 16 to under 40 BSU; large, 40 BSU and over. One BSU equals 2000 European Currency Units of standard gross margins at average 1978–80 values.
Source. *Farm Incomes in the United Kingdom 1987.*

Table 3.16. Part-time agricultural holdings

	1978[1]	1980[1]	1985[1]	1984[2]	1987[2]
England					
Number	70 927	72 287	78 049		
% of all holdings	45	46	51		
Wales					
Number	16 056	16 032	16 696		
% of all holdings	54	54	56		
Scotland					
Number	15 734	16 653	17 400		
% of all holdings	51	53	56		
Northern Ireland					
Number	18 378	17 292	15 727		
% of all holdings	64	63	61		
United Kingdom					
Number	121 095	122 264	127 872	102 700	110 200
% of all holdings	49	50	53	41	43

[1]Holdings needing less than 250 standard man days per year to operate.   [2]Holdings with under 4 BSU.
Source. MAFF: *June Agricultural Censuses.   Farm Incomes in the United Kingdom* 1987.

Table 3.17. Agricultural land prices (£ per hectare)

	England			Wales	Scotland			Northern Ireland
	Vacant possession	Total sold	Tenanted	Vacant possession	Vacant possession	Total sold	Tenanted	Vacant possession
1944		93				68		
1945		98				68		
1950		153				87		
1955		147				84		
1960		249				138		173
1965		440				269		273
1969	570		379	314	182		70	360
1970	526		372	311	240		166	413
1975	1205		797	926	602		441	1143[1]
1980	3470		2336	2326	1853		1560	3227
1981	3418		2381	2118	1834		1204	2897
1982	3669		2490	2321	1791		1340	2683
1983	3789		2404	2737	1969		1073	2866
1984	3895		2780	2485	1628		743	2958
1985	3871		2918	2589	1572		628	3130
1986[2]	3476		2278	2308	1418		691	3128

[1]In 1972 there was a change in the method used for assigning transactions to calendar years.   [2]Provisional.
Source. MAFF: *Agricultural Land Prices in England and Wales. Scottish Agricultural Economics.* HMSO: *Annual Review of Agriculture.*

Table 3.18. Oxford Institute land price series (£ per hectare)[1]

	At current prices	In 1986 money values		At current prices	In 1986 money values		At current prices	In 1986 money values
1945	111	1474	1960	304	2365	1974	1572	5596
1946	146	1916	1961	306	2316	1975	1332	3810
1947	173	2126	1962	331	2410	1976	1814	4462
1948	195	2225	1963	415	2963	1977	2449	5192
1949	188	2096	1964	529	3655	1978	3279	6427
1950	198	2146	1965	581	3840	1979	4371	7562
1951	217	2157	1966	598	3803	1980	4265	6227
1952	188	1760	1967	638	3949	1981	4272	5596
1953	180	1658	1968	692	4097	1982	4557	5468
1954	185	1676	1969	734	4125	1983	5145	5917
1955	198	1732	1970	605	3195	1984	4888	5377
1956	193	1619	1971	647	3119	1985	4781	4924
1957	180	1462	1972	1473	6628	1986	4193	4193
1958	210	1661	1973	1871	7727	1987	4944	4746
1959	250	1965						

[1]England and Wales, with vacant possession, average of land sold at auction. New series from 1970 onwards.
Source. Oxford Institute of Agricultural Economics.

Appendix 4: Labour

Table 4.1. Numbers of farmers and agricultural workers: Great Britain ('000)

	Total	Workers	Farmers		Total	Workers	Farmers
	Population census						
1851	2000	1697	303	1951		812	
1861	1913	1601	312	1952		804	
1871	1690	1385	305	1953		780	
1881	1500	1221	279	1954		755	
1891	1402	1124	278	1955		732	
1901	1325	1047	278	1956		700	
1911	1382	1103	279	1957		696	
1921	1317	996	316	1958		679	
	Agricultural census			1959		669	
1923		892		1960		645	
1924		924		1961		617	
1925		925		1962		589	
1926		921		1963		569	
1927		894		1964		544	
1928		890		1965		514	
1929		888		1966		488	
1930		857		1967		451	
1931	1162[1]	829	294[1]	1968		418	
1932		809		1969		402	
1933		828		1970		400	
1934		801		1971		396	
1935		787		1972		381	
1936		751		1973		385	
1937		742		1974	618	368	250
1938		697		1975	604	354	250
1939		711		1976	610	348	262
1940		712		1977	689[2]	344	259
1941		759		1978	691[2]	340	264
1942		824		1979	685[2]	338	265
1943		843		1980	661[2]	334	260
1944		863		1981	650[2]	324	257
1945		887		1982	646[2]	320	256
1946		889		1983	638[2]	315	253
1947		891		1984	632[2]	305	256
1948		849		1985	634[2]	306	256
1949		855		1986	623[2]	296	255
1950		843		1987	610[2]	286	252

[1]Population Census.   [2]Includes spouses of farmers, partners and directors engaged in farm work.
Source. Agricultural Departments: *Agricultural Census.*
MAFF: *Agricultural Labour in England and Wales.*

Table 4.2. UK labour force in Annual Work Units ('000)

	Number of persons in agriculture	Number of annual work units	AWU per person
1975	757.6	625.7	0.83
1979–80	723.7	582.8	0.81
1983	723.1	562.1	0.78
1985	736.6	543.0	0.74

Note. An Annual Work Unit represents the agricultural work done by one full-time worker in one year. Part-time and seasonal work is expressed as a fraction of an AWU. Each person is counted according to the time actually worked on the holding (excluding work in the household). The Annual Work Unit (AWU) used in the publications of the Statistical Office of the European Community is the same concept as the Annual Labour Unit (ALU) used by the Ministry of Agriculture, Fisheries and Food in the UK publications. (See Table 4.3) The statistics do not correspond closely because they are based on different sources.
Source. Eurostat: *Agriculture: Statistical Yearbook.*

Table 4.3. UK labour force in Annual Labour Units (ALU) ('000)

	ALU	Average ALU per person working in agriculture
1977	556.8	0.74
1978	555.4	0.73
1979	543.8	0.73
1980	529.2	0.73
1981	517.5	0.73
1982	513.1	0.73
1983	508.1	0.73
1984	500.8	0.72
1985	496.6	0.72
1986	486.8	0.71

Annual Labour Units (ALU). One ALU represents the labour input of a full-time worker in a year.
Note. Part-time workers are converted to a full-time basis according to the annual average number of hours worked relative to those of a full-time worker.
Source. MAFF: *Agricultural Labour in England and Wales.*

Table 4.4. UK Family and non-family members of the labour force ('000 AWU)

	Family	Non-family	Total	Family as % of total
1973	343.2	253.9	597.1	57.5
1978	325.8	229.6	555.4	58.7
1983	304.0	204.2	508.1	59.8
1986	303.8	183.0	485.8	62.5

Note. Annual Work Unit (AWU) represents the agricultural work done by one full-time worker in one year. Part-time and seasonal work is expressed as a fraction of an AWU. Each person is counted according to the time actually worked on the holding (excluding work in the household). The Annual Work Unit (AWU) used in the publications of the Statistical Office of the European Community is the same concept as the Annual Labour Unit (ALU) used by the Ministry of Agriculture, Fisheries and Food in the UK publications. (See Table 4.3) The statistics do not correspond closely because they are based on different sources.
Source. Eurostat: *Agriculture: Statistical Yearbook.*

Table 4.5. Holdings by number of full-time workers: England and Wales ('000)

	Number of workers on the holding				Total number of holdings employing full-time workers
	1	2–4	5–9	10 or more	
1951	68.3	59.9	13.6	5.0	146.8
1960	57.9	46.2	9.7	3.7	117.5
1966	46.8	35.2	7.2	2.5	91.7
1971	38.8	31.7	6.6	2.6	79.7
1976	33.0	26.8	5.5	2.1	67.4
1981	27.7	21.4	4.6	1.7	55.4
1986	26.2	19.3	3.8	1.4	50.7

Note. Before 1970 the basis of classification was the number of regular full-time men aged 20–64. After 1970 it was the number of full-time workers, irrespective of age or sex.

Table 4.6. Number of agricultural workers by country ('000)[1]

	England and Wales	Scotland	Great Britain	Northern Ireland	United Kingdom
1921	869	127	996		
1922		125			
1923	772	120	892		
1924	806	117	924		
1925	803	122	925		
1926	795	126	921		
1927	774	119	894		
1928	773	117	890		
1929	770	118	888	41	929
1930	742	116	857	38	895
1931	717	112	829	36	865
1932	697	111	809	38	847
1933	716	112	828	37	865
1934	688	113	801	37	838
1935	673	113	787	45	831
1936	641	111	751	100	850
1937	632	111	742	96	838
1938	593	104	697	88	786
1939	607	104	711	92	804
1940	609	104	712	94	806
1941	650	110	759	90	850
1942	708	115	824	92	915
1943	719	124	843	112	955
1944[2]	741	122	863	112	975
1945[2]	770	117	887	95	981
1946[2]	774	115	889	87	976
1947[2]	777	115	891	89	980
1948[2]	741	109	849	82	932
1949[2]	749	107	855	79	934
1950[2]	737	105	843	75	918
1951	708	104	812	70	882
1952	702	102	804	65	869
1953	683	96	780	62	841
1954	658	97	755	60	815
1955	639	93	732	56	788
1956	610	90	700	55	754
1957	607	90	696	54	750
1958	591	88	679	51	730
1959	585	85	669	50	719
1960	562	83	645	49	693
1961	535	82	617	45	661
1962	513	76	589	44	633
1963	496	73	569	41	611
1964	476	68	544	39	584
1965	451	64	514	37	551
1966	430	58	488	34	522
1967	397	54	451	34	485
1968	367	50	418	32	450
1969	354	49	402	31	433
1970	352	48	400	30	430
1971	349	47	396	27	423
1972	340	41	381	25	407
1973	346	39	385	25	410
1974	331	37	368	23	391
1975	318	36	354	21	375
1976	312	36	348	22	369
1977	307	36	344	21	364
1978	304	36	340	20	360
1979	303	35	338	19	357
1980	299	35	334	19	352
1981	291	33	324	18	342
1982	289	31	320	18	339
1983	285	30	315	19	334
1984	277	28	305	19	325
1985	278	28	306	19	324
1986	271	25	296	19	315
1987	263	23	286	19	305

[1]Regular full-time, part-time, seasonal and casual. [2]Including Women's Land Army and Prisoners of War.
Source. Agricultural Departments: *Agricultural Census*.

Table 4.7. Holdings by number of full-time workers:
England and Wales ('000)

	Number of workers on the holding				Number of holdings employing full-time workers	Number of workers
	1	2–4	5–9	10 or more		
1946	67.2	56.1	13.2	5.2	141.7	
1948	66.6	58.5	13.6	5.1	143.8	
1951	68.3	59.9	13.6	5.0	146.8	
1955	63.6	49.5	12.7	4.1	129.9	
1960	57.9	46.2	9.7	3.7	117.5	
1963	54.7	43.2	9.3	3.3	110.5	263.2
1964	51.8	40.7	8.5	3.0	104.0	249.8
1965	47.4	37.8	7.9	2.9	96.0	235.9
1966	46.8	35.2	7.2	2.5	91.7	221.6
1967	44.8	33.5	7.0	2.4	87.7	213.8
1968	43.3	31.5	6.4	2.3	83.5	203.1
1969	41.6	30.1	6.1	2.1	79.9	194.0
				New series		
1971	38.8	31.7	6.6	2.6	79.7	213.5
1972	38.5	30.9	6.4	2.5	78.3	206.5
1973	38.5	30.8	6.1	2.4	77.8	203.4
1974	36.6	28.7	5.8	2.3	73.4	192.9
1975	34.6	27.5	5.6	2.3	70.0	184.1
1976	33.0	26.8	5.5	2.1	67.4	177.6
1977	30.6	25.2	5.2	2.0	63.0	169.2
1978	29.5	24.0	5.0	2.0	60.5	162.3
1979						
1980	28.0	21.7	4.6	1.9	56.2	149.2
1981	27.7	21.4	4.6	1.7	55.4	145.4
1982	27.4	21.5	4.4	1.6	54.9	142.7
1983	26.9	21.4	4.4	1.6	54.3	140.2
1984	26.9	20.5	4.2	1.5	53.1	135.2
1985	26.8	20.2	4.0	1.5	52.5	131.7
1986	26.2	19.3	3.8	1.4	50.7	126.3

Note. Before 1970 the basis of classification was the number of regular whole-time men aged 20–64. After 1970 it was the number of full-time workers, irrespective of age or sex.

Table 4.8. Estimated percentage distribution of hired regular
whole-time men and youths by age and occupation:
England and Wales (1986)

	Youths 15–19	Males 20–44	45–54	55–64	65 and over	Total
Foremen	0.2	52.9	24.5	21.0	1.4	100.0
Dairy cowmen	3.2	63.6	19.9	12.0	1.3	100.0
Other stockmen	10.1	63.4	13.6	11.9	0.9	100.0
Tractor drivers	2.5	55.9	21.8	19.1	0.6	100.0
General farm workers	12.7	56.3	14.6	15.7	0.7	100.0
Horticultural workers	14.3	62.6	11.3	11.6	0.2	100.0
Other farm workers	8.6	55.2	15.7	20.4	–	100.0
All hired males	9.2	57.6	16.6	15.8	0.8	100.0

Source. MAFF: *Agricultural Labour in England and Wales, 1986 Report.*

Table 4.9. Minimum wages and basic hours of ordinary adult male agricultural workers in England and Wales (£ per week)

	Minimum wage (£)	Basic hours (£)	Wage per basic hour (£)
1914	0.900	(58)	0.015
1918	1.500	52	0.029
1920	2.014		
October–September years			
1921–22	1.695	49.9	0.034
1925–26	1.575	50.1	0.031
1930–31	1.585	50.4	0.031
1935–36	1.600	50.6	0.032
1938–39	1.735	50.2	0.035
1945–46	3.610	48.4	0.075
Effective annual date			
7 April 1946	3.50	48.0	0.073
12 November 1950	5.00	47.0	0.106
25 July 1955	6.35	47.0	0.135
22 February 1960	8.00	46.0	0.217
4 January 1965	10.10	45.0	0.224
2 February 1970	13.15	43.0	0.306
21 July 1975	30.50	40.0	0.763
21 January 1980	58.00	40.0	1.450
21 January 1981	64.00	40.0	1.600
21 January 1982	70.40	40.0	1.760
20 January 1983	75.40	40.0	1.885
1 September 1983	79.20	40.0	1.980
3 June 1984	82.80	40.0	2.070
2 June 1985	89.70	40.0	2.243
1 June 1986	94.45	40.0	2.361
1 June 1987	99.20	40.0	2.480

Source. *Agricultural Labour in England and Wales.*

Table 4.10. Farmers' expenditure on labour (£ million)

	At current prices	In 1986 money values	Index (1950 = 100)		At current prices	In 1986 money values	Index[1] (1950 = 100)
1938	66	1463	56	1963	310	2213	85
1939	69	1500	57	1964	313	2163	83
1940	86	1576	60	1965	318	2102	80
1941	114	1732	66	1966	322	2048	78
1942	135	1918	73	1967	323	1999	77
1943	148	2038	78	1968	328	1942	74
1944	162	2190	84	1969	337	1894	73
1945	174	2311	88	1970	354	1869	72
1946	194	2545	97	1971	384	1851	71
1947	217	2667	102	1972	437	1967	75
1948	230	2624	100	1973	510	2104	81
1949	238	2654	102	1974	615	2187	84
1950	241	2612	100	1975	758	2170	83
1951	249	2475	95	1976	883	2169	83
1952	260	2434	93	1977	981	2080	80
1953	269	2477	95	1978	1101	2155	83
1954	274	2482	95	1979	1257	2170	83
1955	280	2450	94	1980	1445	2114	81
1956	290	2433	93	1981	1573	2057	79
1957	294	2387	91	1982	1695	2041	78
1958	299	2365	91	1983	1835	2113	81
1959	302	2374	91	1984	1897	2080	80
1960	300	2334	89	1985	2052	2121	81
1961	299	2263	87	1986	2052	2052	79
1962	302	2199	84	1987	2077	1992	76

[1]In 1986 money values.

Table 4.11. Expenditure on labour (£ million)

	1972	1975	1980	1981	1982	1983	1984	1985	1986	1987[4]
Hired Labour										
Wages and salaries		486.3	906.1	973.8	1051.4	1148.8	1179.5	1276.6	1256.6	1270.1
Insurance[1]		41.9	114.8	123.6	124.5	126.1	123.7	118.0	102.4	100.4
Other charges[2]		0.8	2.0	3.1	4.1	4.2	5.7	7.0	7.0	7.9
Total hired labour	305.1	528.8	1022.9	1100.3	1179.9	1279.0	1308.8	1401.5	1366.0	1378.5
Family and partners' labour										
Wages and salaries		209.1	370.6	414.9	455.6	496.5	528.2	587.3	623.9	636.5
Insurance[1]		19.6	51.4	57.5	59.2	59.0	60.0	62.3	62.2	62.6
Total family and partners' labour	131.8	228.7	422.0	472.4	514.9	555.5	588.1	649.6	686.1	699.1
Total labour (hired and family)	436.9	757.7	1444.6	1572.8	1694.8	1834.5	1896.9	2051.1	2052.1	2077.6

[1]National Insurance and Employers' Liability Insurance. [2]Redundancy payments, workers' pension scheme, youth training scheme. [3]Including family and partners' labour. [4]Forecast.
Source. MAFF: *Departmental Net Income Calculation.*

Table 4.12. Average weekly earnings of regular full-time men: England and Wales[1]

	Weekly earnings	
	At current prices	In 1986 money values
1914	0.99	34.41
1915		
1916		
1917	1.38	27.16
1918	1.65	28.17
1919	1.89	30.50
1920	2.35	32.74
1921	2.44	37.50
1922	1.78	33.66
1923	1.54	30.63
1924	1.56	30.87
1925	1.67	32.87
1926	1.74	35.15
1927	1.74	35.90
1928	1.74	36.30
1929	1.74	36.89
1930	1.74	38.14
1931	1.74	40.94
1932	1.72	41.47
1933	1.69	41.79
1934	1.69	41.52
1935	1.74	42.23
1936	1.77	41.65
1937	1.83	41.05
1938	1.88	41.68
1939	2.15	46.74
1940	2.50	45.82
1941	3.04	46.18
1942	3.50	49.74
1943	3.66	50.40
1944	3.90	52.73
1945	4.13	54.85
1946	4.66	61.14
1947	5.11	62.80
1948	5.42	61.84
1949	5.58	62.22
1950	5.83	63.20
1951	6.27	62.32
1952	6.69	62.62
1953	7.13	65.67
1954	7.66	69.40
1955	8.14	71.22

continued overleaf

Table 4.12 continued

	Weekly earnings			
	At current prices	In 1986 money values		
1956	8.71	73.08		
1957	9.25	75.11		
1958	9.74	77.04		
1959	9.92	77.97		
1960	10.32	80.29		
1961	10.96	82.97		
1962	11.40	82.99		
1963	12.17	86.89		
1964	12.63	87.27		
1965	13.64	90.16		
1966	14.48	92.09		
1967	15.08	93.35		
1968	15.93	94.31		
1969	17.32	97.34		
1970	18.61	98.26		
1971	21.06	101.51		
1972	23.67	106.52		
1973	27.62	114.07		
1974	34.52	122.89		
			GB	UK
1975	43.15	123.41		
1976	50.50	124.23	50.45	50.28
1977	54.84	116.26	54.77	54.69
1978	61.80	121.13	61.99	61.75
1979	72.04	124.63	72.04	71.75
1980	86.48	126.26	86.26	85.95
1981	97.07	127.16	96.52	96.29
1982	106.65	127.98	105.87	105.44
1983	117.93	135.62	117.02	116.57
1984	124.16	136.58	123.11	122.59
1985	136.09	140.17	134.67	134.10
1986	142.77	142.77	141.32	140.76

[1]Hired regular full-time men, 20 years and over.

Table 4.13. Average weekly earnings and hours of hired regular whole-time workers: England and Wales

	Men		Youths		Females	
	20 and over		under 20			
	Earnings (£)	Hours	Earnings (£)	Hours	Earnings (£)	Hours
1960	10.32					
1965	13.64					
1966	14.48	49.3	8.74	47.9	8.89	45.0
1970	18.61	48.3	11.15	47.0	12.07	43.1
1975	43.15	46.5	29.31	45.3	29.06	41.9
1980	86.48	46.2	56.01	44.6	65.16	42.0
1981	97.07	46.8	62.13	45.0	70.00	41.1
1982	106.65	46.6	69.68	45.1	80.10	42.8
1983	117.93	47.1	76.19	45.9	88.08	42.8
1984	124.16	46.6	80.10	45.0	93.87	42.0
1985	136.09	47.3	86.32	45.1	102.30	43.1
1986	142.77	47.1	89.93	45.7	108.01	42.7

Note. Earnings include pay for statutory holidays and benefits in kind which are valued at rates set by the Agricultural Wages Board. Hours include all hours worked and statutory holidays.
Source. MAFF: *Agricultural Labour in England and Wales.*

Table 4.14. Composition of costs of employing regular whole-time men by occupation: England and Wales (£ per week)[1]

	Foremen	Dairy cowmen	All other stockmen	Tractor drivers	General farm workers	Hort. workers	Others	All hired men
Total cash earnings	172.07	164.21	144.16	146.20	128.28	126.53	145.85	139.29
Payment in kind of which:								
allowable	1.35	2.10	3.58	1.97	4.22	0.48	1.41	3.07
other	1.20	0.40	0.31	0.51	0.26	0.29	0.66	0.40
Total earnings	174.62	166.71	148.06	148.67	132.76	127.29	147.92	142.77
National Insurance	17.98	17.16	15.06	15.28	11.55	11.39	15.24	12.54
Employers' Liability Insurance	1.08	1.03	0.92	0.92	0.82	0.79	0.92	0.89
Total cost to employer	193.67	184.90	164.04	164.87	145.13	139.47	164.08	156.20

[1]Year ending 31 December 1986.
Source. MAFF: *Agricultural Labour in England and Wales, 1986 Report.*

Table 4.15. Total cost to employer of employing regular full-time men by occupation: England and Wales (£ per week)

	1981	1982	1983	1984	1985	1986
Foremen	131.92	144.74	159.99	170.80	187.87	193.67
Dairy cowmen	136.17	146.18	163.19	165.32	176.91	184.90
Other stockmen	114.30	122.21	135.54	143.71	154.51	164.04
Tractor drivers	112.70	123.55	136.62	141.87	159.10	164.87
General farm workers	102.32	111.29	121.34	129.34	139.61	145.13
Horticultural workers	99.21	110.15	114.60	125.10	133.55	139.47
Other farm workers	106.81	129.38	139.02	139.77	144.83	164.08
All hired men	110.65	120.61	132.28	138.53	150.83	156.20

Source. MAFF: *Agricultural Labour in England and Wales.*

Table 4.16. Average earnings of full-time men in agriculture and in other industries and services (£ per week)

	Agriculture[1]	Industry and services	Agricultural earnings as % of earnings in industry and services
1960	10.32	14.10	73
1961	10.96	15.07	73
1962	11.40	15.64	73
1963	12.17	16.15	75
1964	12.63	17.62	72
1965	13.64	18.91	72
1966	14.48	20.25	72
1967	15.08	20.58	73
1968	15.93	22.26	72
1969	17.32	23.91	72
1970	18.61	26.90	69
1971	21.06	29.50	71
1972	23.67	32.90	72
1973	27.62	38.20	72
1974	34.52	43.70	79
1975	43.15	55.50	78
1976	50.50	65.00	78
1977	54.84	71.40	77
1978	61.80	80.60	77
1979	72.04	93.00	77
1980	86.48	111.40	78
1981	97.07	121.90	80
1982	106.65	133.80	80
1983	117.93	141.60	83
1984	124.16	152.70	81
1985	136.09	163.60	83
1986	142.77	176.56	81

[1]In England and Wales.
Source. MAFF: Lund, P. J., Morris, T. G., Temple, J. D. and Watson, J. M.: *Wages and Employment in Agriculture: England and Wales, 1960–80.*
Agricultural Labour in England and Wales (annual).
Central Statistical Office: *United Kingdom Abstract of Statistics.*

Appendix 5: Mechanisation

Table 5.1. Numbers of horses on farms: Great Britain ('000)

	Agricultural use[1]	Others[2]
1870	966	
1875	951	
1880	980	441
1885	976	
1890	1039	394
1895	1085	
1900	1078	422
1905	1122	
1910	1137	408
1915	858	
1920	927	653
1925	910	
1930	803	315
1935	697	
1940	642	317
1945	545	
1950	347	147
1955	161	113
1960	54	103
1965	21	125

[1] Including mares for breeding from 1890 onwards. [2] Before 1950, mostly unbroken horses.
Source. MAFF: *A Century of Agricultural Statistics 1866–1966.*

Table 5.2. Estimated number of agricultural machines and implements: England and Wales ('000)

	1942	1946	1950	1956	1960	1965	1971	1975	1980	1985	1986
Tractors	102	180	295	426	417	420	416	441	421	431	425
Cereals Machinery											
Corn drills	84	90	91	88	79[1]	60	58[7]	58[7]	36	34	34
Corn drills and combined seed and fertiliser drills				127	120		40	39	34	31	31
Binders	102	119	120	108	75	42					
Combine harvesters	1	3	10	31	48	58	57	56	47	45	45
Corn driers		1	1	7	17	27[2]	44	38	30	30	30
Potato and root crop machinery											
Potato planters		6	11	20[3]	27	27[4]	26	25	21	19	19
Potato spinners	29	47	60	63[3]	57	50[4]	30	25			
Potato elevator diggers and Shaker diggers	1	4	10	9[3]	13	13[4]	14	6	21	19	13
Complete potato harvesters			1	1[3]	2	3[4]	9	11	12[8]	12	12
Sugar beet harvesters		0.2	1	2[3]	9	13[4]	15		11	11	10
Milking machines (installations)	24	40	69	91[3]	107[5]			98			
Milking machines (units)				280	300	296[6]					

[1] 1959. [2] 1964. [3] 1954. [4] 1963. [5] 1961. [6] Numbers of teat cup clusters. [7] Corn, root and seed drills. [8] Complete root harvesters.
Note: The precise definitions of the different categories of machinery may vary. The figures may not be entirely comparable but they illustrate broad trends.
Source. MAFF: *Agricultural Statistics.*

Table 5.3. Estimated number of agricultural machines and implements: Scotland ('000)

	1942	1946	1950	1956	1961	1964	1971	1975	1980
Tractors	15	24	37	51	60	61	62	62	60
Cereals machinery									
Corn drills	10	9	9	9	7	7	5	5	6
Corn drills and combined seed and fertiliser drills	1	1	1	4	7	7	7	7	7
Binders	29	30	30	29	25	22	11	7	
Combine harvesters	--	--	--	2	4	6	8	8	8
Corn driers	--	--	--	--	1	3	8	11	9
Potato and root crop machinery									
Potato planters	--	1	1	3	5	5	5	5	5
Potato spinners	8	12	14	16	16	15	12	9	9
Potato elevator diggers and Shaker diggers		1	4	3	3	3	4	3	
Complete potato harvesters	--	--	--	--	--	1	1	1	1
Sugar beet harvesters	--	--	--	--	--	--	--	--	--
Milking machines (installations)	6	8	10	12		15	33	29	

- -Negligible: less than 500.   Note. At the time of writing the most recent Scottish machinery census statistics related to March 1980.
Source. MAFF: *Agricultural Statistics.*

Appendix 6: Capital and investment

Table 6.1. Indices of gross capital formation[1] (1986 = 100)

	At current prices	At constant 1980 prices[2]
1963	16.9	101.1
1964	17.8	103.2
1965	17.9	102.8
1966	17.9	99.3
1967	19.2	104.1
1968	22.4	119.4
1969	22.1	113.3
1970	24.3	114.6
1971	27.7	121.6
1972	31.4	136.1
1973	40.5	152.3
1974	49.9	155.4
1975	54.7	138.8
1976	61.3	134.5
1977	74.5	140.1
1978	86.2	144.9
1979	96.6	140.1
1980	103.0	124.7
1981	93.9	106.7
1982	116.7	131.8
1983	131.6	146.0
1984	132.1	145.1
1985	118.4	121.6
1986	100.0	100.0
1987[3]	88.1	85.0

[1]Buildings and works, plant, buildings and machines. [2]The 1980 series has been carried back before 1975 by splicing with the 1970 constant price series. [3]Forecast.
Source. Based on MAFF *Departmental Net Income Calculation.*

Table 6.2. Capital formation at current prices (£ million)

	1972	1973	1974	1975	1976	1977	1978	1979	1980	1981	1982	1983	1984	1985	1986	1987[1]
Plant, machinery	125	169	219	271	352	440	461	501	425	361	484	599	552	592	488	430
Buildings, works	159	209	252	240	225	251	331	397	557	506	610	638	684	515	440	380
Vehicles	40	40	44	54	56	79	99	100	82	103	112	122	129	116	105	100
Gross fixed capital formation	324	418	515	565	633	770	891	998	1064	970	1206	1359	1365	1223	1 033	910
Breeding livestock capital formation	34	36	−21	−37	−7	−25	15	−34	−35	3	28	−7	−28	12	5	−57
Stock appreciation	76	226	310	266	312	204	161	275	342	308	126	281	−34	208	−50	38
Value of physical increase	25	53	35	−171	−33	172	−7	−5	−51	−33	19	28	90	−228	21	−40
Increase in book value of stocks and works in progress	101	279	344	96	279	376	154	270	291	275	145	310	56	−21	−28	−2

[1]Forecast.
Source. MAFF: *Departmental Net Income Calculation.*

Table 6.3. Capital formation at constant 1980 prices (£ million)

	1975	1976	1977	1978	1979	1980	1981	1982	1983	1984	1985	1986	1987[1]
Plant, machinery	563	606	633	581	559	425	347	444	527	473	477	393	337
Buildings, works	503	436	443	526	522	557	469	583	618	664	475	389	325
Vehicles	118	104	118	129	114	82	94	97	100	101	85	71	63
Gross fixed capital formation	1184	1147	1195	1236	1195	1064	910	1124	1245	1238	1037	853	725
Breeding livestock capital formation	−79	−12	−35	20	−37	−35	3	24	−6	−24	9	2	−48
Value of physical increase in stocks and works in progress	−278	−61	223	−13	−2	−51	−26	32	29	90	−185	−42	−29

[1]Forecast.
Source. MAFF: *Departmental Net Income Calculation.*

Table 6.4. Estimated balance sheet for agriculture (£ million)

	1970	1971	1972	1973	1974	1975	1976	1977	1978	1979	1980	1981	1982	1983	1984	1985	1986 Prov.	1987 (F)
Assets																		
Land and buildings	5250	6450	14 700	15 850	12 150	12 350	15 800	22 200	28 400	37 100	34 900	34 700	36 200	41 200	38 300	34 550	33 300	34 300
Machinery	950	1000	1150	1350	1700	2100	2600	3100	3550	4000	4200	4150	4300	4450	4600	4700	4700	4700
Livestock	1200	1600	2150	2350	2150	2950	3450	4200	4900	4800	5200	6000	6550	6800	6350	6500	5750	5700
Crops and stores	450	450	600	800	1200	1200	1450	1350	1600	2050	2050	2150	2300	2600	2800	2500	2650	2550
Debtors cash deposits	500	550	600	750	750	900	1000	1050	1150	1050	1100	1300	1400	1500	1550	1600	1850	1850
Total assets	8350	10 050	19 200	21 100	17 950	19 500	24 300	31 900	39 600	49 000	47 450	48 300	50 750	56 550	53 600	49 850	48 250	49 100
Liabilities																		
Bank borrowing	500	550	650	800	950	950	1050	1450	1850	2400	2900	3400	4100	4800	5000	5500	5550	5700
Other	900	900	900	1100	1150	1250	1350	1450	1550	1800	1900	2100	2200	2300	2600	2800	2900	3000
Total liabilities	1 400	1 450	1 550	1 900	2 100	2 200	2 400	2 900	3 400	4 200	4 800	5 500	6 300	7 100	7 600	8 300	8 450	8 700
Net worth	6950	8600	17 650	19 200	15 850	17 300	21 900	29 000	36 200	44 800	42 650	42 800	44 450	49 450	46 000	41 550	39 800	40 400
As % of national wealth						←		4.6[1]	→					3.6	3.0	2.6	2.3	
In 1986 money values (1980 = 100)																		
Total assets	64	70	125	126	92	81	86	98	112	122	100	91	88	94	85	74	70	68
Total liabilities	105	100	100	112	107	90	84	88	95	104	100	103	108	117	119	122	121	119
Net worth	59	67	128	127	91	79	87	99	114	124	100	90	86	91	81	69	64	62

[1]Average, 1976–78.
Source. MAFF: 1970–75. Private information supplied to Christopher Johnson, Lloyds Bank for paper "The Balance Sheet of British Agriculture", Statistics Users Council, November 1986.
1976 onwards. *Farm Incomes in the United Kingdom,* 1987 and 1988 editions.

Appendix 7: Output, expenses and income

Table 7.1. Economic indicators for agriculture in 1986 money values

	Net product[1]	Farming income[2]	Farm business income[3]	Cash flow of farmer and spouse[1]
1971	123	217	141	148
1972	124	215	142	147
1973	150	278	183	184
1974	128	198	143	143
1975	126	200	141	188
1976	133	222	117	177
1977	119	188	132	126
1978	117	174	127	132
1979	111	140	115	115
1980	102	108	102	104
1981	105	125	109	120
1982	112	148	122	123
1983	103	115	102	93
1984	118	160	131	127
1985	95	78	89	90
1986	100	100	100	100
1987	95	95	94	107

[1]Net product is a measure of the value added by the agricultural industry to all the goods and services purchased from outside agriculture after provision has been made for depreciation. [2]Farming income is the return to farmers and spouses for their labour, management skills and own capital invested, after providing for depreciation. [3]Farm business income is the return to farmers, spouses, non-principal partners and directors for their labour and management skills and on all capital (own or borrowed) invested in the industry, after providing for depreciation. [4]Cash flow is the pre-tax revenue accruing to farmer and spouse, less cash outlays in the specific year i.e. spending on material inputs and services and on capital items. Capital grants are included.

Table 7.2. Gross agricultural output, gross input, gross product, net product and farming income at current prices (£ million)

	Gross output	Gross input	Gross product	Net product	Farming income
1938	300	134	166	156	52
1939	342	140	202	191	82
1940	440	151	289	275	149
1941	513	156	357	339	187
1942	556	164	392	372	202
1943	598	176	422	400	218
1944	606	185	421	397	202
1945	625	197	428	402	195
1946	655	206	449	421	191
1947	711	226	485	452	202
1948	818	258	559	523	259
1949	921	312	609	568	297
1950	987	382	605	554	280
1951	1087	447	641	580	297
1952	1186	500	686	616	322
1953	1277	575	701	624	319
1954	1347	659	688	608	297
1955	1396	692	705	622	303
1956	1448	724	724	636	305
1957	1519	751	768	676	339
1958	1557	782	775	679	335
1959	1576	811	764	664	315
1960	1607	820	787	685	334
1961	1680	863	817	712	358
1962	1758	908	850	743	383
1963	1781	935	846	737	369
1964	1888	983	905	786	409
1965	1979	1034	945	815	427
1966	2031	1052	979	839	442
1967	2119	1092	1028	880	476
1968	2177	1149	1028	870	455
1969	2281	1201	1080	907	477
1970	2458	1318	1140	953	501
1971	2665	1421	1244	1031	553
1972	2949	1499	1450	1198	676
1973	3774	1904	1870	1572	945
1974	4278	2315	1962	1561	796
1975	5012	2592	2419	1902	991
1976	6132	3186	2946	2339	1280
1977	6876	3724	3153	2432	1262
1978	7306	3880	3426	2605	1265
1979	8178	4430	3748	2791	1149
1980	9000	4845	4155	3022	1044
1981	9842	5150	4693	3490	1361
1982	11 192	5875	5317	4048	1478
1983	11 607	6425	5182	3870	1416
1984	12 635	6603	6032	4676	2070
1985	11 996	6572	5424	3996	1085
1986	12 314	6517	5797	4347	1427
1987[1]	12 260	6480	5780	4294	1404

[1]Forecast.
Source. MAFF: *Departmental Net Income Calculation.*

Table 7.3. Gross agricultural output, gross input, gross product, net product and farming income in 1986 money values (£ million)

	Gross output	Gross input	Gross product	Net product	Farming income
1938	6651	2971	3680	3459	1153
1939	7435	3044	4391	4152	1783
1940	8065	2768	5297	5041	2731
1941	7792	2370	5423	5149	2841
1942	7901	2330	5570	5286	2870
1943	8234	2424	5811	5508	3002
1944	8193	2501	5692	5367	2731
1945	8300	2616	5684	5339	2590
1946	8594	2703	5891	5524	2506
1947	8738	2778	5961	5555	2483
1948	9333	2944	6378	5967	2955
1949	10269	3479	6790	6333	3312
1950	10699	4141	6558	6005	3035
1951	10805	4443	6372	5765	2952
1952	11101	4680	6421	5766	3014
1953	11761	5296	6456	5747	2938
1954	12204	5971	6233	5508	2691
1955	12215	6055	6169	5443	2651
1956	12149	6074	6074	5336	2559
1957	12334	6098	6236	5489	2753
1958	12316	6186	6130	5371	2650
1959	12387	6374	6005	5219	2476
1960	12502	6380	6123	5329	2599
1961	12718	6533	6185	5390	2710
1962	12798	6610	6188	5409	2788
1963	12716	6676	6040	5262	2635
1964	13046	6793	6254	5431	2826
1965	13081	6835	6246	5387	2822
1966	12917	6691	6226	5336	2811
1967	13117	6759	6363	5447	2946
1968	12888	6802	6086	5150	2694
1969	12819	6750	6070	5097	2681
1970	12978	6959	6019	5032	2645
1971	12845	6849	5996	4969	2665
1972	13271	6746	6525	5391	3042
1973	15587	7864	7723	6492	3902
1974	15230	8241	6984	5557	2834
1975	14334	7413	6918	5440	2834
1976	15085	7838	7247	5754	3149
1977	14577	7895	6684	5156	2675
1978	14320	7605	6715	5106	2479
1979	14148	7664	6484	4828	1988
1980	13140	7074	6066	4412	1524
1981	12893	6747	6148	4572	1783
1982	13430	7050	6380	4858	1774
1983	13348	7389	5959	4451	1628
1984	13899	7263	6635	5144	2277
1985	12356	6769	5587	4116	1118
1986	12314	6517	5797	4347	1427
1987[1]	11757	6214	5543	4118	1346

[1]Forecast.

Table 7.4. Index numbers of prices of agricultural products (1986 = 100)

	At current prices	In 1986 money values
1969	25.0	140.5
1970	26.3	138.9
1971	27.6	133.0
1972	30.4	136.8
1973	36.0	148.7
1974	41.3	147.0
1975	50.0	143.0
1976	65.5	161.1
1977	67.1	142.3
1978	68.6	134.5
1979	75.6	130.8
1980	79.6	116.2
1981	88.3	115.7
1982	95.2	114.2
1983	100.2	115.2
1984	100.3	110.3
1985	98.7	101.7
1986	100.0	100.0
1987	101.6	97.4

Source. MAFF: *Agricultural Statistics, United Kingdom.*

Table 7.5. Index numbers of prices goods and services bought by farmers (1986 = 100)

	Currently consumed in agriculture		Contributing to agricultural investment		Labour costs		All goods and services	
	At current prices	In 1986 money values	At current prices	In 1986 money values	At current prices	In 1986 money values	At current prices	In 1986 money values
1970	20.6	108.8	13.3	70.2				
1971	22.7	109.4	14.6	70.4				
1972	23.8	107.1	18.1	81.5				
1973	30.9	127.6	20.5	84.6	18.9	78.1		
1974	38.4	136.7	24.7	87.9	24.4	86.9		
1975	41.7	119.3	31.4	89.8	30.8	88.1		
1976	51.6	126.9	37.8	93.0	36.7	90.3	46.1	113.4
1977	59.6	126.4	45.4	96.2	40.0	84.8	53.0	112.4
1978	61.0	119.6	51.1	100.2	46.0	90.2	56.1	110.0
1979	68.0	117.6	57.7	99.8	53.6	92.7	63.2	109.3
1980	76.2	111.3	67.4	98.4	65.1	95.0	72.3	105.6
1981	83.8	109.8	72.8	95.4	71.9	94.2	79.4	104.0
1982	89.7	107.6	78.6	94.3	78.5	94.2	85.5	102.6
1983	96.0	110.4	83.2	95.7	85.1	97.9	91.5	105.2
1984	99.7	109.7	88.5	97.4	90.0	99.0	95.7	105.3
1985	100.9	103.9	93.4	96.2	96.1	99.0	98.6	101.6
1986	100.0	100.0	100.0	100.0	100.0	100.0	100.0	100.0
1987	101.1	97.0	105.7	101.4	105.3	100.7	102.7	98.5

Table 7.6. Ratio of product price index to input price index (1986 = 100)

	Agricultural product prices	Prices of agricultural goods and services	Ratio of product prices to goods and services prices
1976	65.5	46.1	142.1
1977	67.1	53.0	126.6
1978	68.6	56.1	122.3
1979	75.6	63.2	119.6
1980	79.6	72.3	110.1
1981	88.3	79.4	111.2
1982	95.2	85.5	111.3
1983	100.2	91.5	109.5
1984	100.3	95.7	104.8
1985	98.7	98.6	100.1
1986	100.0	100.0	100.0
1987	101.6	102.7	98.9

Table 7.7. Changes in the percentage composition of farmers' expenditure

	Feed	Fertilisers	Machinery	Labour	Rent and interest	Other	Total
1938–39	27.8	3.9	9.5	26.8	17.8	14.2	100
1943–44	7.8	7.7	16.5	39.0	11.7	17.3	100
1946–47	7.1	6.4	17.2	43.4	10.4	15.5	100
1951–52	21.6	6.6	19.7	30.2	7.8	14.1	100
1956–57	29.8	8.0	16.7	24.4	7.0	14.1	100
1961–62	28.6	9.0	16.4	22.3	8.7	15.0	100
1966–67	30.2	8.3	16.0	19.9	10.3	15.3	100
1970	31.9	9.2	16.5	18.7	4.2	19.5	100
1972	29.5	9.1	16.9	19.5	3.8	21.2	100
1975	33.9	9.3	19.5	21.7	4.2	11.4	100
1980	32.2	9.6	20.5	21.3	7.8	8.6	100
1985	28.3	9.4	20.6	21.6	9.1	11.0	100
1986	29.0	8.6	19.9	21.6	9.2	11.7	100
1987[1]	28.5	7.9	20.6	22.2	8.7	12.1	100

[1]Forecast.

Table 7.8. Changes in the volume of agricultural output

Official annual estimates of changes in the volume of agricultural output were not made before 1939. However, a study by Ojala published in 1952 gave average estimates for certain periods beginning with 1867–69, as follows:

	Index of volume of gross agricultural output	Conversion to 1970 = 100	Corrected to exclude Southern Ireland from pre-1922 figures
1867–69	89	48	38
1870–76	93	50	40
1877–85	90	48	38
1886–93	94	50	40
1894–1903	95	51	41
1904–10	99	53	42
1911–13	100	54	43
1920–22	95	51	41
1924–29	81	43	43
1930–34	84	45	45
1935–39	84	45	45
1940–44	82	44	44

Source. Ojala, E. M. 1952, *Agriculture and Economic Progress,* Oxford University Press.

Table 7.9. Indices of volume of agricultural output, gross product and net product (value at constant 1980 prices)

	Output	Gross product	Net product
1965	78.9	74.1	68.5
1966	79.7	74.7	68.6
1967	80.7	77.2	70.9
1968	82.0	74.6	68.6
1969	82.2	75.5	70.0
1970	85.5	75.5	69.2
1971	85.7	82.8	77.0
1972	88.0	82.5	76.5
1973	89.8	83.6	77.4
1974	91.0	84.6	78.0
1975	89.8	76.7	68.6
1976	86.4	70.6	61.0
1977	89.0	81.3	76.1
1978	95.2	89.5	86.8
1979	96.8	89.3	86.1
1980	100.0	100.0	100.0
1981	100.3	103.0	103.6
1982	106.0	109.9	112.5
1983	104.7	104.4	104.6
1984	111.5	123.2	130.2
1985	111.2	116.7	120.7
1986	110.4	118.2	122.6
1987	108.2	115.7	119.2

Sources. *Annual Abstract of Statistics,* 1971 and 1979.
HMSO: *Annual Review of Agriculture, 1988.*

Appendix 8: Public expenditure on agriculture

Table 8.1. Public expenditure on agriculture 1955–56 to 1971–72 (£ million)

	1955–56	1956–57	1957–58	1958–59	1959–60	1960–61	1961–62	1962–63	1963–64	1964–65	1965–66	1966–67	1967–68	1968–69	1969–70	1970–71	1971–72
Implementation of price guarantees																	
Cereals	35.9	26.0	51.2	52.6	58.4	63.4	73.3	63.9	77.1	63.3	43.1	49.4	41.8	57.9	62.5	23.8	62.8
wheat	(25.2)	(15.8)	(22.2)	(19.3)	(20.4)	(18.1)	(22.0)	(16.6)	(30.3)	(15.9)	(14.2)	(13.5)	(10.9)	(17.7)	(17.4)	(13.9)	(34.5)
barley	(10.7)	(8.8)	(17.1)	(23.5)	(25.2)	(33.6)	(33.2)	(36.3)	(36.8)	(37.4)	(21.6)	(29.2)	(23.5)	(29.5)	(35.5)	(7.8)	(16.8)
oats & mixed corn	(–)	(1.4)	(11.9)	(9.8)	(12.8)	(11.7)	(18.1)	(11.0)	(10.0)	(10.0)	(7.3)	(6.7)	(7.4)	(10.7)	(9.6)	(2.1)	(11.5)
Potatoes	0.7	1.2	8.3	6.9	1.0	5.7	8.0	0.4	0.4	0.7	6.8	3.5	1.8	6.3	2.0	6.2	19.7
Eggs, hen & duck	19.3	40.3	46.7	33.7	33.1	22.5	16.2	21.5	20.2	32.3	18.2	18.0	19.2	16.2	12.1	9.3	6.0
Fatstock	52.3	74.7	82.6	45.1	50.9	46.2	113.3	101.1	80.6	47.5	49.8	34.2	63.7	40.5	46.7	48.2	45.5
cattle	(0.4)	(36.1)	(34.1)	(12.5)	(3.4)	(12.3)	(46.4)	(30.5)	(40.8)	(9.8)	(5.0)	(19.6)	(41.1)	(19.3)	(26.2)	(31.0)	(2.8)
sheep	(5.2)	(8.4)	(11.7)	(11.7)	(25.3)	(13.9)	(30.7)	(18.9)	(13.3)	(5.7)	(5.3)	(8.9)	(10.6)	(6.9)	(3.1)	(9.7)	(16.4)
pigs	(46.7)	(30.2)	(36.8)	(20.9)	(22.2)	(20.0)	(36.2)	(51.7)	(26.5)	(32.0)	(39.5)	(5.7)	(12.0)	(14.3)	(17.4)	(7.5)	(26.3)
Milk	34.5	21.3	12.9	10.1	8.5	10.8	11.8	–	–	–	–	–	–	–	–	–	–
Wool	–	0.2	1.5	6.3	2.8	2.6	2.9	3.2	0.6	2.3	3.8	3.7	8.5	6.3	4.6	6.1	6.9
Total	142.7	163.7	203.2	154.7	154.7	151.2	225.5	190.1	178.9	146.1	121.7	108.8	135.0	127.2	127.9	93.6	140.9
Farming grants and subsidies																	
Fertilisers	14.8	19.8	22.8	25.8	29.4	32.2	33.0	33.9	33.6	31.3	29.6	30.0	33.9	30.9	31.5	40.9	35.1
Lime	10.2	9.3	10.4	9.2	11.0	8.7	8.8	10.0	8.0	9.9	8.1	6.4	4.9	4.6	4.6	5.0	5.2
Ploughing	5.4	10.0	10.0	9.2	9.4	10.9	11.5	11.3	9.9	8.1	7.6	5.7	2.5	1.1	0.4	0.3	–
Field drainage	1.9	2.0	2.0	1.9	2.6	2.7	2.7	3.0	2.6	3.1	3.1	3.2	4.0	4.5	5.6	7.1	–
Water supply	0.9	0.9	0.9	0.8	0.7	0.8	0.8	0.8	0.7	0.7	0.6	0.5	0.4	0.5	0.5	0.4	–
Livestock rearing land	1.5	1.6	1.4	1.5	1.5	1.5	1.6	1.5	1.4	1.4	1.3	1.0	0.9	0.6	0.5	0.4	–
Marginal production assistance	1.6	2.1	2.4	2.2	1.7	1.0	0.8	0.7	0.7	–	–	–	–	–	–	–	–
Tuberculosis eradication scheme	10.2	9.8	8.0	8.5	9.0	9.0	7.2	5..2	3.2	1..5	0.6	–	–	–	–	–	–
Brucellosis eradication incentives	–	–	–	–	–	–	–	–	–	–	–	–	–	–	–	0.5	1.9
Calves	7.7	11.4	12.9	14.3	16.5	17.6	17.8	17.7	19.4	20.4	22.7	24.7	22.6	26.8	27.7	29.1	31.0
Beef cows	–	–	–	–	–	–	–	–	–	–	–	2.5	2.9	4.0	5.0	5.8	6.7
Hill cattle and hill cows	2.6	2.7	2.9	3.1	4.1	4.6	5.0	5.4	5.6	5.7	6.7	7.5	8.7	10.3	11.8	13.9	14.7
Hill sheep	1.1	1.1	–	–	–	0.7	0.8	1.4	2.4	6.0	4.4	8.0	5.9	7.2	7.2	9.0	9.8
Farm improvements	–	–	0.2	3.3	6.6	7.8	9.2	10.3	10.2	11.5	11.6	11.1	12.5	13.6	15.1	15.8	–
Small farmers	–	–	–	–	1.1	5.9	7.1	7.2	5.6	4.8	3.4	2.3	1.8	1.8	1.7	1.1	–
Farm capital grants	–	–	–	–	–	–	–	–	–	–	–	–	–	–	–	1.5	18.3
Investment incentives	–	–	–	–	–	–	–	–	–	–	–	–	6.2	9.3	11.5	15.0	–
Winter keep	–	–	–	–	–	–	–	–	–	2.5	3.4	3.1	4.5	4.6	4.9	5.1	5.1
Others	0.2	0.1	1.4	1.1	1.5	1.1	1.2	1.0	0.8	0.8	0.7	2.4	2.1	8.0	10.7	12.1	54.0[1]
Total	58.1	70.8	75.3	80.9	95.1	104.5	107.5	109.4	104.1	107.7	103.8	108.4	113.8	127.8	138.7	163.0	181.8
Administrative expenses	5.1	4.7	4.7	5.0	5.9	6.1	8.7	9.0	9.4	9.7	9.8	10.3	10.9	12.4	13.1	14.5	15.6
Other services																	
Payment of benefit to NI producers	–	–	0.9	0.8	1..2	1.1	0.9	1.1	1.5	0.8	1.3	1.6	1.8	1.7	1.7	–	–
Agricultural training	–	–	–	–	–	–	–	–	–	–	–	–	–	–	–	1.9	–
Total estimated cost of agricultural support	205.9	239.2	284.1	241.4	256.9	262.9	342.6	309.6	293.9	264.3	236.6	229.1	261.5	269.1	281.4	273.0	338.3

[1]Includes £37.1 million grants absorbed by Farm Capital Grant Schemes.
Source. HMSO: *Annual Review of Agriculture.*

Table 8.2. Public expenditure on agriculture 1972–73 to 1987–88 (£ million)

	1972 –73	1973 –74	1974 –75	1975 –76	1976 –77	1977 –78	1978 –79	1979 –80	1980 –81	1981 –82	1982 –83	1983 –84	1984 –85	1985 –86	1986 –87	1987 –88[6]
Market regulation and price guarantees																
Cereals	33.9	30.1	13.4	46.2	29.8	–4.3	28.9	43.0	157.2	242.7	337.2	110.6	367.9	654.0	114.5	191.1
Potatoes	11.4	1.0	1.6	0.5	0.8	9.1	23.0	5.7	8.7	9.6	1.9	9.3	7.6	7.5	–	–
Eggs	3.4	5.7	0.3	–	–	–	–	–	–	–	–	–	–	–	–	–
Beef and veal	1.0	1.2	63.7	113.0	16.3	11.4	–20.8	10.3	131.6	41.8	93.8	263.9	343.2	328.3	229.7	243.0
Sheepmeat	1.9	–	8.5	7.5	0.2	0.4	0.1	11.1	75.2	72.2	126.1	158.3	113.3	110.0	102.3	124.7
Pigmeat	2.7	19.0	53.3	38.6	18.5	10.4	0.2	0.5	–16.7	–33.0	–39.8	–14.8	–10.6	–1.2	–2.4	–2.7
Sugar	–	2.6	45.7	41.2	71.2	86.7	84.7	44.6	21.3	35.6	60.6	53.2	83.4	83.9	114.9	136.8
Processed goods	–	9.7	14.1	3.4	8.8	13.4	21.0	27.8	16.7	16.7	27.4	28.3	32.8	40.9	41.6	45.5
Milk products	30.9	132.7	35.8	61.8	24.1	141.0	198.4	201.3	187.0	168.8	342.5	556.6	250.6	353.7	299.6	282.1
Oilseeds	–	–	–	–	5.2	3.6	9.9	19.5	50.6	51.2	76.3	87.2	49.2	88.6	118.4	195.9
Wool	1.5	–5.2	4.3	2.0	–2.4	–2.2	–	–	3.9	7.5	6.2	0.6	–7.8	1.5	8.1	2.5
	86.7	196.8	240.7	314.2	172.5	269.5	345.4	363.8	635.5	613.1	1032.2	1253.2	1229.6	1667.2	1026.7	1218.9
Other payments																
Milk Outgoers Scheme	–	–	–	–	–	–	–	–	–	–	–	–	5.2	9.6	9.5	61.9[3]
Dairy herd conversion scheme	–	2.1	10.0	11.8	4.4	5.6	3.4	–	–	–	–	–	–	–	–	–
Milk non-marketing premiums	–	–	–	–	–	2.1	7.1	15.8	30.5	21.2	17.8	13.3	12.6	2.6	–	–
Suckler cow premium	–	–	–	–	–	–	–	–	14.6	16.9	16.4	15.7	27.3	26.9	26.9	37.0
Annual premium on ewes	–	–	–	–	–	–	–	–	–	28.1	21.4	66.3	76.7	128.2	101.7	143.8
Calves	31.9	33.9	48.9	61.6	26.1	22.8	6.8	–	–	–	–	–	–	–	–	–
Beef cows	7.1	9.2	22.1	8.1	10.5	2.7	–	–	–	–	–	–	–	–	–	–
Fertilisers	27.5	14.6	6.1	–	–	–	–	–	–	–	–	–	–	–	–	–
Lime	5.0	4.5	4.5	4.7	4.6	0.1	–	–	–	–	–	–	–	–	–	–
Support for capital and other improvements																
Agriculture and hortic. development scheme	–	–	0.1	0.8	3.7	22.4	43.6	77.8	101.7	85.7	100.3	104.1	93.2	65.6	45.3	43.1
insurance premiums	–	–	0.1	0.6	2.2	7.4	10.1	13.1	10.2	6.5	5.5	4.0	3.6	3.8	3.2	2.0
Northern Ireland agric. development programme	–	–	–	–	–	–	–	–	–	–	11.2	9.6	13.4	4.9	4.0	2.2
Agriculture & hortic. grant scheme	67.5	84.4	86.5	69.3	56.9	63.0	62.2	78.6	88.8	76.5	83.6	96.2	85.1	65.4	25.6	1.9
Agriculture improvement scheme	–	–	–	–	–	–	–	–	–	–	–	–	–	0.2	16.4[4]	38.4[5]
Cooperation grants	–	–	0.9	1.1	0.8	0.8	1.1	1.2	1.4	2.1	2.4	3.8	4.5	4.3	2.7	2.5
Total	67.5	84.4	87.6	71.8	63.6	93.6	117.0	170.7	202.1	170.8	203.0	217.7	199.8	144.2	97.2	90.1
Support for Agriculture in upland areas																
Hill Livestock compensatory allowance:																
sheep[1]	9.1	10.4	19.8	13.7	39.0	24.8	18.4	54.6	53.8	47.4	50.3	52.6	53.9	59.4	68.5	64.5
cattle[1]	15.5	16.9	35.4	7.5	43.9	25.4	18.1	41.8	41.2	37.1	38.0	38.9	39.9	45.5	53.2	50.3
Additional benefits under AHDS, NIADP and AHGS and AIS	3.2	4.8	3.4	5.9	7.0	6.6	8.9	14.9	17.1	16.6	28.7	29.7	32.5	28.8	29.9	25.3
Total	27.8	32.1	58.6	27.1	89.9	56.8	45.4	111.3	112.1	101.1	117.0	121.2	126.3	133.7	151.6	140.1
Others[2]	13.5	14.4	16.0	12.3	6.8	6.9	11.8	15.4	17.6	21.2	25.0	29.5	32.2	49.9	29.9	44.2
Grand total	267.0	392.0	494.5	511.6	378.4	460.1	536.9	677.0	1012.4	972.4	1432.8	1716.9	1709.7	2162.3	1443.5	1736.0
of which receipts from EAGGF	0.3	76.7	169.6	264.0	180.3	188.8	329.2	412.1	606.3	742.4	804.8	1220.9	1203.4	1282.3	1480.8	1046.7

[1]Including hill sheep and hill cattle subsidies until 1975–76.　[2]Includes eggs, poultry meat, fruit and vegetables, hops, herbage seeds, dried fodder, peas and beans, fisheries, flax and aid to beekeepers as well as insurance premiums, farm accounts and farm structure payments. Payments for small cereal producers and environmentally sensitive areas are also included.　[3]Including £51.0 million payments to producers giving up milk production.　[4]Including £7.5 million Agriculture Improvement Scheme (EC).　[5]Including £29.8 million Agriculture Improvement Scheme (EC).　[6]Forecast.
Source. HMSO: *Annual Review of Agriculture.*

Appendix 9: Food consumption and expenditure

Table 9.1. Household food expenditure as a proportion of total consumer expenditure (£ million)

	Total[1]	Food and beverages	Food only	% of T.C.E.[1] spent on food
1938	4394	1285[2]		29.2[3]
1946	7159	1816[2]	1730	24.2
1947	7909	2104[2]	2011	25.4
1948	8471	2265[2]	2164	25.5
1949	8831	2471[2]	2366	26.8
1950	9348	2734[2]	2629	28.1
1951	10065	2987[2]	2876	28.6
1952	10584	3282[2]	3151	29.8
1953	11256	3584[2]	3436	30.5
1954	11978	3830[2]	3657	30.5
1955	12763	4122[2]	3917	30.7
1956	13829	3820	3584	25.9
1957	14599	3962	3706	25.4
1958	15296	4028	3775	24.7
1959	16106	4158	3887	24.1
1960	16909	4228	3958	23.4
1961	17810	4370	4093	23.0
1962	18906	4565	4284	22.7
1963	20118	4869	4397	21.9
1964	21463	4888	4580	21.3
1965	22846	5057	4748	20.8
1966	24211	5309	4987	20.6
1967	25428	5464	5127	20.2
1968	27338	5669	5324	19.6
1969	29102	5979	5614	19.3
1970	31644	6375	5971	18.9
1971	35165	6976	6551	18.6
1972	39716	7434	6990	17.6
1973	45044	8440	7961	17.7
1974	51832	9869	9270	17.9
1975	63373	12092	11262	17.8
1976	75873	13941	13046	17.2
1977	86757	16047	14886	17.2
1978	100023	17927	16620	16.6
1979	118361	20364	18905	16.0
1980	137470	22876	22274	16.2
1981	153027	24207	22647	14.8
1982	167599	25649	24054	14.4
1983	183068	27385	25489	13.9
1984	195912	28642	26535	13.5
1985	213720	30064	27725	13.0
1986	234167	32342	29756	12.7

[1]Total Consumer Expenditure. [2]Including alcoholic beverages. [3]Food and beverages.
Source. Central Statistical Office: *United Kingdom National Accounts.*

Table 9.2. Household expenditure on food (£ million)

	At current prices	In 1986 money values
1946	1730	22698
1947	2011	24715
1948	2164	24691
1949	2366	26381
1950	2629	28498
1951	2876	28587
1952	3151	29493
1953	3436	31646
1954	3657	33132
1955	3917	34274
1956	3584	30070
1957	3706	30093
1958	3775	29860
1959	3887	30552
1960	3958	30793
1961	4093	30984
1962	4284	30925
1963	4397	31395
1964	4580	31648
1965	4748	31384
1966	4987	31717
1967	5127	31736
1968	5324	31518
1969	5614	31551
1970	5971	31527
1971	6551	31576
1972	6990	31455
1973	7961	32879
1974	9270	33001
1975	11262	32209
1976	13046	32093
1977	14886	31558
1978	16620	32576
1979	18905	32706
1980	22274	32520
1981	22647	29667
1982	24054	28865
1983	25489	29312
1984	26535	29189
1985	27725	28557
1986	29756	29756

Source. Central Statistical Office: *United Kingdom National Accounts.*

Table 9.3. Household expenditure on food and beverages at current prices (£ million)

	1938	1946	1950	1955	1960	1965	1970	1975	1980	1981	1982	1983	1984	1985	1986
Bread and cereals		292	437	497	558	674	822	1589	3056	3311	3497	3676	3855	4069	4504
Meat and bacon		319	529	956	1140	1387	1791	3330	6471	6715	7215	7400	7495	7849	8173
Fish		84	77	103	153	189	213	363	731	768	806	913	938	1049	1190
Milk, cheese and eggs		288	418	556	640	748	924	1632	3423	3658	3874	4003	4114	4251	4412
Oils and fats		62	105	213	220	250	267	504	920	933	941	958	1000	1037	1021
Fruit		90	169	262	260	306	365	682	1273	1318	1362	1571	1599	1708	1979
Potatoes								546	789	904	1059	1153	1356	1247	1349
Vegetables		190	280	383	437	551	766	914	1621	1747	1786	2047	2140	2316	2587
Sugar								260	322	350	357	371	356	327	318
Preserves and Confectionery		119	206	390	413	485	597	981	1959	2135	2313	2448	2666	2892	3093
Coffee, tea, cocoa								311	746	725	739	890	1056	1146	1200
Soft drinks		86	105	205	270	309	404	430	856	843	856	1006	1051	1193	1386
Other manufactured food		87	99	116	137	158	216	419	709	800	844	949	1016	980	1130
Total food and beverages	1285[1]	1617	2425	3681	4228	5057	6365	11 961	22 876	24 207	25 649	27 385	28 642	30 064	32 342

[1] Including other personal food expenditure.
Source. Central Statistical Office: *United Kingdom National Accounts.*

Table 9.4. Household expenditure on food and beverages at constant 1980 prices (£ million)

	1972	1973	1974	1975	1976	1977	1978	1979	1980	1981	1982	1983	1984	1985	1986
Bread and cereals	3050	3121	3053	3017	3044	3034	3034	3055	3056	3086	3105	3140	3133	3146	3284
Meat and bacon	5963	5761	5809	5976	5971	6116	6272	6475	6471	6275	6228	6137	5903	5989	6055
Fish	714	713	625	688	690	635	648	668	731	750	752	784	767	791	845
Milk, cheese and eggs	3562	3657	3606	3613	3617	3480	3520	3480	3423	3341	3303	3361	3425	3434	3592
Oil and fats	908	939	939	952	937	927	950	931	920	894	861	855	817	810	814
Fruit	1178	1208	1173	1133	1203	1105	1148	1193	1273	1248	1185	1261	1211	1200	1303
Potatoes	737	786	786	730	644	675	750	779	789	823	843	884	911	1020	986
Vegetables	1381	1476	1432	1456	1449	1452	1540	1563	1621	1659	1618	1681	1662	1715	1879
Sugar	430	391	375	325	353	348	345	332	322	320	298	287	267	246	236
Preserves and confectionery	2058	2237	2158	1949	2013	2026	2098	2054	1959	2032	2141	2183	2257	2295	2315
Coffee, tea and cocoa	765	740	787	760	770	665	694	733	746	734	732	763	724	710	732
Soft drinks	493	618	637	701	763	735	776	874	856	815	843	974	1002	1084	1256
Other manufactured food	708	795	742	701	705	685	726	756	709	736	733	799	812	835	877
Total food and beverages	21 947	22 442	22 122	22 001	22 159	21 883	22 501	22 893	22 876	22 713	22 642	23 109	22 891	23 275	24 174

Source. Central Statistical Office: *United Kingdom National Accounts.*

Table 9.5. Household food consumption (ounces per head per week)[1,2]

	1942[3]	1946[3]	1950	1955	1960	1965	1970	1975	1980	1981	1982	1983	1984	1985	1986
Milk and cream (pints)[1]	3.8	4.4	5.21	5.09	5.14	5.19	5.08	5.12	4.58	4.53	4.38	4.30	4.31	4.13	4.15
Cheese	3.6	2.5	2.54	2.83	3.04	3.20	3.59	3.79	3.89	3.89	3.80	4.01	3.84	3.91	4.16
Carcase meat	13.8	13.7	14.39	18.23	17.39	16.78	15.88	15.30	16.76	15.03	14.67	13.97	12.88	13.22	13.24
beef and veal			8.06	9.36	8.74	8.08	7.80	8.32	8.13	6.96	7.06	6.57	6.27	6.51	6.58
mutton and lamb			5.43	6.55	6.63	5.90	5.25	4.25	4.51	4.25	3.59	3.87	3.32	3.27	3.01
pork			0.30	2.32	2.02	2.80	2.83	2.73	4.13	3.82	4.02	3.53	3.29	3.45	3.64
Other meat and meat products	12.5	13.0	15.46	16.19	18.50	20.82	23.65	21.82	23.43	24.32	24.04	24.16	23.72	23.55	28.48
uncooked poultry			0.35	0.48	1.68	3.38	4.84	5.55	6.44	7.03	6.56	6.69	6.97	6.57	6.91
bacon and ham (uncooked)	4.0	3.2	4.52	5.35	5.32	5.43	5.32	3.99	4.20	4.14	3.95	4.02	3.58	3.69	3.68

continued overleaf

Table 9.5 continued

	1942[3]	1946[3]	1950	1955	1960	1965	1970	1975	1980	1981	1982	1983	1984	1985	1986
Fish	6.6	10.5	6.62	5.95	5.86	5.78	5.35	4.46	4.80	4.92	5.03	5.14	4.89	4.90	5.16
Eggs (number)	1.4	2.5	3.50	4.19	4.64	4.78	4.66	4.14	3.69	3.68	3.51	3.53	3.21	3.15	3.01
Fats	8.7	8.3	11.61	11.88	11.97	11.86	11.95	11.14	11.22	11.06	10.98	10.69	10.29	10.07	10.49
butter	2.0	2.8	4.56	4.47	5.68	6.10	5.99	5.63	4.05	3.69	3.17	3.27	2.87	2.83	2.27
margarine	4.2	3.5	3.94	4.68	3.66	3.04	2.86	2.60	3.83	4.11	4.33	4.08	4.08	3.76	4.10
Sugar	8.4	9.6	10.13	17.64	17.76	17.56	16.94	11.29	11.17	11.08	10.31	9.84	9.15	8.41	8.04
Preserves	4.9	5.4	6.30	4.09	3.21	2.99	2.57	2.43	2.05	2.08	1.99	2.05	1.95	1.87	1.98
Vegetables	102.4	111.3	98.68	97.06	95.44	92.62	92.37	83.98	85.37	86.60	85.28	83.74	82.84	84.93	86.27
fresh potatoes	66.2	70.5	62.04	59.90	56.03	53.24	51.84	43.90	40.95	41.87	41.11	39.88	39.82	40.96	38.76
fresh green vegetables	11.9	14.9	13.91	14.79	15.81	15.22	14.45	11.58	12.42	11.98	11.24	10.78	10.83	9.78	11.11
other fresh vegetables	16.9	15.6	15.28	14.64	15.05	14.33	13.95	13.78	15.83	15.74	15.66	15.71	15.26	15.70	16.82
processed vegetables	2.6	4.1	5.43	5.77	7.38	8.29	11.72	14.72	16.17	16.39	17.27	17.36	16.94	18.48	19.56
Fruit	9.7	12.8	18.90	21.91	24.62	25.56	25.52	23.94	28.06	27.87	26.97	28.69	27.85	27.06	30.80
fresh fruit	6.9	10.7	14.41	20.65	18.41	18.79	19.14	17.51	20.81	19.95	18.75	19.64	18.99	18.52	20.33
fruit juices (fl. oz.)[1]			0.25	0.29	0.48	0.67	0.60	1.33	3.08	3.99	4.30	5.20	5.28	5.21	6.84
other fruit and fruit products	2.8	2.1	3.42	6.20	5.73	6.10	5.78	5.11	4.17	3.93	3.92	3.85	3.58	3.33	3.63
Bread	60.6	59.9	55.52	55.13	45.47	40.60	38.11	33.67	31.12	31.23	31.03	30.74	30.57	30.99	30.79
white bread, standard loaf			50.84	36.64	34.31	32.23	27.68	21.87	21.85	21.70	20.81	20.05	19.31	16.54	
brown, whole wheat and wholemeal			1.69	3.34	3.53	2.92	3.30	5.56	5.56	5.40	5.89	6.57	7.33	9.18	
Other cereals	20.9	22.9	26.15	24.91	25.09	25.73	25.08	23.51	24.29	24.54	23.92	23.95	23.46	22.85	24.15
flour	6.4	6.1	7.25	8.57	6.76	6.09	5.68	5.16	5.67	5.96	5.28	4.97	4.34	4.05	4.14
breakfast cereals	0.8	1.0	1.40	1.69	1.80	1.97	2.74	3.05	3.50	3.53	3.54	3.83	4.13	4.04	4.38
Beverages			2.72	3.54	3.57	3.44	3.61	3.11	3.00	2.95	2.93	3.02	2.76	2.70	2.76
tea			2.16	2.79	2.80	2.61	2.59	2.18	2.05	1.98	2.02	2.04	1.80	1.74	1.74
coffee			0.21	0.36	0.39	0.44	0.56	0.65	0.67	0.65	0.64	0.69	0.69	0.68	0.72

[1]Retail statistics are recorded in non-metric measures.　[2]Ounces per head per week unless otherwise stated.　[3]Urban working class households only.
Source. MAFF: *Household Food Consumption and Expenditure.*

Table 9.6. Indices of retail food prices (1970 = 100)

	Liquid milk	Beef and veal	Mutton and lamb	Pork	Bacon and ham unsmoked	Poultry	Fresh fish	Eggs	Butter	Margarine	Sugar	Fresh potatoes	Fresh green vegetables	Bread	Cheese
1970	100	100	100	100	100	100	100	100	100	100	100	100	100	100	100
1971	117	113	110	105	106	111	114	110	135	116	108	88	102	108	121
1972	122	127	126	117	120	108	131	97	147	118	123	97	113	117	156
1973	125	165	163	149	162	137	164	144	121	122	127	114	128	126	163
1974	113	171	186	156	191	155	201	171	126	164	164	136	161	161	181
1975	147	186	201	195	226	188	220	172	161	207	347	243	196	183	211
1976	198	222	238	219	264	215	236	194	222	209	302	937	227	204	245
1977	250	249	280	234	275	255	281	221	279	263	313	882	283	255	309
1978	283	284	324	275	299	280	308	221	315	272	335	348	216	300	348
1979	323	320	347	290	332	320	323	256	378	282	381	447	325	341	412
1980	371	357	378	317	366	354	356	292	408	299	432	532	312	398	477
1981	414	396	401	339	386	362	374	314	437	307	471	437	347	422	513
1982	448	436	458	355	421	392	396	330	476	307	516	776	410	448	557
1983	467	455	441	382	431	420	436	319	478	324	559	948	423	461	574
1984	477	466	484	413	463	448	447	370	492	373	575	548	469	488	588
1985	502	477	505	416	470	466	554	375	484	406	576	531	502	489	621
1986	525	487	520	422	476	492	595	380	521	364	583	635	482	517	633

Source. MAFF: *Household Food Consumption and Expenditure.*

Appendix 10: Cereals

Table 10.1. Value of output of cereals (£ million)

	Wheat	Barley	All cereals[2]
1937–38	10	6	20
1938–39	10	6	20
1939–40	11	8	24
1940–41	13	14	33
1941–42	22	29	59
1942–43	32	39	83
1943–44	53	28	90
1944–45	45	25	77
1945–46	29	30	68
1946–47	24	24	54
1947–48	24	29	58
1948–49	39	30	78
1949–50	36	28	72
1950–51	48	30	86
1951–52	41	48	97
1952–53	43	33	83
1953–54	61	54	128
1954–55	74	50	134
1955–56	67	57	136
1956–57	74	52	139
1957–58	68	56	135
1958–59	63	53	126
1959–60	69	69	151
1960–61	75	74	159
1961–62	59	86	155
1962–63	99	92	200
1963–64	71	102	181
1964–65	94	119	222
1965–66	95	129	232
1966–67	81	142	231
1967–68	44	146	201
1968–69	89	134	233
1969–70	91	144	245
1970–71	126	137	275
1971–72	137	139	286
1972	125	153	292
1973	226	248	491
1974	283	319	619
1975	296	329	640
1976	318	379	717
1977	366	414	801
1978	449	550	1019
1979	605	557	1184
1980	786	651	1463
1981	855	811	1693
1982	1137	894	2062
1983	1115	851	1996
1984	1461	930	2420
1985	1409	842	2281
1986	1366	776	2174
1987[1]	1256	641	1927

[1]Forecast. [2]All cereals includes oats, mixed corn and other cereals.
Source. MAFF: *Departmental Net Income Calculation.*

Table 10.2. Wheat area ('000 hectares)

	England and Wales	Scotland	Great Britain	Northern Ireland	United Kingdom
1866	1311	45	1356		
1867	1318	45	1363		
1868	1427	51	1478		
1869	1438	55	1493		
1870	1366	51	1417		
1871	1392	54	1446		
1872	1401	55	1456		
1873	1364	49	1412		
1874	1420	49	1469		
1875	1311	41	1352		
1876	1181	32	1212		
1877	1249	33	1282		
1878	1272	30	1302		
1879	1139	31	1170		
1880	1147	30	1177		
1881	1105	30	1136		
1882	1184	32	1216		
1883	1030	28	1057		
1884	1055	28	1083		
1885	981	22	1003		
1886	902	23	925		
1887	917	20	938		
1888	1010	28	1038		
1889	967	24	991		
1890	941	25	966		
1891	912	21	934		
1892	873	25	898		
1893	750	18	768		
1894	762	18	780		
1895	560	14	573		
1896	670	15	686		
1897	744	20	764		
1898	828	23	851		
1899	791	19	810		
1900	727	20	747		
1901	674	15	688		
1902	679	19	699		
1903	623	17	640		
1904	541	15	556		
1905	707	20	727		
1906	690	20	711		
1907	638	19	658		
1908	641	17	658		
1909	718	20	738		
1910	711	21	732		
1911	746	26	771		
1912	754	25	779		
1913	689	22	711		
1914	731	25	756		
1915	878	31	909		
1916	774	25	799		
1917	776	25	801		
1918	1035	32	1067		
1919	899	32	931		
1920	759	22	781		
1921	800	26	826	3	829
1922	796	26	822	3	825
1923	704	24	728	3	731
1924	625	20	645	2	647
1925	607	20	626	2	628
1926	644	22	666	3	669
1927	662	27	689	2	691
1928	565	23	588	2	590
1929	538	21	559	2	561
1930	545	22	567	2	569
1931	484	20	505	1	506

continued opposite

Table 10.2 continued

	England and Wales	Scotland	Great Britain	Northern Ireland	United Kingdom
1932	521	21	542	1	543
1933	672	32	704	3	707
1934	712	40	752	4	756
1935	717	41	758	4	762
1936	690	38	728	3	731
1937	701	40	741	2	743
1938	741	37	778	2	780
1939	681	32	713	1	714
1940	687	40	727	5	732
1941	866	43	909	7	916
1942	968	46	1013	5	1018
1943	1327	69	1397	6	1403
1944	1240	62	1301	2	1303
1945	883	37	919	1	920
1946	802	32	834	1	835
1947	840	35	875	1	876
1948	885	35	920	2	922
1949	769	25	794	1	795
1950	970	32	1002	1	1003
1951	834	28	862	--	862
1952	794	26	821	1	822
1953	867	29	896	1	897
1954	962	32	993	1	994
1955	767	21	788	--	788
1956	896	31	927	1	928
1957	822	31	853	2	855
1958	856	36	892	2	894
1959	746	34	780	1	781
1960	811	38	849	2	851
1961	701	37	737	2	739
1962	868	44	911	2	913
1963	743	36	779	1	780
1964	854	37	892	1	893
1965	984	39	1023	2	1025
1966	879	26	905	1	906
1967	900	32	932	1	933
1968	941	36	977	1	978
1969	794	37	832	1	833
1970	969	40	1009	1	1010
1971	1060	36	1096	1	1097
1972	1093	33	1126	1	1127
1973	1114	31	1145	1	1146
1974	1199	33	1232	1	1233
1975	1006	28	1034	1	1035
1976	1204	26	1230	1	1231
1977	1054	22	1076	--	1076
1978	1236	21	1256	1	1257
1979	1348	24	1371	1	1372
1980	1415	26	1441	--	1441
1981	1460	30	1491	--	1491
1982	1622	40	1662	1	1663
1983	1646	47	1693	2	1695
1984	1865	71	1936	3	1939
1985	1816	82	1897	5	1902
1986	1904	89	1993	4	1997
1987	1885	104	1989	5	1994
1988[1]					1891

-- Negligible. [1]Provisional.
Source. Agricultural Departments: *Agricultural Census.*

Table 10.3. Barley area ('000 hectares)

	England and Wales	Scotland	Great Britain		England and Wales	Scotland	Great Britain	Northern Ireland	United Kingdom
1866	819	87	905	1921	581	69	650	1	651
1867	826	88	914	1922	552	64	616	1	617
1868	782	89	870	1923	537	64	601	1	602
1869	818	93	911	1924	532	62	593	1	594
1870	861	99	960	1925	533	62	595	1	596
1871	864	102	966	1926	465	49	514	1	515
1872	835	102	937	1927	425	47	472	1	473
1873	846	100	945	1928	480	45	525	1	526
1874	826	100	926	1929	453	41	494	1	495
1875	909	107	1016	1930	413	43	456	1	457
1876	916	109	1025	1931	416	36	452	1	453
1877	869	109	979	1932	389	28	416	--	416
1878	895	105	1000	1933	304	24	328	1	329
1879	967	113	1079	1934	348	39	387	1	388
1880	892	107	998	1935	321	31	351	1	352
1881	878	110	988	1936	331	29	361	1	362
1882	807	106	913	1937	333	33	366	1	367
1883	828	100	928	1938	358	40	398	1	399
1884	784	93	878	1939	368	40	409	1	410
1885	817	96	913	1940	493	42	535	7	542
1886	819	88	907	1941	543	47	590	7	597
1887	760	84	844	1942	552	60	612	6	618
1888	753	91	844	1943	631	87	717	6	723
1889	768	90	859	1944	696	96	792	7	799
1890	767	87	854	1945	803	88	891	6	897
1891	765	90	855	1946	811	81	892	3	895
1892	738	86	824	1947	760	71	831	3	834
1893	754	86	840	1948	768	73	841	2	843
1894	760	88	848	1949	763	69	832	2	834
1895	789	88	877	1950	657	61	717	2	719
1896	763	88	852	1951	701	70	771	1	772
1897	730	94	824	1952	840	81	921	2	923
1898	674	96	771	1953	820	79	898	3	901
1899	705	97	802	1954	758	74	833	2	835
1900	708	97	805	1955	853	74	927	2	929
1901	703	95	798	1956	858	80	938	3	940
1902	680	93	773	1957	967	89	1056	5	1061
1903	665	87	752	1958	1022	86	1108	7	1115
1904	664	81	745	1959	1134	92	1226	11	1237
1905	608	86	694	1960	1237	103	1341	24	1365
1906	620	89	709	1961	1374	130	1504	45	1549
1907	608	85	693	1962	1417	144	1562	52	1614
1908	595	80	675	1963	1679	169	1847	60	1907
1909	592	81	673	1964	1775	195	1970	67	2036
1910	622	78	700	1965	1883	226	2109	74	2183
1911	576	70	647	1966	2140	272	2412	69	2481
1912	590	78	667	1967	2113	265	2377	62	2439
1913	631	80	711	1968	2057	288	2345	56	2401
1914	609	79	688	1969	2112	297	2411	56	2467
1915	499	60	559	1970	1949	293	2242	51	2293
1916	539	69	608	1971	1961	321	2282	57	2339
1917	591	64	655	1972	1904	332	2237	51	2288
1918	607	62	669	1973	1873	346	2219	48	2267
1919	611	70	681	1974	1811	354	2165	49	2214
1920	662	83	745	1975	1927	369	2295	50	2345
				1976	1746	386	2132	50	2182
				1977	1941	407	2348	52	2400
				1978	1866	426	2292	56	2348
				1979	1859	436	2295	52	2347
				1980	1770	444	2214	51	2265
				1981	1682	439	2121	51	2172
				1982	1642	454	2096	47	2143
				1983	1647	450	2098	46	2144
				1984	1495	438	1933	46	1979
				1985	1502	417	1918	47	1965
				1986	1451	418	1869	47	1916
				1987	1398	387	1785	45	1830
				1988[1]					1895

-- Negligible.   [1]Provisional.
Source. Agricultural Departments: *Agricultural Census.*

Table 10.4. Oats area ('000 hectares)

	England and Wales	Scotland	Great Britain		England and Wales	Scotland	Great Britain	Northern Ireland	United Kingdom
1866	711	406	1117	1922	876	400	1276	144	1420
1867	709	403	1113	1923	800	392	1192	142	1334
1868	707	409	1116	1924	825	387	1211	135	1346
1869	714	412	1126	1925	756	375	1131	130	1261
1870	706	413	1118	1926	754	380	1135	129	1264
1871	691	408	1099	1927	709	363	1072	125	1197
1872	687	408	1095	1928	713	355	1069	124	1193
1873	673	410	1083	1929	750	360	1110	127	1237
1874	644	406	1051	1930	720	349	1068	124	1192
1875	671	407	1078	1931	669	338	1006	116	1122
1876	719	414	1132	1932	639	351	991	116	1107
1877	700	415	1115	1933	605	346	951	117	1068
1878	674	418	1092	1934	567	330	898	113	1011
1879	669	407	1075	1935	574	335	909	110	1019
1880	712	420	1132	1936	575	335	910	107	1017
1881	757	417	1174	1937	495	331	826	104	930
1882	721	425	1147	1938	527	323	849	120	969
1883	781	423	1204	1939	550	314	864	118	982
1884	756	423	1180	1940	847	368	1215	161	1376
1885	766	423	1190	1941	983	433	1417	182	1599
1886	819	429	1247	1942	1011	469	1480	192	1672
1887	819	431	1250	1943	890	409	1300	190	1490
1888	756	411	1166	1944	901	401	1301	178	1479
1889	758	411	1169	1945	931	406	1337	181	1518
1890	764	410	1175	1946	872	405	1276	167	1443
1891	772	401	1173	1947	794	390	1185	154	1339
1892	809	404	1213	1948	806	386	1192	158	1350
1893	872	412	1284	1949	788	377	1165	151	1316
1894	902	414	1316	1950	743	374	1117	140	1257
1895	926	408	1334	1951	665	363	1028	128	1156
1896	845	408	1253	1952	678	365	1044	122	1166
1897	837	392	1229	1953	673	359	1033	117	1150
1898	794	387	1181	1954	594	344	939	108	1047
1899	810	388	1198	1955	603	340	943	102	1045
1900	841	384	1225	1956	603	331	934	104	1038
1901	826	387	1212	1957	534	319	853	96	949
1902	851	386	1237	1958	505	304	809	88	897
1903	877	394	1271	1959	450	291	742	81	823
1904	919	397	1316	1960	442	276	717	82	799
1905	845	390	1235	1961	371	256	627	74	701
1906	844	387	1231	1962	318	231	549	66	615
1907	879	385	1264	1963	249	216	465	59	524
1908	874	384	1258	1964	214	190	405	51	456
1909	825	382	1207	1965	196	175	371	39	410
1910	835	388	1223	1966	172	161	334	33	367
1911	828	390	1219	1967	211	165	377	33	410
1912	839	387	1226	1968	213	140	352	30	382
1913	799	380	1179	1969	229	131	359	23	382
1914	781	372	1153	1970	233	125	358	18	376
1915	845	398	1243	1971	235	112	347	15	363
1916	844	401	1244	1972	208	94	303	12	315
1917	914	421	1335	1973	194	78	271	10	281
1918	1125	503	1628	1974	173	71	244	9	253
1919	1038	450	1487	1975	158	66	224	9	232
1920	919	418	1337	1976	172	56	228	7	235
1921	870	410	1279	1977	138	51	188	6	195
				1978	129	46	175	5	180
				1979	95	36	131	4	136
				1980	105	38	143	4	148
				1981	100	40	140	3	144
				1982	96	31	127	3	129
				1983	81	24	105	3	108
				1984	78	25	103	3	106
				1985	102	29	131	3	133
				1986	68	27	95	2	97
				1987	68	27	95	3	99
				1988[1]					121

[1]Provisional.

Source. Agricultural Departments: *Agricultural Census.*

161

Table 10.5. Total cereal area ('000 hectares)[1]

Great Britain

1866	3402
1890	3251
1900	2969
1914	2811
1920	3139

United Kingdom

1929	2365	1949	3244	1969	3695
1930	2291	1950	3346	1970	3712
1931	2145	1951	3149	1971	3811
1932	2125	1952	3271	1972	3799
1933	2155	1953	3300	1973	3752
1934	2202	1954	3137	1974	3747
1935	2181	1955	2958	1975	3652
1936	2159	1956	3085	1976	3684
1937	2087	1957	3013	1977	3706
1938	2196	1958	3029	1978	3811
1939	2148	1959	2941	1979	3872
1940	2860	1960	3104	1980	3938
1941	3513	1961	3057	1981	3979
1942	3554	1962	3199	1982	4030
1943	3869	1963	3260	1983	3961
1944	3801	1964	3425	1984	4036
1945	3547	1965	3656	1985	4015
1946	3380	1966	3787	1986	4024
1947	3265	1967	3822	1987	3935
1948	3381	1968	3811	1988	3920

[1]Including rye and mixed corn for threshing.
Source. Agricultural Departments: *Agricultural Census.*

Table 10.6. Number and size of holdings with cereals,
England and Wales

Hectares	1964	1976	1981	1986
Less than 1		7.5		
1–1.9	30.1[1]	16.2	4.7	3.5
2–4.9	17.2[2]	15.6	13.7	12.7
5–9.9	10.1[3]	17.2	14.5	13.4
10–19.9	12.2[4]	9.9	17.1	16.4
20–29.9	6.8[5]	6.5	10.6	10.8
30–39.9	6.7[6]	5.0	7.2	7.9
40–49.9		7.9	5.4	5.8
50–74.9	11.4[7]	4.7	9.0	10.0
75–99.9		2.9	5.5	6.1
100–124.9	3.1[8]	1.9	3.4	4.0
125–149.9	2.4[9]	2.1	2.3	2.6
150–199.9		1.6	2.8	3.2
200 and over		0.9	3.6	4.2
Total	100.0	100.0	100.0	100.0
No. of holdings	134 604	84 950	75 155	68 675
Average cereals area per holding (ha)	21.4	37.5	45.3	49.9

[1]1.9 ha or less.   [2]2.0–8.0 ha.   [3]8.1–12.0 ha. [4]12.1–20.1 ha.   [5]20.2–28.2 ha.
[6]28.3–40.4 ha.   [7]40.5–80.8 ha.   [8]80.9–121.3 ha.   [9]121.4 ha and over.
Source. MAFF: *Agricultural Statistics, England and Wales.*
 Agricultural Statistics, United Kingdom.

Table 10.7. Number and size of holdings with wheat,
England and Wales

Hectares	1964	1976	1981	1986
Less than 1		2.0	1.0	0.7
1–1.9	32.9[1]	4.3	2.5	1.9
2–4.9	22.8[2]	16.5	12.6	10.1
5–9.9	12.6[3]	17.8	16.2	13.3
10–19.9	12.9[4]	20.4	20.7	19.3
20–29.9	6.6[5]	11.2	12.1	12.5
30–39.9	5.3[6]	6.7	7.5	8.2
40–49.9		5.1	5.8	6.7
50–74.9	5.2[7]	6.9	8.7	10.2
75–99.9		3.6	4.7	5.8
100–124.9	1.1[8]	1.9	2.8	3.6
125–149.9	0.6[9]	1.1	1.7	
150–199.9		1.1	3.7	7.7
200 and over		1.1		
Total	100.0	100.0	100.0	100.0
No. of holdings	65 029	42 184	40 082	42 668
Average wheat area per holding (ha)	13.1	28.5	36.4	44.6

[1]1.9 ha or less. [2]2.0–8.0 ha. [3]8.1–12.0 ha. [4]12.1–20.1 ha. [5]20.2–28.2 ha.
[6]28.3–40.4 ha. [7]40.5–80.8 ha. [8]80.9–121.3 ha. [9]121.4 ha and over.
Source. MAFF: *Agricultural Statistics, England and Wales.*
Agricultural Statistics, United Kingdom.

Table 10.8. Number and size of holdings with barley,
England and Wales

Hectares	1964	1976	1981	1986
Less than 1		2.0	1.3	0.9
1–1.9	32.7[1]	5.8	4.1	3.3
2–4.9	19.4[2]	19.0	16.9	15.7
5–9.9	11.3[3]	18.1	17.9	18.2
10–19.9	12.8[4]	20.1	19.6	22.9
20–29.9	7.1[5]	11.0	12.4	13.5
30–39.9	6.2[6]	6.8	7.7	8.1
40–49.9		4.7	5.2	5.1
50–74.9	7.3[7]	6.1	7.4	6.4
75–99.9		2.8	3.3	2.7
100–124.9	1.8[8]	1.5	1.7	2.0
125–149.9	1.4[9]	0.8	1.0	
150–199.9		0.7	1.7	1.2
200 and over		0.6		
Total	100.0	100.0	100.0	100.0
No. of holdings	106 545	73 417	67 966	59 154
Average barley area per holding (ha)	16.7	23.8	27.0	24.5

[1]1.9 ha or less. [2]2.0–8.0 ha. [3]8.1–12.0 ha. [4]12.1–20.1 ha. [5]20.2–28.2 ha.
[6]28.3–40.4 ha. [7]40.5–80.8 ha. [8]80.9–121.3 ha. [9]121.4 ha and over.
Source. MAFF: *Agricultural Statistics, England and Wales.*
Agricultural Statistics, United Kingdom.

Table 10.9. Average cereal yields
(tonnes per hectare) Great Britain

	Wheat	Barley	Oats	All cereals
1885–89	2.06	1.96	1.66	
1890–94	2.02	2.00	1.75	
1895–99	2.17	2.02	1.71	
1900–04	2.07	1.93	1.75	
1905–09	2.31	2.08	1.81	
1910–14	2.17	1.96	1.71	
1915–19	2.12	1.85	1.73	
1920–24	2.21	1.87	1.70	
1925–29	2.25	2.10	1.98	
1930–34	2.23	2.02	1.97	
1935–39	2.27	2.10	1.99	

United Kingdom

	Wheat	Barley	Oats	All cereals
Pre-war	2.31	2.09	2.05	2.06
1942	2.56	2.37	2.16	
1946	2.81	2.23	2.05	2.17
1950–54	2.81	2.62	2.35	2.56
1955–59	3.26	3.05	2.49	2.81
1960–64	3.96	3.45	2.76	3.45
1965–69	3.93	3.61	3.22	3.65
1970–74	4.24	4.41	3.73	4.01
1975–79	4.66	3.96	3.73	4.19
1980	5.88	4.43	4.07	4.95
1981	5.84	4.39	4.30	4.93
1982	6.20	4.93	4.43	5.44
1983	6.37	4.65	4.32	5.38
1984	7.71	5.59	4.89	6.59
1985	6.33	4.95	4.59	5.60
1986	6.96	5.22	5.16	6.09
1987[1]	6.03	5.02	4.38	5.51

[1]Forecast.
Source. MAFF: *Output and Utilisation of Farm Produce in the United Kingdom.*
HMSO: *Annual Review of Agriculture 1988.*

Table 10.10. Production of cereals ('000 tonnes)
Great Britain

	Wheat	Barley	Oats	Total
1885	2179	1930	1956	6065
1890	2061	1800	2172	6033
1895	1044	1672	2204	4920
1900	1478	1517	2072	5067
1905	1654	1415	2102	5171
1910	1526	1360	2196	5082
1914	1734	1389	2066	5189
1918	1540	1320	3013	5873
1920	1539	1413	2251	5203
1925	1437	1172	2129	4738
1930	1145	845	2020	4010
1935	1771	744	1849	4364

United Kingdom

	Wheat	Barley	Oats	All cereals[1]
Pre-war	1533	794	1950	4513
1943	3502	1671	3113	8783
1946	1999	1995	2950	7338
1947	1694	1645	2549	6302
1948	2399	2060	3011	8043
1949	2239	2163	3043	8156
1950	2648	1738	2735	7905
1951	2353	1970	2658	7846
1952	2344	2371	2816	8426
1953	2707	2561	2866	9060
1954	2828	2280	2479	8190
1955	2641	2983	2752	8913
1956	2891	2845	2526	8700
1957	2726	3004	2179	8264
1958	2755	3221	2172	8448
1959	2830	4080	2222	9409
1960	3113	4309	2091	9754
1961	2614	5054	1851	9709
1962	3974	5866	1775	11788
1963	3046	6705	1461	11354
1964	3793	7523	1346	12790
1965	4171	8191	1232	13709
1966	3475	8724	1120	13424
1967	3903	9215	1386	14634
1968	3469	8271	1221	13128
1969	3364	8664	1308	13566
1970	4236	7592	1217	13252
1971	4824	8558	1368	14964
1972	4780	9244	1250	15509
1973	5002	9007	1080	15304
1974	6130	9133	955	16382
1975	4489	8511	795	13937
1976	4740	7648	765	13268
1977	5274	10531	790	16727
1978	6613	9849	705	17267
1979	7170	9525	540	17320
1980	8470	10325	600	19479
1981	8707	10230	620	19629
1982	10316	10954	575	21911
1983	10802	9980	466	21307
1984	14958	11064	517	26602
1985	12046	9740	614	22466
1986	13911	10014	503	24488
1987[2]	12011	9219	436	21725

[1]All cereals includes rye mixed corn and other cereals for threshing.　[2]Forecast.
Source. MAFF: *Agricultural Statistics.*
HMSO: *Annual Review of Agriculture 1988.*

Table 10.11. Production of wheat by country ('000 tonnes)

	England and Wales	Scotland	Great Britain	Northern Ireland	United Kingdom
1928	1286	63	1349	5	1354
1935	1648	122	1770	11	1781
1938	1884	106	1990	6	1996
1942	2459	138	2597	11	2608
1946	1912	84	1996	2	1998
1950	2554	91	2645	2	2648
1955	2567	72	2640	1	2641
1960	2889	146	3035	4	3040
1965	4003	162	4165	6	4170
1970	4047	182	4229	5	4235
1975	4331	154	4485	3	4489
1980	8327	137	8464	2	8466
1981	8505	200	8705	2	8707
1982	10021	290	10311	6	10317
1983	10454	340	10794	8	10802
1984	14372	575	14947	22	14969
1985	11558	477	12035	11	12046
1986	13201	690	13891	21	13911
1987[1]					12011

[1]Forecast.
Source. MAFF: *Agricultural Statistics.*

Table 10.12. Production of barley by country ('000 tonnes)

	England and Wales	Scotland	Great Britain	Northern Ireland	United Kingdom
1928	1035	105	1140	2	1142
1935	666	77	743	4	747
1938	816	100	916	2	918
1942	1293	162	1455	14	1469
1946	1783	204	1987	7	1994
1950	1568	167	1735	4	1738
1955	2723	254	2977	6	2983
1960	3880	355	4235	74	4309
1965	7078	876	7954	236	8191
1970	6195	1176	7371	160	7529
1975	6558	1766	8324	187	8511
1980	8179	1947	10126	196	10322
1981	7895	2158	10053	174	10227
1982	8513	2240	10753	203	10956
1983	7726	2055	9781	199	9981
1984	8489	2360	10849	222	11072
1985	7784	1794	9578	162	9740
1986	7725	2097	9822	192	10014
1987[1]					9219

[1]Forecast.
Source. MAFF: *Agricultural Statistics.*

Table 10.13. Estimated areas of winter and spring wheat

	Area ('000 hectares)	Winter %	Spring %
1968	978	86	14
1969	833	77	23
1970	1010	86	14
1971	1097	91	9
1972	1127	92	8
1973	1146	92	8
1974	1233	92	8
1975	1035	88	12
1976	1231	96	4
1977	1076	94	6
1978	1257	95	5
1979	1371	96	4
1980	1441	97	3
1981	1491	97	3
1982	1664	97	3
1983	1695	98	2
1984	1939	99	1
1985	1902	98	2
1986	1997	99	1
1987	1992		

Source. MAFF: *Agricultural Statistics.*

Table 10.14. Estimated areas of winter and spring barley

	Area ('000 hectares)	Winter %	Spring %
1968	2401	5	95
1969	2413	5	95
1970	2243	7	93
1971	2288	8	92
1972	2288	9	91
1973	2267	10	90
1974	2214	10	90
1975	2345	10	90
1976	2182	14	86
1977	2400	14	86
1978	2348	18	82
1979	2343	25	75
1980	2330	31	69
1981	2329	36	64
1982	2221	41	59
1983	2143	43	57
1984	1978	53	47
1985	1965	52	48
1986	1916	50	50
1987	1836	53	47

Source. MAFF: *Agricultural Statistics.*

Table 10.15. Supply and disposal of wheat 1937–70 ('000 tonnes)

	New crop	Imports (excluding flour)[1]	Total supply	Human food	Animal feed	Seed	Industry	Total	Exports
1937–38	1533	4917	6450						
1939–40	1671	5585	7257	6281	1031	137	--	7450	
1942–43	2608	3298	5906	5083	434	283	--	5801	
1946–47	1999	4047	6046	5228	458	185	--	5872	2
1951–52 to 1955–56[2]	2575	4793	7367	5891	1358	174	6	7429	26
1956–57 to 1960–61[2]	2848	4917	7765	5782	1800	160	5	7747	22
1961–62 to 1965–66[2]	3520	4478	7997	5556	2188	175	5	7923	37
1966–67	3475	3964	7439	5159	2191	184	5	7538	9
1967–68	3903	3950	7853	5088	2407	190	5	7691	11
1968–69	3469	4469	7937	5187	2564	163	5	7918	13
1969–70	3364	4656	8020	5218	2732	196	5	8152	6

[1]Imports of wheat flour amounted to about 300 000 tonnes pre-war and about 280 000 in 1961–1962 to 1965–1966. Imports of wheat flour totalled 152 000 in 1966–1967, 84 000 in 1967–1968, 75 000 in 1968–1969 and 84 000 in 1969–1970. [2]Averages. -- Negligible.
Source. MAFF: *Output and Utilisation of Farm Produce in the United Kingdom.*

Table 10.16. Supply and disposal of wheat 1970–87 ('000 tonnes)

	1970	1975	1977	1978	1979	1980	1981	1982	1983	1984	1985	1986	1987[1]
Production	4236	4488	5275	6615	7170	8472	8707	10316	10802	14958	12046	13911	12011
Imports[2]	5352	3634	3855	3095	2615	2256	1772	1554	1326	1123	1614	1707	1495
Exports[2]	30	252	210	350	165	1055	1511	2354	1400	2215	1890	3990	4354
Total new supplies	9557	7870	8920	9360	9620	9673	8968	9516	10728	13866	11770	11628	9152
Production as % of new supplies	44	57	59	71	75	88	97	108	101	108	102	120	131

Utilisation	1970– 1971[6]	1975	1977	1978	1979	1980	1981	1982	1983	1984	1985	1986[7]
Milling[3,4]	5012	5175	5115	5075	5020	4890	4710	4530	4478	4697	4749	4828
of which home grown		(2125)	(2080)	(2760)	(2805)	(3165)	(3115)	(3256)	(3675)	(3615)	(3081)	
Cereal, breakfast foods	68	90	115	110	125	110	110	105	112	111	127	121
Malting, flaking, roasting	10	5	10	10	10	10	5	5	13	13	15	15
Starch, glucose			20	20	20	20	40	75	130	82	255	308
Animal feed[5]	4093	3370	2760	2930	3590	4065	3305	4340	4695	5162	5202	6378
Seed	213	250	235	270	285	280	290	295	338	330	347	340
Waste on farm	53	70	60	70	85	105	105	130	120	169	167	168
Waste in distribution	15	25	25	25	30	40	50	55	47	60	59	75
Total	9465	9015	8350	8510	9165	9520	8615	9535	9933	10625	10921	12233

[1]Forecast. [2]Includes wheat equivalent of flour imports, excludes re-exports. [3]Excludes wheat milled and exported as flour: 1978: 84 000 tonnes; 1979: 31 000 tonnes; 1980: 66 000 tonnes; 1981: 69 000 tonnes; 1982: 85 000 tonnes; 1983: 107 000 tonnes; 1984: 104 000 tonnes; 1985: 108 000 tonnes; 1986: 101 000 tonnes. [4]Excludes millers' rejects. [5]Includes millers' rejects. [6]July–June year. [7]Provisional.
Source: MAFF: *Output and Utilisation of Farm Produce in the United Kingdom.*
HMSO: *Annual Review of Agriculture 1988.*

Table 10.17. Supply and disposal of barley 1937–70 ('000 tonnes)

	New crop	Imports	Total supply	Malting, distilling	Feed	Seed	Total	Exports
1937–38	669	1004	1673					
1939–40	906	640	1546					
1943–44	1671		1671	1532	413	137	2083	
1946–47	1995	66	2061	933	866	144	1943	8
1950–51	1738	774	2512	993	1835	145	2973	
1955–56	2983	664	3648	991	2251	162	3403	205
1960–61	4302	965	5267	1125	3732	255	5112	124
1965–66	8191	195	8387	1364	5851	406	7621	680
1969–70	8664	956	9620	1515	7642	373	9530	12

Source. MAFF: *Output and Utilisation of Farm Produce in the United Kingdom.*

Table 10.18. Supply and disposal of barley 1970–87 ('000 tonnes)

	1970	1975	1977	1978	1979	1980	1981	1982	1983	1984	1985	1986	1987[1]
Production	7530	8513	10530	9850	9625	10325	10227	10954	9980	11064	9740	10014	9219
Imports	1050	502	915	350	300	207	133	39	77	109	198	280	175
Exports	171	1068	470	2035	835	1639	3127	2302	2523	3868	3014	4111	3091
Total new supplies	8409	7947	10980	8160	9090	8893	7232	8691	7534	7305	6924	6183	6303
Production as % of new supplies	90	107	96	121	106	116	141	127	132	151	141	162	146

Utilisation	1970–1971[2]	1975	1977	1978	1979	1980	1981	1982	1983	1984	1985	1986
Malting, flaking and roasting	1146	1465	1495	1555	1735	1785	1765	1745	1690	1647	1620	1564
Distilling	413	420	395	475	310	255	155	155	214	212	84	33
Pearl and pot barley	12	10	10	10	10	10	10	10	12	12	12	12
Animal feed	6485	6240	6215	6315	6405	6045	5740	5395	5388	4934	4536	4731
Seed	378	400	415	410	410	405	360	330	331	286	279	275
Waste on farm	75	90	85	105	95	105	110	110	98	110	105	101
Waste in distribution	24	40	35	60	45	50	75	65	67	85	70	83
Total	8534	8670	8650	8930	9015	8655	8215	7810	7800	7286	6707	6799

[1]Forecast. [2]July–June year.
Source: MAFF: *Output and Utilisation of Farm Produce in the United Kingdom.*
HMSO: *Annual Review of Agriculture 1988.*

Table 10.19. Supply and disposal of oats 1937–70 ('000 tonnes)

	New crop	Imports	Total supply	Human consumption	Animal feed	Seed	Total	Exports
1937–38	1877	61	1937					
1939–40	2035	99	2134					
1943–44	3113		3113	485	2445	341	3271	
1946–47	2949	179	3128	377	2420	317	3114	
1950–51	2735	73	2808	280	2278	290	2848	
1955–56	2752	34	2786	165	2400	190	2755	
1960–61	2091	48	2139	139	1842	153	2135	
1965–66	1232	34	1266	131	1060	82	1273	
1969–70	1308	19	1318	120	1065	92	1276	4

Source. MAFF: *Output and Utilisation of Farm Produce in the United Kingdom.*

Table 10.20. Supply and disposal of oats 1970–87 ('000 tonnes)

	1970	1975	1977	1978	1979	1980	1981	1982	1983	1984	1985	1986	1987[1]
Production	1217	795	790	705	540	600	619	575	466	517	614	503	436
Imports	19	29	45	20	65	25	5	2	28	40	9	17	13
Exports	124	4	5	10	5	–	–	5	2	–	–	1	6
Total new supplies	1113	820	830	715	600	625	624	572	492	557	623	519	443
Production as % of new supplies	109	97	95	99	90	96	99	101	95	93	99	97	98

Utilisation	1970–1971[2]	1975	1977	1978	1979	1980	1981	1982	1983	1984	1985	1986
Milling	120	135	145	145	145	140	145	140	144	143	156	158
Animal feed	1037	720	570	560	530	390	475	430	361	313	399	397
Seed	92	60	45	40	30	40	25	25	21	27	19	19
Waste on farm	23	15	15	15	10	10	10	10	9	8	10	10
Waste in distribution	4	5	5	5	5	5	5	5	4	4	4	5
Total	1276	935	780	765	720	585	660	610	539	495	588	589

[1]Forecast. [2]July–June year.
Source: MAFF: *Output and Utilisation of Farm Produce in the United Kingdom.*
HMSO: *Annual Review of Agriculture 1988.*

Table 10.21. All cereals: estimated total supplies[1] ('000 tonnes)

	1961–1963[2]	1967–1969[2]	1970	1975	1977	1978	1979	1980	1981	1982	1983	1984	1985	1986	1987[3]
Production	10951	13773	13255	13936	16725	17250	17415	19480	19621	21910	21307	26602	22466	24488	21725
Imports	9179	8418	9398	7702	9120	6850	6215	5315	4197	3746	3225	2744	3287	3488	3172
Exports	287	575	340	1416	720	2425	1030	2707	4718	4825	3934	6093	4910	8114	7488
Total new supplies	19844	21616	22314	20222	25130	21685	22605	22088	19100	20831	20598	23253	20843	19862	17409
Production as % of new supplies	55	64	59	69	67	80	77	88	103	105	103	114	108	123	125

[1]Including mixed corn, rye, maize and sorghum. [2]Averages. [3]Estimated.
Source. MAFF: *Output and Utilisation of Farm Produce in the United Kingdom.*
    HMSO: *Annual Review of Agriculture 1988.*

Table 10.22. Imports of Wheat (1871–1938) ('000 tonnes)

1871	1970	1910	5350
1880	2807	1915	4500
1885	3124	1920	5550
1890	3070	1925	4920
1895	4150	1930	5320
1900	3490	1935	5140
1905	4960	1938	5160

Source. Mitchell, B. R., in collaboration with Deane, P., 1976, *Abstract of Historical Statistics,* University of Cambridge, Dept. of Applied Economics, Monograph 17. *Statistical Abstract for the United Kingdom, 1871–1885.*

Table 10.23. Imports of wheat 1937–87 ('000 tonnes)

	1937–39[2]	1942	1946	1950	1955	1960	1965	1970	1975	1980	1981	1982	1983	1984	1985	1986	1987
Argentina	783	316	113	–	389	302	509	16	–	–	–	–	–	–	–	–	–
Australia	1132	335	–	304	504	692	623	1179	–	–	–	–	–	–	–	219	–
Belgium	35	–	–	–	64	17	105	93	469	–	–	3	4	7	9	32	44
Canada	1663	2890	2930	2501	2290	2164	2064	1534	970	1513	1468	1326	992	791	815	474	462
France	187	–	–	–	654	94	303	396	691	218	46	39	139	88	518	697	623
Netherlands	–	–	–	–	–	19	435	367	944	31	83	20	55	57	43	29	10
United States	556	2	382	455	481	570	322	685	311	244	121	70	–	37	31	20	–
Other countries	801	–	1	59	181	312	49	658	244	250	54	96	136	143	198	237	538[1]
Total	5157	3543	3426	3319	4563	4170	4410	4928	3629	2256	1772	1554	1326	1123	1614	1708	1677

[1]324000 tonnes from Spain. [2]Average.
Source. *Customs and Excise.*

Table 10.24. Imports of barley (1871–1938) ('000 tonnes)

1871	435	1910	930
1880	764	1915	620
1885	780	1920	640
1890	850	1925	800
1895	1200	1930	770
1900	870	1935	870
1905	1090	1938	1010

Source. Mitchell, B. R., in collaboration with Deane, P., 1976, *Abstract of Historical Statistics,* University of Cambridge, Dept. of Applied Economics, Monograph 17. *Statistical Abstract for the United Kingdom, 1871–1885.*

Table 10.25. Imports of barley 1937–87 ('000 tonnes)

	1937–39[1]	1942	1946	1950	1955	1960	1965	1970	1975	1980	1981	1982	1983	1984	1985	1986	1987
Australia	55	–	–	97	51	60	23	275	58	–	–	–	–	34	–	–	–
Canada	202	–	–	–	837	601	242	673	1	–	–	3	–	–	–	–	–
Denmark									80	–	–	–	–	–	76	92	34
France	--	–	–	–	–	1	11		181	–	23	–	5	–	43	30	15
Iraq	201	–	–	148	–	–	–										
Irish Republic									24	194	108	33	64	37	78	130	181
United States	121	–	–	–	12	5	1			–	–	–	–	–	–	–	–
USSR	96	–	–	330	–	30	–			–	–	–	–	–	–	–	–
Other countries	202	–	112	201	43	17	9	263	158	13	1	3	8	38	1	27	7
Total	877	–	112	776	943	714	286	1211	502	207	132	39	77	109	198	279	237

-- Negligible.   [1]Average.
Source. *Customs and Excise.*

Table 10.26. Exports of wheat, wheat flour and meal 1885–1965 ('000 tonnes)

1885	50	1930	270
1890	40	1935	170
1895	40	1938	180
1900	70	1942	10
1905	80	1945	260
1910	120	1950	10
1915	110	1955	10
1920	20	1960	10
1925	450	1965	20

Source. Mitchell, B. R., in collaboration with Deane, P., 1976, *Abstract of Historical Statistics,* University of Cambridge, Dept. of Applied Economics, Monograph 17. *Statistical Abstract for the United Kingdom, 1871–1885.*

Table 10.28. Exports of barley 1885–1965 ('000 tonnes)

1885	–
1890	–
1895	–
1900	–
1905	–
1910	–
1915	–
1920	–
1925	–
1930	–
1935	–
1938	1
1942	–
1945	40
1950	40
1955	90
1960	220
1965	200

Source. Mitchell, B. R., in collaboration with Deane, P., 1976, *Abstract of Historical Statistics,* University of Cambridge, Dept. of Applied Economics, Monograph 17. *Statistical Abstract for the United Kingdom, 1871–1885.*

Table 10.27. Exports of wheat 1970–87 by destination ('000 tonnes)

	1970	1975	1980	1981	1982	1983	1984	1985	1986	1987
Algeria	–	–	–	–	123	107	103	128	–	–
Belgium/ Luxembourg	–	–	449	64	118	80	80	89	184	111
Cuba	–	–	–	–	326	–	112	–	–	–
GDR	–	–	–	184	71	101	262	116	–	141
France	–	–	139	190	504	145	81	–	58	79
Irish Republic	54	–	155	238	122	96	159	106	133	136
Italy	–	–	–	–	68	25	163	131	803	503
Morocco	–	–	–	–	74	53	–	–	63	–
Netherlands	–	–	94	124	116	149	95	184	366	128
Poland	–	–	–	129	133	140	237	–	50	424
Romania	–	–	46	263	80	–	–	–	–	–
USSR	–	–	–	74	–	–	282	42	508	1091
FR Germany	–	–	110	111	237	120	346	738	737	343
Other countries	18	216	62	134	382	384	295	356	1085[1]	1165
Total	72	216	1055	1511	2354	1400	2215	1890	3987	4121

[1]Of which Denmark 108 000 tonnes and Spain 643 000 tonnes.
Source. *Customs and Excise.*

Table 10.29. Exports of barley 1970–87 by destination ('000 tonnes)

	1970	1975	1980	1981	1982	1983	1984	1985	1986	1987
Algeria	–	–	74	128	294	295	573	206	2	–
Belgium/ Luxembourg	47	235	185	610	500	341	1091	503	697	280
Cyprus	–	–	–	110	–	54	116	92	86	39
Denmark	–	20	–	65	37	118	70	–	7	–
GDR	–	–	91	228	–	–	–	–	–	–
France	–	–	–	–	148	62	63	–	36	24
Iran	–	–	–	101	–	–	184	101	–	–
Irish Republic	4	18	–	45	–	38	40	–	–	–
Italy	1	–	156	245	178	230	459	78	422	410
Netherlands	13	302	79	241	308	158	86	53	121	94
Poland	–	–	625	606	41	–	–	56	–	–
Saudi Arabia	–	–	–	135	328	266	578	321	610	626
Spain	–	–	236	122	–	647	50	–	720	27
USSR	–	–	–	116	–	–	152	819	584	1063
FR Germany	48	295	105	168	313	192	92	149	139	146
Other countries	–	198	88	207	155	122	314	636	695	378
Total	113	1068	1639	3127	2302	2523	3868	3014	4119	3087

Source. *Customs and Excise.*

Table 10.30. Imports of maize ('000 tonnes)

1871	855	1930	1740	1975	3030
1885	1602	1935	3020	1980	2810
1890	2210	1938	2930	1981	2260
1895	1720	1942	130	1982	2130
1900	2750	1945	520	1983	1810
1905	2140	1950	990	1984	1460
1910	1880	1955	1520	1985	1420
1915	2470	1960	3130	1986	1473
1920	1720	1965	3250	1987	1510
1925	1400	1970	3140		

Source. Mitchell, B. R., in collaboration with Deane, P., 1976, *Abstract of Historical Statistics,* University of Cambridge, Dept. of Applied Economics, Monograph 17.
Customs and Excise.
Statistical Abstract for the United Kingdom, 1871–1885.

Table 10.31. Cereal prices (England and Wales)[1] (£ per tonne)

	Wheat		Barley		Oats	
	At current prices	In 1986 money values	At current prices	In 1986 money values	At current prices	In 1986 money values
1780	8.92		4.98			
1790	13.00		7.42			
1800	27.21		17.07			
1810	24.38		13.72			
1820	16.05		9.65			
1830	15.24		9.25			
1840	15.75		10.36			
1850	9.55		6.71			
1860	12.60		10.36			
1870	11.07		9.86			
1880	10.47		9.34			
1890	7.30		7.87		6.56	
1900	6.15	247.5	6.89	277.3	6.23	250.8
1910	7.30	264.4	6.40	231.8	6.15	222.8
1914	8.04	279.5	7.46	259.3	7.38	256.5
1918	16.73	285.6	16.24	277.2	17.47	298.2
1920	18.54	258.2	24.61	342.8	20.09	279.8
1925	11.97	235.6	11.56	227.6	9.60	189.0
1930	7.87	172.5	7.79	170.8	6.07	133.1

continued opposite

Table 10.31 continued

	Wheat		Barley		Oats	
	At current prices	In 1986 money values	At current prices	In 1986 money values	At current prices	In 1986 money values
1935	5.09	123.5	7.79	189.0	6.56	159.2
1938	6.64	147.2	10.01	222.0	7.46	165.4
1942	15.67	222.7	44.95	638.9	14.68	208.7
1945	14.19	188.4	24.03	319.1	16.16	214.6
1950	25.43	275.6	27.48	297.8	21.24	230.2
1955	22.55	197.3	25.59	223.9	25.84	226.1
1960	21.00	163.4	20.91	162.6	22.14	172.2
1965	22.14	146.3	22.47	148.4	22.31	147.4
1970	27.10	143.0	28.41	150.0	24.68	130.3
1972	35.99	162.0	31.58	142.2	26.72	120.3
1975	65.64	187.9	65.14	186.4	60.45	173.0
1980	104.98	153.6	95.50	139.7	97.00	141.9
1981	112.38	147.0	106.32	139.0	99.79	130.5
1982	119.08	143.4	114.56	138.0	104.60	126.0
1983	124.33	143.2	121.97	140.4	111.94	128.9
1984	111.26	122.0	110.05	120.7	114.57	125.6
1985	112.20	116.0	106.02	109.6	92.95	96.1
1986	112.70	112.7	111.30	111.3	114.10	114.1
1987[2]	113.90	109.2	111.60	107.0	129.13	123.8

[1]These prices reflect all qualities spot and forward transactions.   [2]Forecast.
Source. MAFF.

Table 10.32. Average total returns for cereals (United Kingdom)[1] (£ per tonne)

	Wheat		Barley		Oats	
	At current prices	In 1986 money values	At current prices	In 1986 money values	At current prices	In 1986 money values
1966–67[2]	25.00	159.0	25.00	159.0	26.96	171.5
1967–68[2]	25.39	157.2	24.01	148.6	26.96	166.9
1968–69[2]	26.97	159.7	24.80	146.8	27.39	162.1
1969–70[2]	28.54	160.4	25.59	143.8	27.39	153.9
1970–71[2]	30.76	162.4	28.28	149.3	27.39	144.6
1971–72[2]	32.08	154.6	28.54	137.6	28.34	136.6
1972	34.50	155.3	30.71	138.2	29.72	215.0
1973	58.54	241.8	52.51	216.9	47.77	197.3
1974	57.61	205.1	58.11	206.9	55.44	197.4
1975	65.40	187.0	64.26	183.8	59.52	170.2
1976	84.50	207.9	83.00	204.2	77.73	191.2
1977	83.33	176.7	77.95	165.3	74.91	158.8
1978	85.63	167.8	78.35	153.6	73.26	143.6
1979	96.06	166.2	89.78	155.3	88.58	153.2
1980	99.30	145.0	92.83	135.5	97.52	142.4
1981	108.91	142.7	100.45	131.6	97.30	127.5
1982	113.68	136.4	108.65	130.4	101.08	121.3
1983	124.80	143.5	119.46	137.4	113.11	130.1
1984	114.58	126.0	112.48	123.7	123.06	135.4
1985	112.25	119.1	106.50	109.7	99.19	102.2
1986	111.18	111.2	105.89	105.9	100.87	100.9
1987[3]	112.35	107.7	106.18	101.8	114.16	109.5

[1]Including any deficiency payments up to 1975–76 inclusive. As market prices tended to be above guaranteed prices there were, in fact, only relatively small payments after 1971–72.
[2]Averages.   [3]Forecast.
Source. MAFF: *Annual Review of Agriculture.*

Appendix 11: Oilseed rape

Table 11.1. Value of output of oilseed rape (£ million)

1937–1971	–
1972	1
1973	2
1974	9
1975	9
1976	15
1977	23
1978	28
1979	43
1980	69
1981	87
1982	157
1983	174
1984	254
1985	244
1986	270
1987[1]	291

[1]Forecast.
Source. MAFF: *Departmental Net Income Calculation.*

Table 11.4. Oilseed rape yields (tonnes per hectare)

1968–70[1]	1.8
1975	1.7
1976	2.3
1977	2.6
1978	2.4
1979	2.7
1980	3.3
1981	2.7
1982	3.3
1983	2.53
1984	3.43
1985	3.01
1986	3.18
1987[2]	3.37

[1]Average.   [2]Forecast.
Source. MAFF: *Farm Incomes in the United Kingdom.*

Table 11.6. Prices received for oilseed rape (£ per tonne)[1]

	At current prices	In 1986 money values
1972	58	261
1973	79	325
1974	172	613
1975	128	366
1976	140	344
1977	162	343
1978	182	356
1979	215	371
1980	230	336
1981	255	334
1982	270	325
1983	310	357
1984	275	302
1985	274	283
1986	284	284
1987[2]	221	212

[1]Average market price.   [2]Forecast.
Source. HMSO: *Annual Review of Agriculture.*

Table 11.2. Area of oilseed rape ('000 hectares)

	England and Wales	Scotland	Great Britain	Northern Ireland	United Kingdom
1969	5	–	5	–	5
1970	4	–	4	–	4
1971	5	–	5	–	5
1972	7	–	7	–	7
1973	14	–	14	–	14
1974	25	–	25	–	25
1975	39	–	39	–	39
1976	48	–	48	–	48
1977	55	–	55	–	55
1978	64	–	64	–	64
1979	74	–	74	–	74
1980	92	–	92	–	92
1981	125	–	125	–	125
1982	173	2	175	–	174
1983	218	4	222	–	222
1984	257	11	268	–	269
1985	272	23	295	1	296
1986	277	22	299	- -	299
1987	342	45	387	1	388
1988					348

- - Negligible.
[1]Provisional.
Source. Agricultural Departments: *Agricultural Census.*

Table 11.3. Number of holdings with oilseed rape, 1986

Hectares	England and Wales	Scotland	United Kingdom
Under 2	81	15	96
2–4.9	597	135	732
5–9.9	2122	429	2551
10–19.9	3772	531	4303
20–29.9	2077	202	2279
30–39.9	1128	81	1209
40–49.9	653	38	691
50–74.9	652	16	668
75–99.9	216		
100–124.9	103	8	434
125–149.9	47		
150 and over	60		
Total	11 508	1455	12 963

Source. Agricultural Departments: *Agricultural Census.*

Table 11.5. Oilseed rape supplies ('000 tonnes)

	Production	Imports	Exports	New supply	Production as % of new supply
1968–69	- -	72		72	nil
1970–71	8	57	1	63	13
1975–76	67	61	1	127	53
1980	300	137	- -	437	69
1981	340	139	1	478	71
1982	580	38	14	604	96
1983	562	126	106	582	97
1984	923	67	167	823	112
1985	891	60	295	656	136
1986	951	259	496	714	133
1987[2]	1318	200	293	1225	108

[1]Forecast.   - - Negligible.
Source. HMSO: *Annual Review of Agriculture.*

Appendix 12: Potatoes

Table 12.1. Value of output of potatoes (£ million)

1937–38	14	1954–55	64	1971–72	98
1938–39	14	1955–56	78	1972	113
1939–40	15	1956–57	63	1973	127
1940–41	25	1957–58	89	1974	150
1941–42	38	1958–59	96	1975	328
1942–43	43	1959–60	67	1976	585
1943–44	53	1960–61	65	1977	376
1944–45	54	1961–62	86	1978	261
1945–46	58	1962–63	93	1979	385
1946–47	62	1963–64	71	1980	312
1947–48	57	1964–65	79	1981	392
1948–49	76	1965–66	90	1982	451
1949–50	69	1966–67	112	1983	495
1950–51	69	1967–68	92	1984	585
1951–52	61	1968–69	89	1985	318
1952–53	65	1969–70	123	1986	470
1953–54	66	1970–71	98	1987[1]	538

[1]Forecast.
Source. MAFF: *Departmental Net Income Calculation.*

Table 12.2. Area of potatoes ('000 hectares)

	England and Wales	Scotland	Great Britain		England and Wales	Scotland	Great Britain	Northern Ireland	United Kingdom
1866	144	58	202	1907	166	56	222		
1867	136	64	199	1908	169	58	227		
1868	152	68	219	1909	175	58	233		
1869	164	72	237	1910	163	55	219		
1870	165	73	238	1911	174	58	231		
1871	179	74	254	1912	187	61	248		
1872	157	72	228	1913	179	60	239		
1873	143	65	208	1914	187	62	248		
1874	146	65	210	1915	187	58	246		
1875	148	64	212	1916	173	53	226		
1876	141	63	204	1917	206	60	265		
1877	140	67	207	1918	257	68	324		
1878	139	67	206	1919	192	63	255		
1879	149	71	219	1920	221	66	286		
1880	147	76	223	1921	226	62	288		
1881	158	76	234	1922	227	64	291	70	361
1882	151	69	219	1923	189	55	244	66	310
1883	152	68	219	1924	183	56	239	64	303
1884	162	66	229	1925	200	57	257	62	319
1885	162	60	222	1926	202	57	259	62	321
1886	163	61	224	1927	208	59	268	62	330
1887	166	61	226	1928	198	58	256	63	319
1888	175	64	239	1929	210	59	269	62	331
1889	172	63	234	1930	172	50	222	55	277
1890	157	57	214	1931	181	52	233	54	287
1891	159	57	216	1932	204	60	264	57	321
1892	156	56	212	1933	210	62	272	56	328
1893	158	55	214	1934	197	57	254	55	309
1894	152	53	204	1935	187	53	240	52	292
1895	165	54	219	1936	185	54	239	53	292
1896	176	53	228	1937	184	55	239	51	290
1897	156	49	204	1938	192	55	247	50	297
1898	161	51	212	1939	184	54	238	47	285
1899	170	51	222	1940	217	64	281	55	336
1900	174	53	227	1941	314	76	391	64	455
1901	181	53	234	1942	363	88	452	76	528
1902	180	53	232	1943	387	96	483	80	563
1903	175	53	228	1944	397	97	493	80	573
1904	175	56	231	1945	398	91	488	77	565
1905	188	58	246	1946	408	89	498	78	576
1906	172	57	229	1947	381	84	465	74	539

continued overleaf

Table 12.2. continued

	England and Wales	Scotland	Great Britain	Northern Ireland	United Kingdom
1948	452	90	541	85	626
1949	376	78	454	76	530
1950	350	77	427	72	499
1951	296	70	367	58	425
1952	276	70	346	55	401
1953	272	70	342	56	398
1954	263	67	330	53	383
1955	244	62	306	47	353
1956	257	66	322	51	373
1957	229	58	287	42	329
1958	233	59	292	40	332
1959	231	61	291	39	330
1960	239	62	300	35	335
1961	199	55	254	31	285
1962	210	57	267	31	298
1963	217	61	278	33	311
1964	224	62	286	29	315
1965	218	57	275	25	300
1966	198	49	247	23	271
1967	216	52	264	23	287
1968	211	48	259	20	280
1969	189	42	231	17	248
1970	208	44	251	19	271
1971	199	40	239	17	257
1972	185	36	222	15	236
1973	176	34	209	14	225
1974	170	32	203	13	215
1975	162	31	193	11	204
1976	174	34	208	11	222
1977	176	37	214	19	233
1978	165	34	200	14	214
1979	155	34	189	15	204
1980	155	36	191	15	206
1981	145	34	179	12	191
1982	144	35	179	13	192
1983	148	35	183	12	195
1984	150	35	185	13	198
1985	155	23	178	13	191
1986	136	30	166	12	178
1987	136	29	165	12	177
1988[1]					179

[1]Provisional.
Source. Agricultural Departments: *Agricultural Census.*

Table 12.3. Number of registered potato growers in Great Britain ('000)

1955	86.8	1974	36.9
1960	76.8	1975	35.5
1961	74.9	1976	34.9
1962	70.1	1977	35.3
1963	66.4	1978	33.4
1964	60.9	1979	32.1
1965	57.7	1980	30.2
1966	54.7	1981	28.8
1967	50.3	1982	27.5
1968	48.2	1983	26.5
1969	45.1	1984	25.5
1970	43.3	1985	24.9
1971	42.8	1986	22.6
1972	40.8	1987	21.4
1973	38.8		

Source. *Potato Marketing Board.*

Table 12.4. Number of holdings by area of potatoes England and Wales

Area (ha)	1964[1]	1975[1]	Area (ha)	1981[2]	1986[2]
Under 1.9	49 777	18 378	Under 1	9254	6922
2–3.9	8896	5227	1–1.9	4010	3087
4–7.9	7169	4593	2–4.9	6533	5470
8–11.9	2855	2059	5–9.9	3670	3355
12–15.9	1277	1030	10–14.9	1639	1453
16–19.9	682	648	15–19.9	800	806
20–28.2	717	605	20–29.9	823	782
28.3–40.4	423	372	30–39.9	335	338
40.5 and over	286	289	40–49.9	190	191
			50–74.9	147	169
			75 and over	72	71
Total	72 082	33 201		27 473	22 644

[1]Maincrop potatoes only.   [2]Total potatoes.
Source. MAFF: *Agricultural Statistics, England and Wales.*
   MAFF: *Agricultural Statistics, United Kingdom.*

Table 12.5. Average potato yields 1885–1939 (tonnes per hectare)

Great Britain	
1885–89	14.7
1890–94	14.5
1895–99	15.1
1900–04	14.3
1905–09	15.6
1910–14	15.8
1915–19	15.5
1920–24	15.5
1925–29	16.3
1930–34	16.5
1935–39	17.2

Table 12.6. Average potato yields pre-war–1987 (tonnes per hectare)

	Earlies	Main crop	Total
Pre-war			16.8
1946			17.8
1950–54			19.9
1955–60			19.1
1961			22.3
1962			22.6
1963			21.6
1964	16.1	23.6	22.3
1965	16.8	26.6	25.4
1966	16.8	25.6	24.4
1967	16.6	26.4	25.1
1968	19.3	25.3	24.6
1969	18.1	25.9	25.1
1970	16.7	28.8	27.6
1971	19.8	29.9	28.8
1972	18.4	28.8	27.7
1973	20.1	31.6	30.4
1974	19.1	33.1	31.6
1975	14.3	23.4	22.3
1976	16.6	22.1	21.6
1977	18.1	29.6	28.5
1978	21.6	35.6	34.3
1979	18.4	33.3	31.9
1980	22.6	35.8	34.5
1981	18.6	34.0	32.3
1982	21.7	37.4	35.8
1983	20.5	30.7	29.9
1984	18.7	39.2	37.0
1985	24.1	36.7	35.8
1986	21.2	37.6	36.0
1987[1]	23.7	39.3	37.8

[1]Forecast.
Source. MAFF: *Output and Utilisation of Farm Produce in the United Kingdom.*
HMSO: *Annual Review of Agriculture 1988.*

Table 12.7. Potato production ('000 tonnes)

Great Britain	Earlies	Main crop	Total
1885			3250
1890			2857
1895			3651
1900			2779
1905			3823
1910			3533
1915			3891
1920			4458
United Kingdom			
1923			4567
1925			5464
1930			4530
1937			4726
1938			5197
1942			9543
1946			10 329
1950			9659
1955			6378
1960			7273
1961			6358
1962			6765
1963			6681
1964	774	6289	7063
1965	721	6856	7577
1966	622	5958	6580
1967	593	6607	7200
1968	618	6254	6872
1969	417	5798	6215
1970	452	7029	7482
1971	515	6881	7396
1972	460	6067	6527
1973	463	6382	6845
1974	458	6333	6791
1975	350	4201	4551
1976	371	4418	4789
1977	406	6215	6621
1978	422	6909	7331
1979	362	6124	6486
1980	453	6657	7110
1981	388	5826	6498
1982	432	6498	6930
1983	322	5535	5857
1984	397	7001	7398
1985	403	6489	6892
1986	364	6083	6447
1987[1]	395	6395	6760

[1]Forecast.
Source. MAFF: *Output and Utilisation of Farm Produce in the United Kingdom.*
HMSO: *Annual Review of Agriculture 1988.*

Table 12.8. Production of potatoes by country ('000 tonnes)[1]

	England and Wales	Scotland	Great Britain	Northern Ireland	United Kingdom
1934	3494	1041	4535	938	5472
1938	3542	933	4475	722	5197
1942	6757	1535	8292	1250	9543
1946	6949	1802	8751	1511	10 262
1950	6784	1510	8294	1364	9659
1955	4497	1115	5612	769	6378
1960	5182	1376	6558	714	7273
1965	5818	1248	7066	511	7577
1970	5820	1255	7075	406	7482
1975	3412	896	4308	243	4551
1980	5066	1201	6267	384	6651
1981	4485	1042	5527	312	5840
1982	4899	1194	6093	351	6444
1983	4224	1016	5240	324	5563
1984	5318	1279	6597	403	7001
1985	5027	1148	6175	287	6489
1986	4659	1112	5771	312	6083

[1]Main crop and second earlies.

Table 12.9. Potato supplies ('000 tonnes)

	Production	Output for human consumption[1]	Imports[2]	Exports	New supply[3]	Output as % of new supply[3]
Pre-war	4951	3747	183	50	3880	97
1946–47	10 329	6584	116	81	6619	99
1953–54	8392	4814	185	56	4943	97
1960–61	7273	4720	283	80	4923	96
1965–66	7577	4707	301	225	4783	98
1970–71	7482	4949	448	101	5296	93
1971–72	7396	5049	438	84	5403	93
1972	6527	5383	414	84	5713	94
1973	6845	5552	591	167	5976	93
1974	6791	5328	356	152	5532	96
1975	4551	3659	500	60	5412	68
1976	4789	3575	1114	20	4669	77
1977	6621	4671	867	28	5510	85
1978	7331	5136	487	86	5540	93
1979	6486	5016	553	98	5470	92
1980	7110	5907	582	97	6392	92
1981	6190	4953	641	93	5501	90
1982	6930	5717	969	88	6599	87
1983	5857	4909	875	95	5689	86
1984	7398	6002	780	103	6679	90
1985	6892	5764	718	94	6388	90
1986	6447	5498	868	146	6220	88
1987[4]	6760	5506	998	142	6362	87

[1]Production less chats, waste, retained for stock feed, seed for home crop and exports. [2]Including supplies from Channel Isles. [3]New supply for human consumption. [4]Forecast.

Table 12.10. Imports of potatoes ('000 tonnes)

	1885	1909–13	1919–23	1924–28	1929–33	1935	1938
Belgium		20	11	18	44	1	–
Canary Isles		13	6	11	9	8	12
Channel Isles		61	53	54	57	86	56
Irish Republic		–	2	27	22	9	12
Netherlands		50	24	72	100	15	17
Spain		5	4	33	83	72	18
Other countries		117	78	201	171	3	33
Total	117	266	178	416	486	194	148

Source. *Customs and Excise*
Statistical Abstract for the United Kingdom 1871–1885.

Table 12.11. Imports of potatoes ('000 tonnes)

Raw potatoes (Great Britain)	1955	1960	1965	1970	1975	1980	1981	1982	1983	1984	1985	1986	1987
New													
Canary Isles	44	33	43	28	25	2	3	4	7	7	7	3	2
Channel Isles	50	45	41	36	23	33	27	30	32	31	40	36	44
Cyprus	28	52	74	136	59	108	121	116	120	120	78	98	62
Egypt	2	21	10	36	15	116	79	92	66	88	62	69	63
France	1	2	--	12	23	27	25	41	15	17	23	12	26
Greece	–	8	6	–	–	8	25	5	38	16	16	8	10
Italy	55	45	15	6	4	3	4	7	6	3	5	5	6
Spain	22	64	60	43	31	33	33	32	27	44	43	36	24
Other countries	46	37	32	16	37	--	2	9	1	7	3	4	3
Total	248	307	281	313	217	330	320	336	312	332	277	271	240
Ware													
Belgium	120	–				--	37	7	21	9	30	86	
Netherlands	236	–				22	305	56	60	37	97	161	
Other countries						1	14	2	7	6	11	13	
Total	376	–	–	–	–	24	356	65	88	52	138	260	
Seed	4	11	7	10	12	5	13	12	12	11	13	12	16
Total raw	628	318	288	323	229	359	689	413	412	395	428	543	
Processed[1]													
(United Kingdom)													
Canned				15	16	9	11	14	22	24	17	25	
of which Belgium						3	6	7	9	10	9	13	
Crisped				2		4	3	2	3	4	5	3	
Dehydrated				111	292	79	92	143	168	141	111	106	
of which Netherlands						23	53	93	108	97	79	69	
Frozen				13	80[2]	57	149	186	219	200	215	242	
of which Belgium						16	21	22	22	18	19	19	
Netherlands						36	83	116	129	130	151	195	
West Germany						2	20	30	47	41	40	14	
Total processed			54	141	389	148	254	345	411	369	348	377	

[1] Raw equivalent. [2] Estimated. -- Negligible.
Source. *Customs and Excise.*

Table 12.12. Consumption of potatoes (kg per head per annum)

	Unprocessed potatoes	Crisps[1]	Frozen and par fries[1]	Canned[1]	Dehydrated[1]	Total[1]
Pre-war						86.2
1942						102.0
1946						127.6
1950						109.8
1955						106.2
1960						101.5
1965						100.9
1970	88.9	6.3	3.4		4.9[2]	103.5
1975	80.4	7.8	8.4	0.4	4.9	101.9
1980	77.4	8.3	9.9	0.4	3.3	99.3
1981	79.1	9.1	11.3	0.4	3.5	103.4
1982	77.8	9.6	12.6	0.5	5.0	105.5
1983	76.5	11.8	12.2	0.4	5.2	106.1
1984	74.7	11.2	12.6	0.8	3.7	103.0
1985	77.6	11.5	13.4	1.0	4.1	107.6
1986	81.2	10.8	15.7	0.9	3.8	112.4

[1] Weight of raw equivalent. [2] Including canned.
Source. MAFF: *Food Facts.*

177

Table 12.13. Farm gate potato prices
(£ per tonne)[1]

	At current prices	In 1986 money values
1936	6.05	142.33
1937	5.95	133.47
1938	4.28	94.90
1939	4.05	88.04
1940	5.33	97.67
1941	7.01	106.46
1942	7.27	103.33
1943	7.40	101.92
1944	7.46	100.86
1945	7.75	102.90
1946	8.13	106.69
1947	8.94	109.85
1948	9.94	113.46
1949	10.31	114.97
1950	10.43	113.04
1951	10.97	109.08
1952	11.91	111.53
1953	12.32	113.44
1954	12.57	113.84
1955	14.91	130.44
1956	17.83	149.55
1957	14.29	116.07
1958	21.29	168.32
1959	16.74	131.54
1960	11.98	93.19
1961	15.23	115.22
1962	17.73	129.07
1963	15.83	113.10
1964	14.11	97.56
1965	13.77	90.97
1966	16.74	106.40
1967	16.35	101.25
1968	14.92	88.29
1969	14.70	82.56
1970	14.60	77.06
1971	14.82	71.47
1972	17.43	78.47
1973	20.70	85.42
1974	23.60	83.92
1975	56.80	162.57
1976	143.40	352.17
1977	69.90	148.18
1978	40.00	78.30
1979	58.90	101.68
1980	51.20	74.91
1981	63.00	82.40
1982	78.08	93.70
1983	81.89	94.17
1984	102.13	112.34
1985	48.13	49.57
1986	76.74	76.74
1987[2]	86.48	82.93

[1]Paid by registered merchants to growers for early and main crop potatoes. [2]Forecast.
Source. HMSO: *Annual Review of Agriculture.*

Table 12.14. Main crop and early potato prices (£ per tonne)

	Main crop[1]		Earlies[2]	
	At current prices	In 1986 money values	At current prices	In 1986 money values
1960	11.67	90.79		
1961	17.89	135.43		
1962	17.62	128.27		
1963	14.57	104.03		
1964	13.85	95.70		
1965	13.99	92.47		
1966	19.07	121.29		
1967	14.43	89.32		
1968	15.28	90.46		
1969	21.71	122.01		
1970	14.27	75.35		
1971	14.82	71.43		
1972	19.30	86.85		
1973	18.77	77.52		
1974	25.40	90.42		
1975	103.90	297.15		
1976	131.58	323.69		
1977	42.81	90.76		
1978	44.25	86.73	78.00	152.88
1979	58.81	101.74	61.09	105.69
1980	44.30	64.68	111.71	163.10
1981	83.62	109.54	89.66	117.45
1982	53.10	63.72	100.33	120.40
1983	125.76	144.62	143.28	164.77
1984	48.98	53.88	65.80	72.38
1985	57.13	58.84	104.29	107.40
1986	86.61	86.61	120.16	120.16

[1]United Kingdom main crop price.   [2]Great Britain early price.
Source. *Potato Marketing Board.*

Appendix 13: Sugar beet

Table 13.1. Value of sugar beet output (£ million)

1937–38	5
1938–39	5
1939–40	8
1940–41	10
1941–42	10
1942–43	16
1943–44	15
1944–45	12
1945–46	16
1946–47	19
1947–48	15
1948–49	22
1949–50	20
1950–51	28
1951–52	25
1952–53	24
1953–54	30
1954–55	25
1955–56	27
1956–57	31
1957–58	25
1958–59	32
1959–60	34
1960–61	39
1961–62	33
1962–63	30
1963–64	32
1964–65	43
1965–66	40
1966–67	39
1967–68	42
1968–69	43
1969–70	41
1970–71	44
1971–72	57
1972	49
1973	69
1974	59
1975	85
1976	97
1977	133
1978	159
1979	206
1980	195
1981	192
1982	253
1983	218
1984	251
1985	232
1986[1]	218
1987[1]	211

[1]Forecast.
Source. MAFF: *Departmental Net Income Calculation.*

Table 13.2. Sugar beet area ('000 hectares)

	England and Wales	Scotland	Great Britain	Northern Ireland	United Kingdom
1912	2	–	2	–	2
1913	2	–	2	–	2
1914	1	–	1	–	2
1915	1	–	1	–	1
1916	–	–	–	–	–
1917	–	–	–	–	–
1918	- -	–	- -	–	- -
1919	–	–	–	–	–
1920	1	–	1	–	1
1921	3	–	3	–	3
1922	3	–	3	–	3
1923	7	–	7	–	7
1924	9	–	9	–	9
1925	22	- -	23	–	23
1926	51	2	52	–	52
1927	90	4	94	–	94
1928	71	1	72	–	72
1929	93	- -	93	–	93
1930	140	1	141	–	141
1931	94	- -	95	–	95
1932	103	- -	104	–	104
1933	147	1	148	–	148
1934	160	3	163	–	163
1935	149	3	152	–	152
1936	141	3	144	–	144
1937	124	3	127	–	127
1938	133	3	136	–	136
1939	136	3	140	–	140
1940	131	2	133	–	133
1941	139	3	142	–	142
1942	167	6	172	–	172
1943	163	5	169	–	169
1944	169	5	174	–	174
1945	164	5	169	–	169
1946	172	5	176	–	176
1947	156	4	160	–	160
1948	164	4	167	–	167
1949	167	4	170	–	170
1950	170	4	174	–	174
1951	168	4	172	–	172
1952	161	4	165	–	165
1953	163	4	168	–	168
1954	171	6	177	–	177
1955	167	5	172	–	172
1956	167	6	172	–	172
1957	168	6	174	–	174
1958	171	6	178	–	178
1959	169	6	176	–	176
1960	170	6	176	–	176
1961	166	6	173	–	173
1962	165	6	172	–	172
1963	165	6	171	–	171
1964	175	4	179	–	179
1965	180	4	184	–	184
1966	178	3	180	–	180
1967	182	2	185	–	185
1968	185	4	188	–	188
1969	180	5	185	–	185
1970	182	5	187	–	187
1971	186	4	191	–	191
1972	189	–	189	–	189
1973	194	–	194	–	194
1974	195	–	195	–	195
1975	198	–	198	–	198
1976	206	–	206	–	206

continued overleaf

Table 13.2 continued

	England and Wales	Scotland	Great Britain	Northern Ireland	United Kingdom
1977	202	–	202	–	202
1978	209	–	209	–	209
1979	214	–	214	–	214
1980	213	–	213	–	213
1981	210	–	210	–	210
1982	204	–	204	–	204
1983	199	–	199	–	199
1984	199	–	196	–	196
1985	205	–	205	–	205
1986	205	–	205	–	205
1987	202	–	202	–	202
1988[1]	201	–	201	–	201

- - Negligible.   [1]Provisional.
Source. *Agricultural Department: Agricultural census.*

Table 13.3. Numbers and size of holdings with sugar beet in England and Wales

Hectares of sugar beet	1967	1976	1981	1986
less than 1	} 11 400	614	246	} 525
1–1.9		1098	561	
2–4.9		3794	2594	2045
5–9.9		3479	3229	2834
10–14.9	} 10 300	2075	1920	} 2839
15–19.9		1186	1095	
20–29.9		1397	1376	1312
30–39.9		605	619	609
40–49.9	} 2100	411	418	429
50–74.9		363	407	409
75 and over		237	319	349
Total	23 800	15 259	12 784	11 351

Source. *Agricultural Statistics, United Kingdom.*

Table 13.4. Average sugar beet yields (tonnes per hectare)

Great Britain			
1921–25	18.3[2]		
1926–30	20.2		
1931–35	22.1		
United Kingdom			
Pre-war	20.6	1967	37.4
1946	26.4	1968	38.2
1947	19.1	1969	32.9
1948	26.4	1970	34.4
1949	23.9	1971	41.7
1950	30.9	1972	33.1
1951	26.9	1973	39.4
1952	26.1	1974	25.2
1953	32.1	1975	25.2
1954	26.1	1976	31.5
1955	27.1	1977	31.8
1956	30.6	1978	34.7
1957	26.6	1979	35.9
1958	33.1	1980	35.1
1959	32.1	1981	35.7
1960	41.9	1982	49.8
1961	35.1	1983	38.3
1962	31.6	1984	45.9
1963	31.4	1985	38.3
1964	35.6	1986	40.4
1965	37.4	1987[1]	40.0
1966	36.7		

[1]Forecast.   [2]England and Wales.
Source. MAFF: *Output and Utilisation of Farm Produce in the United Kingdom.*

Table 13.5. Production of sugar beet ('000 tonnes)

1925	497	1965	6812
1930	3109	1966	6599
1935	3459	1967	6883
Pre-war	2785	1968	7118
1946	4594	1969	6034
1947	3007	1970	6412
1948	4388	1971	7869
1949	4025	1972	6216
1950	5299	1973	7427
1951	4607	1974	4588
1952	4304	1975	4864
1953	5359	1976	6325
1954	4593	1977	6382
1955	4629	1978	7081
1956	5252	1979	7659
1957	4612	1980	7380
1958	5834	1981	7395
1959	5598	1982	10008
1960	7330	1983	7494
1961	6031	1984	9017
1962	5398	1985	7717
1963	5338	1986	8118
1964	6317	1987[1]	8000

[1]Forecast.
Source. MAFF: *Output and Utilisation of Farm Produce in the United Kingdom.*

Table 13.6. Utilisation of sugar beet production ('000 tonnes)

	Beet production	Sugar (refined equiv.)	Molasses for distilling, yeast, etc	Molasses for incorporation in pulp	Pulp dry, plain molasses	Pulp wet
Pre-war	2785					
1946–47	4594					
1950–51	5299					
1956–57	5252	709	92	130	377	318
1960–61	7330	888	110	217	552	183
1965–66	6812	860	98	225	558	133
1970–71	6412	906	93	239	591	108
1975	4864	695	118	238	547	71
1980	7380	1106	120	227	651	234
1981	7395	1092	127	230	596	277
1982	10008	1420	165	291	583	318
1983	7494	1062	186	310	681	327
1984	9017	1314	207	195	446	145
1985	7717	1210	197	252	837	145
1986	8118	1318	140	212	697	130
1987[1]	8000	1200				

[1]Forecast.
Source. MAFF: *Output and Utilisation of Farm Produce in the United Kingdom.*

Table 13.7. Sugar supplies ('000 tonnes refined)

	Production	Imports	Exports	New supply	Production as % of new supply
Pre-war	422	2204	349[1]	2277[1]	19[1]
1946–7	602	1595	100[1]	2097[1]	29[1]
1953–4	796	3305	673[1]	3428[1]	23[1]
1960–61	954	2282	490[1]	2746[1]	35
1970–71	954	2159	213	2900	33
1975	641	2225	354	2512	26
1980	1106	1340	94	2352	47
1981	1092	1211	120	2183	50
1982	1420	1215	150	2485	57
1983	1062	1295	316	2041	52
1984	1314	1269	258	2325	57
1985	1210	1303	354	2159	56
1986	1318	1255	173	2400	55
1987[2]	1200	1193	282	2111	57

[1]Author's estimate.   [2]Forecast.
Source. HMSO: *Annual Review of Agriculture.*

Table 13.8. Imports of unrefined sugar ('000 tonnes)

	1935	1938	1942	1945	1950	1955	1960	1965	1970	1975	1980	1981	1982	1983	1984	1985	1986	1987
Australia	244	387	49		251	415	337	408	347	52	–	–	–	–	–	–	–	–
Belize											38	36	49	35	28	40	35	42	50
Cuba	559	611	62	540	886	102	85	92	32	11	–	–	–	–	–	–	.	–
Fiji	69	78	89			46	97	170	13	208	122	195	135	142	201	140	187	148
Guyana	56	56		47	68	144	133	121	174	138	139	179	159	136	173	150	156	164
Jamaica	89[1]	177[1]	157[1]	187[1]	307[1]	216	155	262	241	124	88	130	115	58	128	126	126	111
Mauritius	188	287	190	41	166	447	365	411	411	414	517	346	395	386	437	439	395	405
St Domingo	314	275	121	253	–	–	4	–	–	–	–	–	–	–	–	–	–	–
South Africa	158	218	–	–	15	164	207	20	32		–	–	–	–	–	–	–	–
Swaziland	–	–	–	–	–	–	–	–	10	101	111	75	120	127	127	127	133	80
Zimbabwe	–	–	–	–	–	–	–	–	–	–	–	–	14	–	49	28	48
Other countries	269	317	105	11	432	741	718	637	579	629	140	132	124	150	178	152	147	157
Total	1946	2406	773	1079	2125	2275	2101	2121	1839	1715	1153	1106	1083	1041	1284	1218	1214	1163

[1]British West Indies.
Source. *Customs and Excise.*

Table 13.9. Consumption of sugar and syrups (kg per head per annum)

	Sugar refined[1]	Honey	Glucose	Total[2]
Pre-war	41.2	0.2	3.0	43.5
1942	28.5	0.4	1.5	30.3
1946	34.0	0.2	1.4	35.1
1950	36.4	0.3	1.7	38.0
1955	46.2	0.3	3.2	48.9
1960	47.3	0.3	3.4	53.8
1965	45.4	0.3	4.4	49.2
1970	44.0	0.4	5.3	48.8
New series				
1975	36.0	0.4	7.9	43.0
1980	37.0	0.3	7.9	43.4
1981	36.7	0.4	7.3	42.6
1982	39.0	0.4	7.4	44.9
1983	37.4	0.4	7.3	43.3
1984	37.9	0.4	7.9	44.2
1985	37.1	0.4	7.6	43.2
1986	37.3	0.4	7.9	43.6

[1]Including estimated sugar content of manufactured goods but excluding sugar used in connection with alcoholic drinks.   [2]Sugar content.
Source. MAFF: *Food Facts.*

Table 13.10. Sugar beet prices (£ per tonne)

	At current prices	In 1986 money values
1927–28	2.73	56.32
1928–29	2.56	53.40
1929–30	2.60	55.12
1930–31	2.45	53.70
1931–32	2.08	48.94
1932–33	2.10	50.63
1933–34	1.95	48.22
1934–35	2.36	57.99
1935–36	1.89	46.36
1936–37	1.95	45.88
1937–38	2.03	45.87
1938–39	2.27	50.33
1939–40	2.43	52.83
1940–41	3.21	58.84
1941–42	3.32	50.43
1942–43	4.21	59.82
1943–44	4.19	57.69
1944–45	4.00	54.08
1943–46	4.00	53.12
1946–47	4.47	58.65
1947–48	5.47	67.23
1948–49	5.35	61.04
1949–50	5.17	57.65
1950–51	5.54	60.05
1951–52	5.64	56.06
1952–53	5.83	54.57
1953–54	6.03	54.43
1954–55	5.91	53.54
1955–56	6.33	55.39
1956–57	6.33	53.11
1957–58	6.30	51.16
1958–59	6.37	50.39
1959–60	6.30	49.52
1960–61	6.26	48.70
1961–62	6.18	46.78
1962–63	6.16	44.84
1963–64	6.46	46.12
1964–65	6.90	47.68
1965–66	6.33	41.84
1966–67	6.33	41.84
1967–68	6.33	41.84

Source. MAFF: *Agricultural Statistics.*

Table 13.11. Prices received for sugar beet (£ per tonne)

	Guaranteed price	Minimum beet price	Farm gate price		Total return	
			At current prices	In 1986 money values	At current prices	In 1986 money values
1968–69	6.72	–	5.93	34.20		
1969–70	6.72	–	5.91	32.20		
1970–71	6.84	–	5.98	30.20		
1971–72	7.48	–	6.59	30.70	7.48	34.90
1972	7.87	6.60			7.87	35.40
1973	6.86	6.90			9.41	38.90
1974		9.44			13.96	49.70

	Producer price[1]	
	At current prices	In 1986 money values
1974	13.49	48.00
1975	18.48	52.90
1976	16.42	40.30
1977	21.93	46.50
1978	23.72	46.40
1979	28.28	48.80
1980	27.93	40.90
1981	27.74	36.30
1982	27.15	32.70
1983	31.06	35.80
1984	30.71	33.70
1985[2]	32.79	33.90
1986[2]	29.66	29.66
1987[3]	29.15	27.72

[1]Weighted average price paid to growers by the British Sugar Corporation for sugar beet of average sugar content.   [2]Provisional.   [3]Forecast.
Source. HMSO: *Annual Review of Agriculture.*

Appendix 14: Horticulture

Table 14.1. Value of fruit output (£ million)

1937–38	9	1954–55	34	1971–72	63
1938–39	9	1955–56	39	1972	86
1939–40	12	1956–57	39	1973	88
1940–41	17	1957–58	49	1974	105
1941–42	19	1958–59	39	1975	95
1942–43	33	1959–60	41	1976	116
1943–44	29	1960–61	36	1977	145
1944–45	27	1961–62	49	1978	153
1945–46	22	1962–63	47	1979	158
1946–47	28	1963–64	42	1980	170
1947–48	40	1964–65	54	1981	187
1948–49	34	1965–66	48	1982	212
1949–50	30	1966–67	45	1983	230
1950–51	27	1967–68	47	1984	242
1951–52	33	1968–69	56	1985	232
1952–53	34	1969–70	56	1986	254
1953–54	37	1970–71	56	1987[1]	228

[1]Forecast.
Source. MAFF: *Departmental Net Income Calculation.*

Table 14.2. Cropped area of orchards and small fruit ('000 hectares)

Great Britain		
	Orchards	Soft fruit
1871–75	67	
1876–80	68	
1881–85	77	
1986–90	81	
1891–95	86	27
1896–1900	91	29
1901–05	97	31
1906–10	101	34
1911–15	100	34
1916–20	100	29
1921–25		31
1926–30	100	30
1931–35	102	28

Source. Agricultural Departments.
Agricultural Census.

Table 14.3. Estimated cropped area of fruit ('000 hectares)

	Dessert apples	Culinary apples	Pears	Plums	Cherries	Total orchard fruit	Soft fruit	Total fruit
Pre-war						107.3	25.3	132.6
1946						113.9	15.8	129.7
1947	22.8	33.2	6.0	19.0	7.1	111.8	17.6	129.4
1948	23.4	32.9	6.1	18.9	7.2	112.0	19.8	131.8
1949	24.1	32.8	6.3	18.2	7.3	111.3	23.8	136.1
1950	24.6	31.6	6.6	17.6	7.3	108.3	25.4	134.9
1951	25.1	30.6	6.7	17.4	7.3	107.1	23.7	132.0
1952	25.4	29.9	6.8	16.8	7.3	105.9	22.5	129.7
1953	25.6	29.2	6.8	16.2	7.3	104.7	21.2	127.2
1954	25.8	28.8	6.9	15.5	7.3	103.7	20.7	125.3
1955	26.0	28.1	7.0	14.9	7.3	102.5	19.9	123.7
1956	26.3	27.4	7.1	14.3	7.3	101.4	19.3	121.8
1957	26.5	26.5	7.1	13.4	7.2	99.9	19.7	120.5
1958	26.4	25.4	7.1	12.5	6.7	96.3	20.3	117.4
1959	26.3	24.4	7.2	11.7	6.2	93.1	20.6	114.4
1960	26.4	23.8	7.2	11.4	6.0	91.2	20.6	112.4
1961	25.9	22.1	6.8	10.8	5.7	86.7	19.5	106.9
1962	25.5	20.9	6.7	9.7	5.5	82.7	19.7	103.0
1963	25.2	20.1	6.7	9.3	5.1	80.3	20.2	101.1
1964	24.8	19.1	6.6	9.0	4.7	77.5	20.1	97.6
1965	24.0	18.2	6.3	8.5	4.3	73.5	19.4	92.9
1966	23.3	17.1	6.2	8.0	4.0	70.0	18.6	88.6
1967	23.3	16.2	6.0	7.7	3.7	68.1	17.9	86.0
1968	23.4	15.3	5.8	7.5	3.4	66.7	18.0	84.8
1969	23.1	14.9	5.7	7.3	3.3	65.8	18.0	83.8
1970	23.2	14.7	5.6	6.8	3.0	65.1	18.1	83.2
1971	23.1	14.5	5.5	6.5	2.9	64.1	17.9	82.1
1972	23.1	14.3	5.4	6.4	2.8	63.7	18.1	81.7
1973	23.0	13.8	5.4	6.3	2.7	62.8	17.9	80.8
New series								
1974	21.2	12.6	5.2	6.0	2.6	53.7	17.5	71.1
1975	20.6	12.3	5.1	5.7	2.3	52.2	17.3	69.4
1976	20.3	12.2	4.9	5.4	2.0	50.8	16.4	67.2
1977	19.6	11.9	4.8	5.3	1.8	49.0	15.8	64.7
1978	18.9	11.9	4.7	5.0	1.6	47.1	16.6	63.7
1979	18.7	11.7	4.6	4.8	1.5	46.5	18.3	64.8
1980	17.5	11.3	4.5	4.7	1.5	44.4	18.9	63.4
1981	16.4	10.2	4.4	3.9	1.4	41.3	18.5	59.8
1982	15.3	9.9	4.0	3.6	1.2	38.8	17.7	56.5
1983	14.6	9.5	3.9	3.4	1.1	37.1	17.1	54.2
1984	14.4	9.2	3.9	3.1	1.1	36.3	16.6	52.9
1985	14.1	9.1	3.9	2.8	1.1	35.5	16.0	51.5
1986	14.0	8.9	3.8	2.7	0.9	34.8	15.1	49.9
1987[3]	14.6	8.9	3.9	2.5	0.9	35.2	15.0	50.3

[1]Including cider apples and perry pears as well as other mixed fruit. [2]Including glasshouse fruit and fruit not primarily grown for sale. [3]Provisional.
Source. MAFF: *Basic Horticultural Statistics for the United Kingdom.*

183

Table 14.4. Estimated yields of orchard fruits: England and Wales
(kg per tree)

	Dessert and cooking apples	Plums	Dessert and cooking pears	Cherries
1934	32.9	30.0	11.7	22.7
1935	5.8	3.6	5.4	11.2
1936	24.0	20.1	16.0	21.3
1937	9.1	19.5	5.7	12.3
1938	5.4	6.0	5.3	7.0
1939	28.3	22.3	15.7	20.5
1940	16.7	23.9	17.8	19.6
1941	8.8	9.0	6.9	7.1
1942	22.8	28.7	23.1	33.8
1943	21.5	22.5	17.7	29.4
1944	19.5	17.5	12.1	21.2
1945	17.4	13.5	16.8	21.7
1946	20.6	21.5	11.7	29.1
1947	38.7	25.7	19.0	32.4

Source. MAFF: *Agricultural Statistics, England and Wales.*

Table 14.5. Estimated gross orchard fruit yields: England and Wales
(tonnes per hectare)

	Dessert and cooking apples	Plums	Dessert and cooking pears	Cherries
1947	11.1	7.7	6.5	3.9
1948	6.8	8.4	5.3	3.4
1949	8.4	6.5	6.4	3.5
1950	7.9	3.8	3.6	2.0
1951	10.6	6.3	4.7	2.3
1952	9.2	7.5	6.8	5.2
1953	9.7	4.9	5.3	2.5
1954	9.4^1	6.9^1	5.1^2	2.2
1955	7.0^1	6.1^1	7.4^2	3.5
1956	9.9^1	7.3^1	8.9^2	3.6
1957	8.3^1	3.1^1	6.1^2	3.3
1958	11.7^1	5.3^1	11.0^2	3.8
1959	10.3^1	7.6^1	9.0^2	2.0
1960	12.0^1	5.3^1	9.6^2	4.3
1961	6.5^1	6.4^1	7.6^2	2.6
1962	10.5^1	7.1^1	7.8^2	4.0
1963	11.6^1	8.7^1	9.8^2	2.8
1964	14.6^1	5.5^1	10.2^2	3.3

[1] United Kingdom.   [2] Great Britain.
Source. MAFF: *Agricultural Statistics, United Kingdom.*

Table 14.6. Estimated gross soft fruit yields
(tonnes per hectare)

	Strawberries	Raspberries	Blackcurrants
England and Wales			
1934	2.4	2.4	2.6
1935	1.1	0.9	2.3
1936	1.9	1.9	1.7
1937	3.3	3.7	2.6
1938	2.1	1.7	1.5
1939	3.0	3.1	3.1
1940	2.2	2.5	2.2
1941	2.4	2.2	1.8
1942	4.3	2.8	3.0
1943	4.8	2.6	2.6
1944	3.6	1.8	1.8
United Kingdom			
1945	2.9	1.2	2.2
1946	3.8	2.6	2.5
1947	4.1	2.6	3.4
1948	4.0	3.1	2.7
1949	4.9	3.1	2.2
1950	3.5	3.4	2.5
1951	4.7	3.2	3.8
1952	4.3	4.5	4.5
1953	4.0	3.9	3.9
1954	4.4	4.3	3.4
1955	4.8	4.0	4.4
1956	3.1	5.6	2.6
1957	4.0	3.7	3.1
1958	4.0	3.4	4.2
1959	5.0	4.2	3.0
1960	4.0	4.6	3.6
1961	5.2	3.1	3.4
1962	5.4	3.8	3.5
1963	5.1	4.2	4.5
1964	5.7	4.4	4.4

Source. MAFF: *Agricultural Statistics, United Kingdom.*

Table 14.7. Gross fruit yields (tonnes per hectare)

	Dessert apples	Culinary apples	Pears	Plums	Cherries	Strawberries	Raspberries	Blackcurrants
1972	8.8	11.0	9.4	6.7	4.4	6.7	4.3	6.9
1973	12.8	13.6	8.4	9.5	3.0	7.6	4.0	5.4
1974	9.6	11.8	10.0	7.7	3.6	8.5	5.5	5.7
1975	11.8	11.0	5.4	3.3	3.2	6.5	4.7	5.8
1976	10.8	11.5	13.2	6.0	3.6	5.3	4.4	4.5
1977	6.9	11.2	7.5	8.2	1.6	6.4	5.3	2.2
1978	11.2	15.1	5.7	8.1	2.2	7.8	5.7	4.6
1979	11.8	12.0	15.8	10.1	4.1	7.0	4.9	5.3
1980	10.2	15.9	9.7	10.0	4.8	6.7	5.1	4.3
1981	9.3	7.9	11.1	4.0	2.0	6.8	5.0	4.4
1982	14.1	14.9	10.0	9.4	5.5	7.6	5.6	4.3
1983	12.7	13.3	13.9	10.6	2.6	8.0	5.1	8.0
1984	12.7	17.7	12.5	11.1	5.0	8.4	5.8	4.6
1985	11.3	16.0	13.2	8.4	4.5	7.7	5.6	6.1
1986	11.7	15.6	12.2	12.2	4.1	7.4	6.0	8.1
1987	11.4	13.6	16.4	13.0	3.9	8.6	6.3	5.6

Source. MAFF: *Basic Horticultural Statistics for the United Kingdom.*

Table 14.8. Fruit production 1934–65 ('000 tonnes)

	Apples incl. cider apples	Pears incl. perry pears	Plums	Cherries	Strawberries	Raspberries	Blackcurrants
England and Wales							
1934	535	30	161	19	28	7	10
1935	135	16	20	10	12	2	10
1936	417	37	121	17	19	4	7
1937	188	13	118	10	29	8	10
1938	124	12	36	6	18	3	6
1939	540	37	136	17	23	5	13
1940	309	40	146	16	14	4	9
New series							
United Kingdom							
1941	205	18[1]	55	6[1]	12	10	7
1942	454	54[1]	171	28[1]	19	10	12
1943	412	43[1]	132	24[1]	19	9	9
1944	475	36[1]	102	17[1]	16	6	7
1945–46	323	39[1]	78	18[2]	14	5	8
1946–47	478	35[1]	124	24[2]	21	7	10
1947–48	712	47[1]	147	27[2]	24	8	16
1948–49	486	34[1]	158	24[2]	29	10	14
1949–50	632	45[1]	117	25[2]	43	13	15
1950–51	566	25[1]	66	15[2]	33	16	17
1951–52	709	40[1]	110	17[2]	37	15	25
1952–53	609	62[1]	206	38[2]	31	21	27
1953–54	618	41[1]	81	18[2]	30	16	21
1954–55	572	41[1]	107	16[2]	35	17	16
1955–56	421	53[1]	91	25[2]	38	16	19
1956–57	604	41[1]	105	25[2]	23	22	11
1957–58	510	54[1]	42	23[2]	29	15	15
1958–59	704	68[1]	66	25[2]	30	15	21
1959–60	588	46[1]	89	13[2]	37	18	16
1960–61	686	74[1]	60	25[2]	28	19	20
1961–62	334	53[1]	68	15[2]	35	11	20
1962–63	583	59[1]	69	22[2]	37	12	22
1963–64	581	69[1]	82	15[2]	35	13	30
1964–65	717	73[1]	52	17[2]	40	15	28

[1]Great Britain only. [2]England and Wales only.
Source. MAFF: *Agricultural Statistics, United Kingdom.*

Table 14.9. Fruit production (1972–86) ('000 tonnes)

	Dessert apples	Culinary apples	Pears	Plums	Cherries	Strawberries	Raspberries	Blackcurrants
1972	195.3	149.9	50.6	42.2	12.2	54.2	17.5	26.2
1973	276.0	173.2	44.0	47.7	8.0	58.7	16.7	21.1
1974	203.3	149.7	52.1	46.0	9.4	61.3	23.7	22.9
1975	242.4	136.1	27.5	18.8	7.4	45.2	19.1	23.8
1976	219.5	140.1	64.2	32.3	7.3	37.0	15.9	17.7
1977	136.1	133.8	36.1	42.9	2.9	42.3	18.3	8.4
1978	211.0	180.2	26.6	40.7	3.6	54.3	21.7	17.7
1979	221.8	141.2	72.7	48.6	6.2	54.8	20.4	21.7
1980	178.0	179.2	43.9	46.6	7.1	53.4	22.5	18.9
1981	151.6	80.2	49.2	15.8	2.8	51.8	21.7	19.3
1982	215.7	147.3	40.4	33.9	6.8	56.4	24.1	17.2
1983	186.0	125.6	54.0	36.4	2.9	58.0	21.8	30.0
1984	183.6	163.0	48.1	34.0	5.4	58.5	23.6	16.9
1985	160.5	144.9	50.7	23.7	4.8	53.2	22.6	20.5
1986	163.3	139.3	46.6	33.2	3.8	48.4	23.4	24.8
1987[1]	167.1	121.6	63.4	32.8	3.6	56.7	25.1	17.3

[1]Provisional.
Source. MAFF: *Basic Horticultural Statistics for the United Kingdom.*

Table 14.10. Fruit output[1] ('000 tonnes)

	Pre-war	1946-47	1950-51	1955-56	1960-61	1965-66	New series 1970-71	1972	1975	1980	1981	1982	1983	1984	1985	1986	1987[2]
Orchard																	
Dessert apples	}199	}366	133	173	258	294	256	190	229	159	146	194	169	170	145	153	153
Cooking apples			280	188	272	241	182	148	128	153	78	135	116	138	132	130	115
Cider apples	59	76	88	40	80	48	63	21	34	78							
Pears	16	24	22	50	67	69	65	50	26	38	45	38	49	44	48	39	58
Perry pears	5	10	2	2	5	3	4	3	3	4							
Cherries	11	24	15	25	25	13	13	9	5	6	3	6	3	5	4	3	3
Plums	93	124	65	90	60	46	46	42	16	32	12	29	29	27	20	26	27
Other fruit	1	3	3	3	4	3	3										
Soft fruit																	
Strawberries	24	21	33	38	28	35	45	49	44	42	48	43	51	55	48	43	45
Raspberries	15	7	16	16	19	14	19	15	18	21	21	23	21	23	22	23	21
Blackcurrants	}24	10	17	19	20	28	20	26	23	16	19	16	27	16	19	23	16
Gooseberries		12	9	17	12	16	13	9	7	}							
Red and white currants	}3	2	2	2	1	1	2	1	1	}		Included in total for other fruit (below)					
Loganberries and blackberries		2	2	2	3	2	2	2	3	}							
Other fruit	–	–	1	1	1	1	1	2	1	13	11	10	13	13	13	11	10

[1]Output is the actual quantity which was moved off the national farm and for which revenue was received. It includes fruit sold for juicing. [2]Forecast.
Source. *Basic Horticultural Statistics for the United Kingdom.*

Table 14.11. Value of output of vegetables [1](£ million)

1937–38	19	1954–55	76	1971–72	163
1938–39	20	1955–56	83	1972	189
1939–40	24	1956–57	70	1973	247
1940–41	33	1957–58	77	1974	312
1941–42	58	1958–59	70	1975	370
1942–43	54	1959–60	80	1976	405
1943–44	66	1960–61	79	1977	486
1944–45	63	1961–62	94	1978	460
1945–46	66	1962–63	86	1979	536
1946–47	70	1963–64	88	1980	550
1947–48	71	1964–65	112	1981	583
1948–49	66	1965–66	113	1982	596
1949–50	71	1966–67	125	1983	704
1950–51	52	1967–68	132	1984	786
1951–52	62	1968–69	142	1985	777
1952–53	71	1969–70	152	1986	778
1953–54	60	1970–71	158	1987[2]	839

[1]Including allotment and garden production. [2]Forecast.
Source. MAFF: *Departmental Net Income Calculation.*

Table 14.12. Estimated cropped area of vegetables[1] ('000 hectares)

Pre-war	136
1946–47	253
1947–48	255
1948–49	266
1949–50	241
1950–51	238
1951–52	195
1952–53	199
1953–54	210
1954–55	206
1955–56	210
1956–57	208
1957–58	190
1958–59	191
1959–60	187
1960–61	193
1961–62	179
1962–63	180
1963–64	185
1964–65	172
1965–66	168
1966–67	168
1967–68	182
1968–69	197
1969–70	206
1970–71	220
1971–72	199
1972	193
1973	202
1974	201
1975	199
1976	202
1977	218
1978	207
1979	199
1980	193
1981	191
1982	186
1983	176
1984	178
1985	184
1986	188
1987[2]	190

[1]Including protected crops.   [2]Provisional.
Source. MAFF: *Basic Horticultural Statistics for the United Kingdom.*

Table 14.13. Estimated cropped area of roots and onions ('000 hectares)[1]

	Beetroot	Carrots	Parsnips	Turnips and swedes	Onions, dry bulb	Onions, green
Pre-war		6.7		11.2	0.3	0.8
1946	5.8	16.8	2.5	9.6	4.0	1.9
1947	4.6	14.0	2.2	10.5	3.8	1.2
1948	4.7	14.6	3.7	7.1	5.3	2.4
1949	3.7	13.3	2.3	11.6	2.6	1.7
1950	3.5	12.9	2.1	7.6	2.2	1.4
1951	3.2	10.2	1.5	7.6	1.4	1.3
1952	3.8	11.6	1.4	8.1	1.7	1.4
1953	3.5	13.3	1.5	6.0	2.1	1.3
1954	2.9	11.1	1.4	6.5	1.6	1.1
1955	3.5	13.4	1.6	6.8	1.5	1.2
1956	4.1	13.7	2.0	4.7	1.7	1.3
1957	4.1	11.1	1.6	6.3	1.2	1.3
1958	3.8	14.0	1.7	4.5	1.2	1.1
1959	3.2	12.0	1.6	6.3	0.8	1.3
1960	4.2	14.7	2.0	3.1	0.9	1.4
1961	3.0	11.9	1.7	3.9	0.9	1.5
1962	3.4	13.4	1.9	4.2	1.4	1.5
1963	3.6	13.1	2.0	4.1	1.7	1.3
1964	3.4	11.3	1.9	3.9	1.5	1.4
1965	2.7	10.0	2.0	4.0	2.0	1.4
1966	3.1	11.5	1.9	4.1	2.0	1.4
1967	3.7	12.3	2.3	4.1	2.4	1.5
1968	3.5	14.5	2.2	3.7	3.4	1.6
1969	3.5	17.5	2.7	4.5	2.9	1.4
1970	3.7	16.3	2.7	4.5	3.7	1.6
1971	3.9	14.9	2.7	3.9	5.5	1.8
1972	3.3	13.3	2.1	4.0	4.9	1.9
1973	3.8	14.4	2.4	4.0	5.5	1.8
1974	3.2	12.9	2.1	4.3	6.1	1.7
1975	3.3	14.8	2.3	4.6	6.2	1.7
1976	3.2	16.6	2.8	4.9	7.4	1.8
1977	3.3	19.5	3.4	6.0	8.7	1.8
1978	3.1	18.0	3.2	4.7	7.7	1.9
1979	2.7	15.7	2.7	4.7	6.5	1.7
1980	2.9	13.7	2.5	4.5	6.8	1.7
1981	2.7	14.4	2.6	3.2	7.8	1.7
1982	2.7	13.9	2.6	4.1	6.7	1.7
1983	2.4	13.1	2.4	4.1	6.5	1.5
1984	3.1	13.8	2.6	4.5	6.6	1.5
1985	2.9	14.1	2.8	4.2	8.4	1.8
1986	2.6	14.8	3.1	4.7	7.4	2.1
1987[2]	2.6	14.7	3.1	4.6	7.8	2.2

[1]Prior to 1972, commercially significant holdings. From 1972 onwards area actually cropped plus any adjacent headlands or ditches. Includes an allowance where appropriate for several crops a year.   [2]Provisional.
Source. MAFF: *Basic Horticultural Statistics for the United Kingdom.*

Table 14.14. Estimated area of brassicas and legumes[1] ('000 hectares)

	Brussels sprouts	Cabbage	Cauliflower	Broad beans	Runner beans[3]	Peas for market[3]	Peas for processing[4]
Pre-war	14.7	28.1	12.6	2.2	3.7	23.3	3.3
1946	18.8	39.1	20.9	3.0	4.8	25.0	7.9
1947	20.7	46.4	20.6	1.7	5.0	21.0	8.5
1948	22.2	45.3	22.5	2.6	5.2	22.3	9.7
1949	17.6	35.8	15.5	3.0	4.1	20.9	10.8
1950	18.4	42.3	17.1	2.5	4.4	22.3	10.7
1951	15.7	32.9	14.7	1.6	3.4	16.5	10.1
1952	18.3	31.0	13.4	2.1	3.3	16.0	11.4
1953	21.2	32.8	15.4	2.1	3.7	19.0	14.0
1954	17.6	30.3	14.5	1.9	3.9	17.4	17.5
1955	18.9	30.6	13.5	2.9	4.2	17.7	20.4
1956	19.9	33.8	14.0	3.2	5.0	14.9	20.9
1957	17.2	30.8	15.6	4.0	5.1	12.6	22.6
1958	18.3	28.5	16.2	4.6	5.4	14.1	23.9
1959	18.7	29.8	16.1	3.9	5.5	11.8	26.9
1960	19.2	30.6	18.2	4.4	5.7	13.4	29.8
1961	20.1	31.7	18.9	4.1	5.0	11.1	29.1
1962	20.4	30.0	18.5	5.1	5.5	12.2	28.3
1963	19.2	28.2	17.9	4.9	7.3	10.4	33.5
1964	18.2	24.4	16.2	4.9	7.7	8.3	35.1
1965	17.2	24.1	17.7	4.0	7.0	7.4	33.6
1966	15.2	25.9	16.6	3.1	7.4	6.5	35.2
1967	17.9	26.1	18.4	3.9	8.0	7.3	35.5
1968	20.2	26.7	18.4	3.6	8.3	7.3	43.3
1969	19.9	29.9	16.6	2.8	10.5	5.9	44.0
1970	21.8	27.4	15.5	4.2	10.3	5.0	50.6
1971	17.2	26.6	16.1	4.7	8.8	5.1	41.6
1972	16.2	24.4	16.3	4.4	8.7	4.9	44.8
1973	15.6	21.4	16.4	3.7	12.3	4.5	51.8
1974	14.7	23.8	16.0	3.5	12.8	4.0	57.5
1975	13.7	23.2	15.4	3.8	12.3	4.4	56.9
1976	14.7	22.6	13.7	5.2	12.5	3.6	53.2
1977	14.8	26.8	15.4	4.4	13.4	4.0	55.3
1978	15.0	22.6	17.2	6.1	11.6	4.0	51.8
1979	14.3	21.5	16.6	6.4	11.2	4.5	51.0
1980	14.8	20.7	16.4	4.5	8.1	2.6	54.5
1981	12.9	20.5	17.1	3.4	7.7	2.8	55.7
1982	13.1	20.6	16.6	3.6	8.6	3.2	51.0
1983	11.7	19.7	16.0	3.8	7.0	2.7	43.1
1984	11.6	21.4	16.7	3.9	7.4	3.2	42.4
1985	11.0	22.3	17.6	3.9	7.3	3.1	44.5
1986	11.4	23.0	17.7	2.8	7.2	2.3	46.4
1987[5]	10.9	22.5	18.1	2.3	6.7	2.3	44.0

[1]Prior to 1972 commercially significant holdings. From 1972 onwards area actually cropped plus any adjacent headlands or ditches. Includes an allowance for, if applicable, several crops being taken during the year.   [2]Including french beans.   [3]Peas, green, for market.   [4]Peas, green, for processing (canning and freezing). In the 1940s, 1950s and 1960s there was also a large area devoted to growing peas which were harvested dry. Between 1946–47 and 1950–51 about 68 000 hectares were grown. In recent years there have been about 16 000 hectares grown for human consumption only.   [5]Provisional. Source. MAFF: *Basic Horticultural Statistics for the United Kingdom.*

Table 14.15. Gross vegetable yields: England and Wales
(tonnes per hectare)

	Onions	Carrots
1928	16.6	32.9
1929	16.1	29.6
1930	15.6	31.6
1931	14.3	26.9
1932	14.6	29.6
1933	15.3	21.1
1934	13.8	32.6
1935	13.8	23.1
1936	15.6	35.9
1937	16.8	25.6
1938	13.8	22.3

	Onions, dry bulb	Carrots	Turnips and swedes	Cabbage	Cauliflower
1942	16.3	27.6	26.1	21.1	16.1
1943	18.3	25.1	25.3	17.3	15.6
1944	17.6	26.4	22.6	21.3	14.6
1945	18.1	22.6	25.6	20.6	16.1
1946	19.6	26.4	25.1	16.8	10.5
1947	14.6	26.4	19.8	17.1	13.3
1948	23.9	32.6	22.6	20.8	16.3
1949	16.3	21.6	21.3	14.6	9.8
1950	25.6	32.6	25.1	22.5	14.8
1951	19.3	25.9	22.8	21.1	15.1
1952	24.6	27.6	19.6	17.8	15.3
1953	26.4	23.1	22.6	21.8	14.6
1954	23.3	20.8	22.6	20.8	15.1
1955	20.1	23.1	22.6	16.6	11.5
1956	23.9	28.9	27.6	23.1	16.8
1957	24.4	21.6	22.6	20.3	14.8
1958	22.1	27.6	27.6	21.8	16.1
1959	24.1	26.1	22.6	16.8	14.1
1960	30.4	40.7	35.1	20.6	15.1
1961	30.6	21.8	30.8	19.3	15.1
1962	28.4	21.6	42.4	17.8	10.5
1963	32.1	40.4	39.2	23.9	18.1
1964	36.9	37.4	37.7	22.8	19.8

Source. MAFF: *Agricultural Statistics, United Kingdom.*

Table 14.16. Gross vegetable yields (tonnes per hectare)

	Beetroot	Carrots	Turnips and swedes	Onions, dry bulb	Brussels sprouts	Cabbage winter	Cauliflower	Peas, green for market
1972	29.3	35.0	31.2	33.9	14.1	25.0[1]	20.6	7.8
1973	31.8	42.1	32.0	35.7	13.1	25.3[1]	21.1	8.4
1974	36.4	38.4	34.2	35.0	13.6	26.2[1]	19.9	9.3
1975	31.6	38.7	32.7	35.8	11.8	24.4[1]	19.1	7.7
1976	30.1	29.8	27.2	23.0	9.2	21.3[1]	17.8	5.3
1977	33.6	43.9	36.9	35.0	15.2	33.5	22.5	9.6
1978	34.6	41.8	41.5	29.9	14.6	31.8	21.3	8.5
1979	35.9	43.6	35.9	39.5	15.7	32.3	20.9	8.4
1980	37.5	40.3	36.5	32.2	16.7	32.2	22.4	7.0
1981	36.5	49.3	34.2	29.7	15.3	31.6	19.0	8.8
1982	38.2	52.3	35.6	34.4	16.9	36.4	21.2	8.7
1983	39.1	42.2	33.1	27.0	13.1	31.6	18.7	8.4
1984	37.4	41.3	31.4	35.9	14.6	38.7	20.6	8.4
1985	38.8	42.7	33.4	32.0	13.8	35.5	20.2	8.6
1986	36.9	42.8	34.8	33.3	14.7	34.6	20.3	8.7
1987	36.6	38.5	34.4	33.3	15.1	35.3	21.5	8.3

[1]All types of cabbage.
Source. MAFF: *Basic Horticultural Statistics for the United Kingdom.*

Table 14.17. Gross vegetable production ('000 tonnes)

	1972	1973	1974	1975	1976	1977	1978	1979	1980	1981	1982	1983	1984	1985	1986	1987[1]
Beetroot	96	120	116	96	96	110	109	98	109	97	105	94	115	114	95	94
Carrots	465	606	495	573	494	854	753	684	553	711	725	554	572	600	635	567
Parsnips	44	53	46	45	52	66	65	56	54	53	55	51	57	62	68	66
Turnips and swedes	126	131	147	150	135	223	196	170	163	109	145	135	143	140	163	159
Onions, dry bulb	167	195	219	221	170	306	231	287	224	232	231	175	238	268	247	305
Onions, green	28	28	27	25	29	23	28	26	26	25	27	25	22	25	30	31
Brussels sprouts	228	204	200	162	135	226	223	224	228	197	223	154	169	152	168	165
Cabbage	609	542	623	555	485	799	573	594	576	546	610	518	670	683	688	690
Cauliflower	337	346	324	293	244	348	367	348	367	325	353	299	344	356	360	384
Peas, harvested dry	73[2]	70[2]	58[3]	47[3]	42[3]	53[3]	45[3]	53[3]	53[3]	50[3]	50[3]	51[3]	57[3]	37[3]	52[3]	54[3]
Beans, broad	46	39	15[4]	18[4]	17[4]	21[4]	28[4]	28[4]	18[4]	17[4]	19[4]	17[4]	21[4]	19[4]	14[4]	11[4]
Beans, runner and french	84	125	133	92	94	112	100	109	62	69	92	65	77	65	67	50
Peas, green for market	39	38	37	34	19	38	34	38	18	25	28	23	27	26	20	19
Peas, green for processing	206	258	296	263	170	267	210	229	223	277	238	198	241	206	239	195
Asparagus	1	1	1	1	1	1	- -	- -	1	1	1	1	1	1	1	1
Celery	73	71	64	69	60	70	66	64	54	50	51	46	57	53	65	69
Leeks	28	26	25	24	27	42	35	38	40	40	43	44	53	60	71	77
Lettuce (outdoors)	153	171	164	123	103	145	133	127	135	134	161	155	153	166	160	171
Rhubarb[5]	47	46	43	40	34	40	45	46	43	41	39	29	26	26	28	29
Watercress	5	5	5	5	5	5	6	6	5	5	5	4	4	5	4	4
Other vegetables	129	121	127	121	139	200	193	160	159	162	171	139	154	156	161	157

[1]Provisional. [2]Dried shelled weight excluding factory waste. [3]Dried shelled weight excluding factory waste, for human consumption only. [4]Shelled weight. [5]Including rhubarb grown in sheds.
Source. MAFF: *Basic Horticultural Statistics for the United Kingdom.*

Table 14.18. Vegetable output ('000 tonnes)[1]

	Pre-war	1946-47	1950-51	1955-56	1960-61	New series 1965-66	1970-71	1972	1975	1980	1981	1982	1983	1984	1985	1986	1987[2]
In the open																	
Beetroot		121	73	78	103	83	112	89	91	100	83	95	86	103	95	82	95
Carrots	157	333	338	300	390	289	477	409	487	470	444	576	468	424	466	508	471
Parsnips		64	46	39	45	43	54	41	39	47	45	48	47	50	52	57	57
Turnips and swedes	323	277	192	162	99	134	129	116	133	143	81	124	124	112	116	128	143
Onions – dry, bulb	5	79	53	30	25	52	112	134	158	214	192	214	167	224	241	219	277
Onions – green	16	31	19	12	15	19	21	26	27	25	23	22	24	19	22	27	29
Brussels sprouts	121	142	151	135	166	182	235	215	152	208	138	186	142	144	137	147	148
Cabbages	548	656	583	481	562	576	612	555	524	526	420	532	479	546	536	585	622
Cauliflowers	197	217	252	151	245	328	283	319	254	332	282	312	273	303	321	307	361
Peas – harvested dry	13	97	92	116[3]	31[3]	41[3]	76[3]	62[3]	75[4]	43[4]	41[4]	35[4]	43[4]	47[4]	27[4]	44[4]	41[4]
Beans – broad	12	15	18	23	33	43	39	46	41	16[5]	15[5]	18[5]	16[5]	20[5]	17[5]	13[5]	10[5]
Beans, runner and french	34	45	34	35	66	59	101	82	88	59	65	84	62	71	60	56	44
Peas, green for market	124	142	125	104	102	59	41	37	33	16	22	25	18	25	24	18	17
Peas, green for processing incl. freezing	5	14	30	86	115	138	202	201	255	210	261	226	183	225	177	219	172
Asparagus	4	2	2	2	2	1	1	1	1	1	1	1	1	1	1	1	1
Celery	67	83	63	65	112	66	62	64	60	47	41	50	40	49	48	59	63
Leeks		29	17	9	20	22	30	27	23	33	31	38	40	43	52	62	71
Lettuce (outdoors)	44	72	56	56	96	108	138	139	115	110	114	132	126	144	134	130	136
Rhubarb	73	72	60	39	37	51	43	45	33	39	37	35	28	24	24	26	27
Watercress	–	—	—	7	2	8	6	5	5	5	5	4	4	4	4	4	4
Protected crops																	
Tomatoes	69	100	105	105	88	88	107	109	111	125	120	117	118	125	118	132	126
Cucumbers	20	9	31	31	34	36	34	35	37	55	51	52	57	63	68	72	78
Lettuce	5	3	6	12	10	14	21	22	32	37	37	39	41	48	48	48	45
Mushrooms	3	3	4	6	16	32	45	54	55	61	65	70	76	87	100	101	105

[1]Output is the actual quantity which was moved off the farm and for which revenue was received. [2]Provisional. [3]Dried shelled weight excluding factory waste. [4]Shelled weight excluding factory waste, for human consumption only. [5]Shelled weight.
Source. *MAFF.*

Table 14.19. Estimated cropped area of protected vegetables
(hectares)

	Tomatoes	Cucumber	Lettuce	Mushrooms	Others	Total
1972	1009	165	1029	420	261	2884
1973	1019	138	1264	420	277	3118
1974	986	190	1306	405	185	3072
1975	984	210	1309	388	209	3100
1976	950	235	1321	361	181	3048
1977	943	228	1337	359	232	3099
1978	931	240	1330	360	245	3106
1979	910	217	1310	373	239	3049
1980	859	238	1384	404	267	3152
1981	823	249	1340	418	300	3130
1982	752	239	1555	421	341	3308
1983	744	234	1617	448	311	3354
1984	734	225	1587	481	308	3335
1985	704	230	1576	524	322	3356
1986	707	227	1606	525	308	3373
1987[1]	696	230	1616	525	294	3361

[1]Provisional.
Source. MAFF: *Horticultural Statistics for the United Kingdom.*

Table 14.20. Cropped area of non-edible horticultural crops (hectares)

	Open		Under glass[1]				
	Flowers and bulbs in the open	Hardy nursery stock	Carnations	Roses	Chrysanthemums	Pot plants	Bulb flowers
1974	7004	7465	70	41	316	110	55
1975	6349	7305	68	36	299	113	48
1976	6170	6862	58	34	277	112	42
1977	5875	6725	51	22	238	118	36
1978	5685	6613	47	18	241	121	33
1979	5343	6872	41	21	246	133	38
1980	5424	6843	40	21	234	141	33
1981	5349	6915	36	21	238	147	35
1982	5318	6888	32	19	223	146	29
1983	5116	6859	30	19	214	151	30
1984	5095	7077	26	18	218	143	28[2]
1985	5337	6890	22	15	212	141	28[2]
1986	4982	7045	18	16	212	148	28[2]
1987[3]	5396	7223	12	15	219	143	28[2]

[1]England and Wales only.   [2]Estimated.   [3]Provisional.
Source. MAFF: *Basic Horticultural Statistics for the United Kingdom.*

Table 14.21. Value of output of flowers, bulbs and nursery stock
(£ million)

	Flowers in the open	Flower bulbs	Hardy nursery stock		Protected crops	Total
			Field	Containers		
1974	8.4	1.3	31.3	3.6	37.9	82.5
1975	8.9	1.3	32.4	5.3	41.3	89.2
1976	10.9	2.1	34.6	6.5	50.8	104.9
1977	11.3	2.6	37.3	8.5	60.0	119.7
1978	12.7	3.0	39.6	10.8	66.9	133.0
1979	13.8	3.6	46.9	18.1	74.1	156.5
1980	13.4	4.2	50.8	25.4	85.4	179.2
1981	13.0	4.9	54.6	29.6	86.4	188.5
1982	14.3	5.0	60.6	31.8	92.8	204.5
1983	15.3	5.0	59.1	38.4	98.8	216.6
1984	17.4	8.2	65.3	41.8	99.6	232.3
1985	16.6	9.8	70.6	44.0	110.2	251.2
1986	15.2	9.4	75.3	47.1	127.8	274.8
1987[1]	17.6	10.2	81.3	56.0	136.1	301.2

[1]Provisional.
Source. MAFF: *Basic Horticultural Statistics for the United Kingdom.*

Table 14.22. Supplies of some horticultural crops ('000 tonnes)

	1961–62 to 1963–64	1968–69	1970–71	1973	1975	1980	1981	1982	1983	1984	1985	1986	1987[1]
Apples													
Output – total	415	328	438	426	352	313	224	329	285	325	287	282	266
Dessert	234	192	256	257	226	160	146	194	169	170	154	148	145
Cooking	181	136	182	169	126	153	78	135	116	155	133	134	121
Imports	228	252	255	318	330	374	423	400	405	401	428	442	428
Exports	4	1	11	12	13	13	19	14	21	20	24	19	22
Total new supply	638	579	682	732	669	674	628	715	669	706	691	705	672
Output as % of new supply for use in U.K.	65	57	64	58	53	46	36	46	43	46	42	40	40
Closing stocks						111	64	102	106	118	113	114	105
Total disposals in year						663	675	677	663	682	696	704	681
Pears													
Output	54	66	65	43	27	38	45	38	49	44	48	45	37
Imports	67	57	54	48	51	59	77	64	79	66	69	65	95
Exports	2	1	1	2	1	2	2	1	2	1	1	1	1
Total new supply	119	122	118	89	77	95	120	101	126	109	116	109	131
Output as % of new supply for use in U.K.	45	54	55	48	35	40	38	38	39	40	41	41	28
Closing stocks						16	21	13	23	24	24	18	28
Total disposals in year						110	115	109	116	108	116	103	121
Cauliflowers													
Output	244	290	283	297	255	324	314	291	263	338	307	338	304
Supplies from Channel Isles				8	7	11	13	14	14	17	8	10	10
Imports	34	56	46	16	25	26	31	49	40	51	41	56	40
Total new supply	277	345	329	321	287	361	358	354	317	406	356	404	354
Output as % of total new supply for use in U.K.	88	84	86	93	89	90	88	82	83	83	86	84	86
Tomatoes													
Output	83	93	108	117	122	125	120	114	115	126	125	138	121
Supplies from Channel Isles				61	61	54	46	43	31	26	24	16	12
Imports	217	230	240	142	141	178	207	205	217	235	253	257	249
Exports	1	- -	1	1	1	5	4	7	7	7	7	8	6
Total new supply	300	323	346	319	323	352	368	355	356	380	395	403	376
Output as % of total new supply for use in U.K.	28	29	31	37	38	36	33	32	32	33	32	34	32

[1]Forecast.   - - Negligible.
Source. HMSO: *Annual Review of Agriculture.*

Table 14.23. Imports of fresh fruit ('000 tonnes)

	Pre-war	1952	1955	1960	1965	1970	1975	1980	1981	1982	1983	1984	1985	1986	1987
Apples	318	152	182	190	243	261	329	374	423	399	406	401	428	442	443
Pears	60	44	71	62	52	54	51	60	78	64	79	66	69	64	77
Plums	15	4	6	7	12	9	13	21	21	21	27	21	22	21	24
Cherries							2	4	6	8	8	10	9	7	9
Strawberries[1]							2	7	8	8	9	10	13	14	15
Oranges	543	327	381	430	393	} 438		375	344	315	305	317	284	344	334
Mandarins								92	96	110	123	135	122	131	151
Lemons	62[3]	27[3]	33[3]	34[3]	34[3]			46	43	50	48	50	47	51	52
Other citrus	61[2]	37[2]	50[2]	62[2]	72[2]	35	563	113	112	98	85	79	71	82	83
Bananas	304	169	312	350	376	326	307	323	328	328	307	309	324	343	360
Melons							57	69	80	71	91	98	99	106	108
Peaches							22	48	60	67	84	82	85	79	95
Grapes	44	20	40	50	63	77	59	75	80	65	86	86	106	101	108
Avocados								7	8	9	11	12	14	15	28
Pineapples								12	14	16	16	15	18	19	21
Other	34	24	43	65	81	110	16	28	11	13	13	15	16	19	18
All fresh fruit	1441	804	1118	1250	1326	1310	1421	1652	1573	1713	1697	1706	1728	1839	1927

[1]Excluding imports of strawberries, either frozen or provisionally preserved.   [2]Grapefruit.   [3]Lemons, limes and other citrus.
Source. *Customs and Excise.*

Table 14.24. Imports of vegetables ('000 tonnes)

	Pre-war	1952	1955	1960	1965	1970	1975	1980	1981	1982	1983	1984	1985	1986	1987
Tomatoes, fresh or chilled	143	194	198	160	166	175	143	178	207	205	218	236	254	257	257
Dry bulb onions	253	218	224	226	217	200	149	195	199	177	198	210	228	215	238
Cauliflowers, fresh or chilled	9	35	39	36	30	32	25	26	31	49	40	51	41	56	41
Cabbage	3	8	3	6	9	4	15	28	27	51	30	40	48	44	33
Brussels sprouts							--	--	3	3	3	3	3	2	2
Lettuce and endive	12	7	7	12	12	12	7	12	15	18	21	26	34	45	55
Peas							--	1	1	1	1	1	1	2	2
Beans							2	2	2	3	4	4	6	6	7
Carrots and turnips	13	20	33	23	24	18	24	30	44	75	35	47	56	63	44
Cucumbers	1	2	2	7	21	27	26	32	34	40	40	48	47	47	54
Mushroom and truffles	--	--	--	1	1	1	4	6	6	7	8	11	16	22	24
Sweet peppers							5	14	17	20	21	25	31	33	37
Aubergines, marrows and pumpkins							5	9	11	11	14	15	18	18	17
Celery							14	19	21	21	18	25	25	30	28
Other fresh vegetables	12	6	9	12	13	30	24	32	16	22	19	22	22	22	25
Dried peas	87	20	89	85	71	60	25	24	28	28	30	28	27	30	32
Dried beans (*Phaseolus*)	46	50	47	84	83	87	[1]	92	90	103	106	119	117	125	119
Other dried vegetables	20	8	13	11	13	11	114	25	26	27	25	27	27	25	28

-- Less than 500 tonnes.   [1]Included in other dried vegetables.
Source. *Customs and Excise.*

Table 14.25. Consumption of fruit (kg per head per annum)

	Fresh citrus fruit	Apples	Tropical fruit	Other fresh fruit[1]	Imported canned fruit	Imported fruit juices[2]	Other imported processed fruit	Total (converted to fresh equivalent)
Pre-war	12.9			22.7[3]	4.7	0.5	5.3	56.2
1942	2.1			14.7[3]	1.3	0.6	5.8	36.2
1946	6.2			17.3[3]	1.1	1.8	5.8	44.6
1950	8.0			19.5[3]	3.3	1.7	3.7	46.8
1955	8.4			21.7[3]	6.3	2.0	3.5	51.3
1960	9.4			24.1[3]	7.9	2.1	3.5	55.3
1965	8.7			24.7[3]	8.6	2.2	3.0	55.4
1970	9.9			24.7[3]	8.3	2.4	3.0	56.6
1975	9.3			25.4[3]	5.3	5.7	3.1	61.7
New series								
1980	10.1	12.8	6.3	7.0	4.8	11.6	2.6	72.3
1981	9.7	11.5	6.2	7.2	5.3	14.7	2.5	77.4
1982	9.2	12.7	6.4	7.6	5.3	13.1	2.9	75.8
1983	8.9	11.8	6.5	8.3	5.1	15.6	3.0	79.7
1984	9.4	12.5	6.7	8.2	5.1	16.7	3.2	84.9
1985	8.4	12.5	7.1	8.3	4.8	16.2	3.3	84.1
1986	9.8	13.3	7.5	8.1	4.8	18.0	3.3	90.8

[1]Includes home grown products for canning, freezing and other processing.   [2]In natural strength.   [3]Including apples and tropical fruit.
Source. MAFF: *Food Facts.*

Table 14.26. Consumption of vegetables (kg per head per annum)

	Fresh tomatoes[1]	Cabbage, greens[1]	Leafy salads[1]	Carrots[1]	Peas and beans[1]	Beets, parsnips and swedes	Other vegetables	Imported canned tomatoes	Other imported processed vegetables	Total (converted to fresh equivalent)
Pre-war	4.7	21.1	1.4	4.0	4.2		16.8[2]	0.9	0.9[3]	54.6
1942	3.9	26.1	1.7	7.5	4.9		13.4[2]	1.5	0.7[3]	60.5
1946	4.2	24.7	1.9	5.8	4.8		17.9[2]	0.3	0.9[3]	60.6
1950	6.3	15.3	1.9	4.7	5.4		14.3[2]	2.2	2.0[3]	53.2
1955	7.1	17.0	1.9	5.2	5.7		13.0[2]	2.1	2.2[3]	55.2
1960	6.8	16.3	2.1	5.6	8.3		12.7[2]	2.4	2.5[3]	58.0
1965	5.9	17.0	2.0	5.5	8.8		13.1[2]	2.5	3.6[3]	60.9
1970	6.1	16.4	2.0	5.2	10.2		12.6[2]	3.1	4.5[3]	63.0
New series										
1975	6.5	17.0	2.9	8.9	8.0		18.3	2.9	1.0	68.8
1980	6.6	16.8	2.6	8.8	6.4	12.4	6.9	4.0	0.8	71.7
1981	7.1	15.6	2.8	8.7	7.6	11.9	6.9	4.5	1.5	72.2
1982	6.9	16.3	3.2	9.4	7.4	11.3	7.8	4.5	3.3	77.9
1983	6.8	15.1	3.1	8.8	5.6	11.7	8.0	4.6	3.5	77.0
1984	7.3	17.0	3.6	8.4	6.6	12.0	9.0	4.8	3.5	81.8
1985	7.1	15.9	3.9	8.5	5.9	12.9	9.8	4.7	4.1	82.2
1986	7.3	17.1	4.0	8.8	6.3	12.7	10.4	5.7	4.8	85.7

[1]Includes home grown products for canning, freezing and other processing. [2]Including beets, parsnips and swedes. [3]Other canned vegetables.
Source. MAFF: *Food Facts.*

Table 14.27. Horticultural prices (£ per tonne)

	Apples				Pears (Dessert)		Tomatoes		Cauliflowers	
	Dessert		Culinary							
	At current prices	In 1986 money values	At current prices	In 1986 money values	At current prices	In 1986 money values	At current prices	In 1986 money values	At current prices	In 1986 money values
Pre-war	17	377	16	354	14	310	54	1197	9	200
1946–47	43	564	39	512	61	800	115	1509	23	396
1950–51	69	747	22	238	45	488	101	1095	21	228
1955–56	78	683	35	306	60	525	127	1111	28	245
1960–61	52	405	17	132	40	311	135	1050	49	381
1965–66	67	443	32	212	47	311	163	1077	51	337
1970–71	73	385	37	195	62	327	178	940	46	243
1971–72	81	390	46	222	75	362	187	901	52	251
1972–73	163	733	113	509	131	590	206	927	54	243
1973	121	500	151	624	144	595	212	876	73	301
1974	150	534	112	399	152	541	237	844	92	328
1975	175	501	172	492	185	529	291	832	122	349
1976	191	469	176	433	189	465	346	851	119	293
1977	305	647	242	513	275	583	411	871	143	303
1978	235	461	195	382	251	492	440	862	132	259
1979	194	336	171	296	200	346	387	670	162	280
1980	258	377	207	302	232	339	492	718	186	272
1981	334	438	270	354	281	368	475	622	207	271
1982	306	367	279	335	333	400	431	517	211	253
1983	367	422	280	322	315	362	543	624	238	274
1984	373	410	318	350	314	345	557	613	216	238
1985	369	380	298	307	325	335	507	522	253	261
1986	391	391	327	327	352	352	601	601	201	201
1987[1]	354	339	302	290	340	326	631	605	252	242

[1]Forecast.
Note. Average farm gate prices – estimated prior to 1970–71. English wholesale market prices 1973 onwards.
Source. HMSO: *Annual Review of Agriculture.*

Appendix 15: Hops

Table 15.1. Value of hops output (£ million)

1937–38	2	1954–55	7	1971–72	9
1938–39	2	1955–56	7	1972	9
1939–40	2	1956–57	6	1973	9
1940–41	3	1957–58	7	1974	9
1941–42	4	1958–59	6	1975	9
1942–43	4	1959–60	7	1976	11
1943–44	5	1960–61	7	1977	11
1944–45	5	1961–62	7	1978	13
1945–46	6	1962–63	7	1979	17
1946–47	6	1963–64	8	1980	23
1947–48	6	1964–65	8	1981	25
1948–49	7	1965–66	8	1982	28
1949–50	7	1966–67	8	1983	27
1950–51	7	1967–68	7	1984	26
1951–52	8	1968–69	6	1985	15
1952–53	8	1969–70	7	1986	11
1953–54	7	1970–71	8	1987	12

Source. MAFF: *Departmental Net Income Calculation.*

Table 15.2. Area of hops ('000 hectares)[1]

1866–70	25	1940	8	1965	8
1871–75	26	1941	7	1966	8
1876–80	28	1942	7	1967	8
1881–85	31	1943	8	1968	7
1896–90	25	1944	8	1969	7
1891–95	23	1945	8	1970	7
1896–1900	21	1946	8	1971	7
1901–05	20	1947	9	1972	7
1906–10	16	1948	9	1973	7
1911–15	14	1949	9	1974	7
1916–20	8	1950	9	1975	7
1921–25	11	1951	9	1976	6
1926–30	9	1952	9	1977	6
1928	10	1953	9	1978	6
1929	10	1954	8	1979	6
1930	8	1955	8	1980	6
1931	8	1956	8	1981	6
1932	7	1957	8	1982	6
1933	7	1958	8	1983	6
1934	7	1959	8	1984	5
1935	7	1960	8	1985	5
1936	7	1961	8	1986	4
1937	7	1962	8	1987	4
1938	7	1963	8	1988	4
1939	8	1964	8		

[1] Hops grown only in England.
Source. Agricultural Departments: Agricultural Census.

Table 15.3. Hops yields (tonnes per hectare)

1928–37[1]	1.6
1938–44[1]	1.8
1945–46 to 1954–55[1]	1.7
1954–55 to 1963–64[1]	1.5
1965–66 to 1967–68[1]	1.5
1968–69 to 1970–71[1]	1.6
1975–77[1]	1.3
1980	1.7
1981	1.6
1982	1.8
1983	1.5
1984	1.6
1985	1.4
1986	1.2
1987[2]	1.2

[1] Average.   [2] Provisional.
Source. HMSO: *Annual Review of Agriculture.*
    MAFF: *Agricultural Statistics.*

Table 15.4. Hops supplies ('000 tonnes)

	Production	Imports	Exports	New supply	Production as % of new supply
1928	12				
1930	13				
1935	13				
1938	13				
1942	13				
1946–47	14				
1950–51	19				
1955–56	13				
1960–61	12				
1968–69	10	1	1	10	104
1970–71	12	1	1	12	97
1975–76	8	1	1	9	91
1980	10	2	4	8	126
1981	9	2	2	9	104
1982	10	2	3	10	104
1983	9	3	3	9	99
1984	8	2	2	7	110
1985	7	2	2	7	96
1986	5	2	2	6	86
1987[1]	5	2	1	6	78

[1] Provisional.
Source. HMSO: *Annual Review of Agriculture*
        MAFF: *Agricultural Statistics.*

Table 15.5. Average farm gate selling price for hops
(£ per tonne)

	At current prices	In 1986 money values
1927	226	4662
1930	74	1622
1935	165	4053
1938	167	3702
1946–47	443	5812
1950–51	413	4477
1960–61	638	4964
1968–69	703	4162
1969–70	679	3816
1970–71	660	3485
1972	985	4433
1973	829	3424
1974	876	3119
1975	1063	3040
1976	1356	3336
1977	1520	3222
1978	1415	2773
1979	1628	2816
1980	2356	3440
1981	2636	3453
1982	2754	3305
1983	3140	3611
1984	3307	3637
1985	2297	2366
1986	2233	2233
1987[1]	2298	2201

[1]Forecast.
Source. HMSO: *Annual Review of Agriculture.*
        MAFF: *Basic Horticultural Statistics for the United
        Kingdom.*

Appendix 16: Fodder crops, grass and straw

Table 16.1. Hay production ('000 tonnes)

Great Britain		United Kingdom					
1885	8871	pre-war	7901	1959	7973	1974	7823
1890	10030	1946	6937	1960	8272	1975	6877
1895	7799	1947	7347	1961	8974	1976	8305
1900	8665	1948	7343	1962	8587	1977	8634
1905	8363	1949	7625	1963	8771	1978	8110
1910	9670	1950	6453	1964	9823	1979	7359
1915	7470	1951	7433	1965	8673	1980	6963
1920	9300	1952	7776	1966	8783	1981	6778
1925	8120	1953	7871	1967	8842	1982	6580
1930	8965	1954	6817	1968	8530	1983	6005
1935	7708	1955	7999	1969	8667	1984	5704
		1956	6900	1970	7990	1985	4649
		1957	7459	1971	9692	1986	4669
		1958	8192	1972	9371		
				1973	8892		

Source. MAFF: *Output and utilisation of farm produce in the United Kingdom.*

Table 16.2. Silage production ('000 tonnes)

	Grass	Arable	Total
1969	7946	348	8294
1970	9013	346	9359
1971	10772	358	11130
1972	12979	391	13370
1973	15989	475	16464
1974	16793	672	17465
1975	16779	808	17587
1976	17052	692	17744
1977	19698	1032	20730
1978	22414	1024	23438
1979	24590	1070	25660
1980	27609	1098	28707
1981	29321	872	30193
1982	31593	1913	33506
1983	32643	1427	34070
1984	33826	1146	34972
1985	40851	1497	42348
1986	44187	1497	45864

Source. MAFF: *Output and utilisation of farm produce in the United Kingdom.*

Table 16.3. Area of turnips and swedes for stock feeding[1] ('000 hectares)

	England and Wales	Scotland	Great Britain
1866	677	194	871
1867	684	196	880
1868	679	198	877
1869	681	198	879
1870	693	202	895
1871	673	203	876
1872	640	203	843
1873	652	207	859
1874	660	203	863
1875	663	204	867
1876	661	207	868
1877	634	205	839
1878	621	201	822
1879	617	199	816
1880	622	197	819
1881	625	199	824
1882	620	200	819
1883	623	198	821
1884	624	196	821
1885	620	196	815
1886	614	197	811
1887	603	195	798
1888	592	195	787
1889	584	193	777
1890	593	195	788
1891	582	194	777
1892	591	193	784
1893	605	194	799
1894	596	195	792
1895	580	195	775
1896	570	192	762
1897	550	192	742
1898	528	189	718
1899	514	190	705
1900	495	188	684
1901	488	186	674
1902	467	185	651
1903	464	185	649
1904	466	183	649
1905	463	180	643
1906	462	182	644
1907	452	180	633
1908	449	178	628
1909	451	178	630
1910	454	179	633
1911	455	178	633
1912	434	178	612
1913	426	175	601
1914	423	174	597
1915	377	170	548
1916	380	168	547
1917	393	168	561
1918	369	161	529
1919	398	172	571
1920	401	172	573
1921	362	166	529
1922	332	163	496
1923	349	166	515
1924	337	164	501
1925	326	160	486
1926	310	158	467
1927	290	153	442

continued opposite

Table 16.3 continued

	England and Wales	Scotland	Great Britain	Northern Ireland	United Kingdom
1928	292	153	445	17	462
1929	283	150	433	17	450
1930	272	151	423	16	439
1931	251	146	397	15	412
1932	235	141	376	15	391
1933	225	142	367	15	382
1934	210	143	354	14	368
1935	202	142	344	5	349
1936	182	140	322	5	327
1937	178	134	312	5	317
1938	172	130	302	3	305
1939	160	125	285	9	294
1940	176	123	299	10	309
1941	202	130	332	7	339
1942	210	133	342	5	347
1943	199	134	333	3	336
1944	195	136	331	1	332
1945	193	133	327	2	329
1946	175	129	304	2	306
1947	168	125	292	1	293
1948	148	120	268	1	269
1949	140	119	259	1	260
1950	124	117	241	1	242
1951	126	114	240	1	241
1952	126	113	239	1	240
1953	125	113	238	2	240
1954	118	112	230	2	232
1955	126[2]	110	236[2]	4	240[2]
1956	109[2]	108	217[2]	3	221[2]
1957	104[2]	106	210[2]	3	213[2]
1958	100[2]	104	204[2]	3	206[2]
1959	93[2]	100	193[2]	2	196[2]
1960	83[2]	99	182[2]	2	184
1961	75[2]	93	168[2]	2	170
1962	69[2]	89	158[2]	2	159
1963	64[2]	83	147[2]	1	149
1964	63[2]	80	143[2]	1	144
1965	58[2]	76	133[2]	1	134
1966	53[2]	68	121[2]	1	122
1967	51	66	116	1	117
1968	47	62	108	--	109
1969	46	59	105	--	106
1970	43	57	100	--	100
1971	44	55	99	--	100
1972	41	55	97	--	97
1973	43	55	98	--	98
1974	45	56	101	--	102
1975	51	55	106	--	107
1976	47	55	103	--	103
1977	44	53	96	1	97
1978	41	50	91	1	91
1979	40	47	87	1	87
1980	39	45	84	1	84
1981	35	43	78	1	79
1982	31	40	71	1	71
1983	28	37	65	1	66
1984	27	37	64	1	64
1985	26	36	62	1	62
1986	24	34	58	1	59
1987	24	31	55	1	56
1988[3]					54

[1] Including turnips and swedes for human consumption. [2] Including fodder beet in England and Wales. [3] Provisional. -- Negligible.
Source: *Agricultural Departments: Agricultural Census.*

Table 16.4. Area of fodder beet and mangolds[1]
('000 hectares)

Year		Year		Year		Year		Year		Year		Year		Year	
1866	105	1881	141	1896	137	1911	183	1926	137	1941	107	1956	71	1972	8
1867	104	1882	135	1897	144	1912	197	1927	124	1942	108	1957	62	1973	7
1868	101	1883	134	1898	142	1913	170	1928	121	1943	115	1958	59	1974	7
1869	119	1884	132	1899	151	1914	176	1929	121	1944	124	1959	53	1975	7
1870	124	1885	144	1900	168	1915	168	1930	117	1945	124	1960	54	1976	6
1871	146	1886	141	1901	161	1916	154	1931	110	1946	123	1961	45	1977	7
1872	133	1887	146	1902	178	1917	158	1932	93	1947	110	1962	42	1978	6
1873	132	1888	146	1903	163	1918	163	1933	97	1948	113	1963	36	1979	6
1874	131	1889	132	1904	161	1919	161	1934	100	1949	111	1964	29	1980	6
1875	146	1890	134	1905	163	1920	157	1935	102	1950	112	1965	24	1981	5
1876	141	1891	144	1906	174	1921	153	1936	101	1951	106	1966	17	1982	5
1877	145	1892	146	1907	182	1922	172	1937	85	1952	90	1967	15	1983	5
1878	139	1893	140	1908	173	1923	164	1938	88	1953	87	1968	13	1984	8
1879	147	1894	143	1909	185	1924	158	1939	87	1954	81	1969	11	1985	12
1880	139	1895	136	1910	179	1925	145	1940	93	1955	74	1970	10	1986	13
												1971	9	1987	13
														1988[2]	12

[1] The figures relate to the United Kingdom but virtually no mangolds are grown in either Scotland or Northern Ireland.   [2] Provisional.
Source: *Agricultural Departments: Agricultural Census.*

Table 16.5. Straw production[1] ('000 tonnes)

	Wheat	Barley	Total
Pre-war			5602
1946–47			7836
1950–51	2564	1442	7960
1955–56	2047	1962	7156
1960–61	1724	1980	5800
New series			
1965–66	1930	4100	7245
1970–71	1620	2754	5259
1973	1120	2980	4618
1975	2130	3520	6130
1980	1665	3595	5585
1981	1585	3390	5285
1982	1660	3440	5410
1983	3065	4191	7751
1984	3308	4586	8482
1985	3398	4252	8319
1986[2]	3370	4265	8491

[1] The quantity of straw produced for use or for sale, not including that disposed of by burning or ploughing: England and Wales and Northern Ireland only from 1970–71 onwards.   [2] Provisional.
Source: MAFF: *Output and utilisation of farm produce in the United Kingdom.*

Appendix 17: Beef and veal

Table 17.1. Value of output of slaughter cattle and calves (£ million)

1937–38	37	1954–55	190	1971–72	407
1938–39	37	1955–56	161	1972	468
1939–40	47	1956–57	207	1973	564
1940–41	56	1957–58	222	1974	617
1941–42	45	1958–59	208	1975	897
1942–43	54	1959–60	196	1976	995
1943–44	54	1960–61	201	1977	1060
1944–45	57	1961–62	242	1978	1258
1945–46	64	1962–63	247	1979	1420
1946–47	67	1963–64	271	1980	1500
1947–48	71	1964–65	266	1981	1601
1948–49	79	1965–66	271	1982	1674
1949–50	86	1966–67	274	1983	1834
1950–51	103	1967–68	314	1984	1968
1951–52	121	1968–69	312	1985	1958
1952–53	123	1969–70	337	1986	1804
1953–54	145	1970–71	388	1987[1]	1890

[1]Forecast.

Source. MAFF: *Departmental Net Income Calculation.*

Table 17.2. Cattle numbers ('000)[1]

	England and Wales	Scotland	Great Britain
1866	3848	937	4786
1867	4014	979	4993
1868	4373	1051	5424
1869	4296	1018	5313
1870	4362	1041	5403
1871	4268	1070	5338
1872	4504	1121	5625
1873	4816	1148	5965
1874	4971	1155	6125
1875	4870	1143	6013
1876	4713	1131	5844
1877	4596	1102	5698
1878	4643	1095	5738
1879	4773	1084	5856
1880	4813	1099	5912
1881	4815	1096	5912
1882	4726	1081	5807
1883	4868	1094	5963
1884	5133	1137	6269
1885	5422	1176	6958
1886	5489	1157	6647
1887	5321	1120	6441
1888	5019	1110	6129
1889	5019	1121	6140
1890	5323	1186	6509
1891	5630	1223	6853
1892	5723	1222	6945
1893	5483	1218	6701
1894	5146	1202	6347
1895	5176	1178	6354
1896	5287	1207	6494
1897	5277	1224	6500
1898	5376	1246	6622
1899	5579	1217	6796
1900	5607	1198	6805
1901	5535	1229	6764
1902	5334	1222	6556
1903	5457	1247	6705
1904	5646	1213	6858
1905	5760	1227	6987
1906	5809	1202	7011
1907	5727	1185	6912
1908	5731	1174	6905
1909	5845	1176	7021
1910	5867	1171	7037
1911	5914	1200	7114
1912	5842	1184	7026
1913	5717	1247	6964
1914	5878	1215	7093
1915	6064	1224	7288
1916	6216	1226	7442
1917	6227	1210	7437
1918	6200	1210	7410
1919	6195	1230	7424
1920	5547	1166	6713
1921	5517	1143	6660

continued opposite

[1]Total cattle, including calves.   [2]Provisional.
Source. Agricultural Departments: *Agricultural Census.*

Table 17.2 continued

	England and Wales	Scotland	Great Britain	Northern Ireland	United Kingdom
1922	5723	1147	6869	800	7669
1923	5823	1194	7017	748	7765
1924	5894	1164	7059	736	7795
1925	6163	1205	7368	667	8035
1926	6253	1198	7451	666	8117
1927	6275	1210	7486	697	8183
1928	6026	1214	7240	738	7978
1929	5957	1234	7191	700	7891
1930	5849	1237	7086	673	7759
1931	6065	1209	7274	681	7955
1932	6358	1233	7591	715	8306
1933	6620	1294	7914	733	8647
1934	6660	1313	7973	769	8742
1935	6541	1319	7860	799	8659
1936	6540	1313	7853	770	8623
1937	6619	1290	7909	730	8639
1938	6714	1316	8030	731	8761
1939	6770	1349	8119	753	8872
1940	7001	1360	8361	732	9093
1941	6841	1312	8153	787	8940
1942	6913	1335	8248	827	9074
1943	7050	1377	8427	832	9259
1944	7198	1418	8616	886	9501
1945	7237	1460	8697	919	9616
1946	7244	1472	8716	913	9629
1947	7175	1459	8634	934	9567
1948	7340	1499	8839	966	9806
1949	7695	1569	9260	980	10 244
1950	8014	1616	9630	990	10 620
1951	7912	1600	9512	961	10 473
1952	7727	1576	9303	941	10 244
1953	7861	1647	9508	936	10 444
1954	8070	1710	9780	940	10 720
1955	8039	1725	9764	904	10 668
1956	8253	1736	9989	918	10 907
1957	8130	1779	9909	972	10 881
1958	8157	1820	9977	980	10 956
1959	8435	1892	10 327	964	11 291
1960	8769	2003	10 772	999	11 771
1961	8816	2045	10 861	1075	11 936
1962	8732	2017	10 749	1110	11 859
1963	8616	1989	10 605	1111	11 716
1964	8525	1990	10 515	1112	11 627
1965	8791	2035	10 826	1117	11 943
1966	8926	2091	11 017	1189	12 206
1967	9003	2104	11 017	1235	13 342
1968	8866	2078	10 944	1207	12 151
1969	8978	2153	11 131	1243	12 374
1970	9028	2234	11 262	1320	12 581
1971	9136	2284	11 420	1384	12 804
1972	9652	2388	12 040	1444	13 483
1973	10 344	2567	12 911	1536	14 445
1974	10 907	2675	13 582	1620	15 202
1975	10 368	2640	13 008	1607	14 616
1976	9953	2569	12 522	1548	14 069
1977	9766	2523	12 238	1565	13 854
1978	9680	2441	12 121	1548	13 670
1979	9650	2398	12 048	1541	13 589
1980	9535	2383	11 918	1507	13 426
1981	9410	2291	11 701	1436	13 138
1982	9480	2333	11 813	1429	13 244
1983	9494	2325	11 819	1472	13 290
1984	9419	2287	11 706	1507	13 213
1985	9116	2235	11 351	1514	12 865
1986	8924	2138	11 062	1471	12 533
1987	8677	2052	10 729	1429	12 518
1988[2]					11 884

Table 17.3. Dairy and beef cow numbers by country[1]

	Dairy cows				Beef cows			
	England and Wales	Scotland	Northern Ireland	United Kingdom	England and Wales	Scotland	Northern Ireland	United Kingdom
1955	2415	364			498	175		
1960	2595	358	212	3165	517	263	68	848
1965	2650	340	196	3186	559	317	146	1022
1970	2714	321	208	3244	667	417	220	1304
1975	2701	302	239	3242	1020	550	328	1899
1980	2672	282	270	3224	764	479	224	1467
1981	2638	278	271	3187	741	461	205	1407
1982	2684	282	280	3246	726	453	197	1376
1983	2745	289	294	3328	702	446	194	1342
1984	2696	283	299	3278	701	440	196	1337
1985	2580	273	294	3147	686	433	200	1319
1986	2576	270	292	3138	691	419	198	1308
1987	2490	264	289	3042	728	417	197	1343
1988				2911				1371

[1]Cows and heifers in milk and cows in calf but not in milk.
Source. Agricultural Departments: *Agricultural Census.*

Table 17.4. Number of holdings with beef cows ('000)

No. of cows	1967	1972	1975	1980	1985	1987[1]
1–19	90.6	79.7	72.5	58.7	51.4	50.0
20–49	12.7	16.4	20.8	15.8	13.9	14.0
50 and over	3.9	6.2	9.1	7.0	6.6	6.0
Total	107.2	102.3	102.4	81.6	71.9	70.5
Average size of herd	11	14	19	18	18	19
% of total beef cows in herds of 50 and over	26.4	34.7	41.6	41.5	43.6	43.5

[1]Provisional.
Source. HMSO: *Annual Review of Agriculture.*

Table 17.5. Cattle slaughterings ('000)

	Cattle[1]	Calves	Total
England and Wales			
1928–29	1420	926	2346
1929–30	1410	933	2343
1930–31	1322	808	2130
Great Britain			
1931	1759	858	2617
1932	1704	860	2564
1933	1780	938	2718
1934	1955	1071	3026
1935	2090	1108	3198
1936	2105	1086	3191
1937	2054	1042	3096
United Kingdom			
1938	2209	836	3045
1942	1759	1126	2885
1945	2004	1422	3426
1946	2050	1481	3531
1947	1883	1352	3235
1948	1779	1305	3084
1949	1623	1207	2830
1950	2311	1344	3655
1951	2451	1302	3753
1952	2151	1197	3348
1953	2119	1080	3199
1954	2595	1019	3614
1955	2480	940	3420
1956	2836	1149	3985

continued opposite

Table 17.5 continued

	Cattle[1]		Calves	Total
1957	2967		1002	3969
1958	2952		712	3664
1959	2646		630	3276

	Steers and heifers	Cows and bulls	Calves	Total
1960	2316	694	860	3870
1961	3336[1]		921	4257
1962	3397[1]		871	4268
1963	2861	904	614	4379
1964	2673	687	492	3852
1965 (53 weeks)	2601	589	387	3577
1966	2702	652	508	3862
1967	2936	649	614	4199
1968	2812	716	477	4002
1969	2630	750	419	3799
1970	2896	791	356	4043
1971 (53 weeks)	2881	812	259	3952
1972	2774	706	154	3634
1973	2547	745	141	3433
1974	3134	1045	416	4595
1975	3610	1221	537	5368
1976 (53 weeks)	3196	988	294	4478
1977	2901	947	264	4112
1978	3003	879	157	4039
1979	2909	1003	145	4057
1980	3046	1065	143	4254
1981 (53 weeks)	2966	962	121	4049
1982	2649	887	94	3630
1983	2879	932	117	3928
1984	3073	1107	132	4312
1985	3113	1042	100	4255
1986	2870	957	78	3905
1987 (53 weeks)	2895	1112	65	4072

[1]Including cows and bulls.
Source. *Annual Abstract of Statistics* (MLC).

Table 17.6. Calf disposals ('000)

	Slaughterings	Exports	Total
1928–29	926[1]	–	926
1930–31	808[1]	–	808
1935–36	1020[1]	–	1020
1937–38	920[1]	–	920
1942	1126	–	1126
1946	1481	–	1481
1950	1344	–	1344
1955	940	–	940
1960	860	42[2]	902
1965	380	177[2]	557
1970	356	377	733
1975	530	224	754
1980	144	299	443
1981	118	227	345
1982	94	233	327
1983	117	223	340
1984	132	209	341
1985	100	152	252
1986	78	201	279
1987	65	373	438

[1]England and Wales only.   [2]Cows, bulls and calves not for breeding.
Source. *Meat and Livestock Commission.*

Table 17.7. Average carcase weights of cattle slaughtered (kg dressed weight)

	Steers and heifers	Cows and bulls	Light calves	Heavy calves
1963–64	255.9			
1964–65	258.2			
1965–66	256.4			
1966–67	255.0			
1967–68	251.4			
1968–69	251.8			
1969–70	252.7			
1970–71	250.0			
1971–72	257.7			
1972	261.0			
1973	261.0			
1974	255.0			
1975	248.0			
1976	256.1	249.0		
1977	260.3	251.4		
1978	264.8	259.5		
1979	268.0	261.3	26.7	101.0
1980	268.1	263.0	27.2	103.0
1981	269.3	264.4	27.6	102.0
1982	274.5	264.1	29.9	102.5
1983	279.2	265.1	30.8	102.9
1984	277.2	265.0	28.7	98.7
1985	278.7	268.5		
1986	274.4	264.4		

Source. MLC, based on SOEC statistics.

Table 17.8. Beef and veal (home-killed) production ('000 tonnes)

1905–09	652[1]	1967	922
1924–27	614[1]	1968	906
1929	675	1969	872
1930	651	1970	949
1935	703	1971[2]	954
1938	615	1972	905
1942	489	1973	854
1946	584	1974	1073
1950	644	1975	1216
1955	715	1976[2]	1074
1956[2]	816	1977	1002
1957	826	1978	1028
1958	812	1979	1047
1959	718	1980	1103
1960[2]	821	1981[2]	1058
1961	905	1982	966
1962	917	1983	1052
1963	944	1984	1152
1964	876	1985	1147
1965[2]	832	1986	1046
1966	867	1987[2]	1092

[1]Home fed only. [2]53 week year.
Source. *Annual Abstract of Statistics.*

Table 17.9. Sources of home produced beef (per cent)

	1970	1975	1980	1985	1986	1987[1]
UK-bred steers, heifers and bulls	67	66	72	77	75	74
of which Beef herd	21	25	29	24	23	23
Dairy herd	46	41	43	53	52	51
Cull cows	20	24	24	19	19	22
of which Beef herd	6	9	7	6	5	6
Dairy herd	14	15	17	13	14	16
Irish cattle	13	10	4	4	6	4

[1]Provisional.
Source. *Meat and Livestock Commission.*

Table 17.10. Beef and veal supplies 1905–65 ('000 tonnes)

	Production	Imports[1]	Total supplies	Production as % of supplies
1905–1909	652	587	1239	53
1929	675	732	1407	48
1930	651	732	1383	47
1935	703	722	1425	49
1938	615	610	1225	50
1942	489	466	955	51
1946	584	410	994	59
1950	644	334	978	66
1955	715	350	1065	67
1960	821	353	1174	70
1965	816	293	1109	74

[1]Carcase weight equivalent.
Source. MAFF: *Agricultural Statistics.*

Table 17.11. Beef and veal supplies 1970–87 ('000 tonnes)

	Production[1]	Imports[2]	Exports[3]	Total[4] new supply	Production as % of new supply
1970–72	968	314	65	1214	80
1973	887	337	101	1119	79
1974	1086	294	78	1299	84
1975	1215	247	137	1324	92
1976	1069	249	115	1199	89
1977	1032	298	122	1205	86
1978	1048	319	126	1238	85
1979	1082	317	135	1261	86
1980	1096	289	175	1211	91
1981	1039	240	161	1117	93
1982	980	208	141	1047	94
1983	1044	215	196	1063	98
1984	1136	198	203	1131	100
1985	1123	210	178	1155	97
1986	1046	261	199	1108	94
1987[5]	1097	259	209	1147	96

[1]Home fed. [2]Carcase weight equivalent. [3]Includes live animals. [4]New supply: production plus imports less exports (including supplies sent to Channel Islands). [5]Forecast.
Source. HMSO: *Annual Review of Agriculture.*

Table 17.12. Imports of live cattle[1] ('000)

1879	248	1965	511
1885	373	1970	524
1929	750	1975	504
1930	841	1980	221
1935	599	1981	137
1938	719	1982	137
1942	627	1983	191
1946	449	1984	216
1950	454	1985	221
1955	611	1986	232
1960	508	1987	152

[1]Including animals for breeding.

Table 17.13. Beef and veal imports ('000 tonnes)

	1938	1942	1945	1950	1955	1960	1965	1970	1975	1980	1981	1982	1983	1984	1985	1986	1987
Beef: fresh and chilled																	
Argentina	350	–	–	–	100	184	96	28	- -	1	1	1	–	–	–	–	- -
Australia	27	–	–	–	5	2	- -	–	–	2	2	2	1	1	1	2	3
Brazil	26	–	–	–	–	- -	- -	4	–	–	–	–	–	–	–	–	–
Denmark	–	–	–	–	–	–	–	–	15	2	2	1	1	1	1	1	2
Irish Republic	- -	–	–	3	12	14	26	93	59	134	81	79	83	73	72	106	111
New Zealand	18	–	–	–	16	2	1	–	–	–	–	–	–	–	–	–	–
Uruguay	28	–	–	–	- -	21	3	–	–	–	–	–	–	–	–	–	–
FR Germany	–	–	–	–	–	–	–	–	14	1	3	2	- -	- -	- -	3	1
Other countries	6	6	–	–	–	2	13	26	11	1	5	5	8	7	9	16	15
Total	455	6	–	3	133	225	139	151	99	141	94	90	93	82	83	128	132
Beef: frozen																	
Argentina	10	344	116	166	60	22	13	29	2	12	14	6	–	–	- -	1	3
Australia	84	10	40	55	112	63	90	32	13	6	3	7	4	2	2	3	3
Botswana	–	–	–	–	–	–	–	–	7	- -	3	7	7	4	6	4	1
Brazil	2	–	3	- -	–	- -	- -	10	–	- -	2	8	17	15	15	7	7
Canada	1	–	67	–	–	–	–	–	–	–	–	–	–	–	–	–	–
Denmark	–	–	–	1	–	–	–	–	–	3	3	3	3	3	2	2	1
France	–	–	–	–	–	–	–	–	20	13	10	8	5	6	5	5	8
Irish Republic	–	–	–	–	–	–	–	—	37	25	19	18	11	11	12	15	16
Netherlands	–	–	–	–	–	–	–	–	- -	4	4	4	5	3	4	4	8
New Zealand	27	27	17	57	39	17	29	15	6	6	6	4	1	- -	- -	–	–
Uruguay	4	31	18	45	1	12	2	–	–	–	–	–	–	–	–	–	1
FR Germany	–	–	–	1	–	–	–	–	1	12	14	8	10	7	7	11	10
Other countries	1	50	–	–	4	13	17	28	8	5	8	8	11	12	15	16	17
Total	129	462	261	325	216	127	151	114	94	86	86	81	74	63	68	68	75
Veal: Total	13	–	8	13	9	6	5	1	3	6	6	5	4	3	3	3	2
Total beef and veal	597	468	269	341	358	358	295	266	196	233	185	176	170	148	154	200	209

- - Negligible.
Source. *Customs and Excise.*

Table 17.14. Beef and veal exports ('000 tonnes)

	1970	1975	1980	1981	1982	1983	1984	1985	1986	1987
Belgium/Luxembourg	–	–	4	3	4	4	3	3	4	7
France	4	64	80	62	61	84	79	86	66	80
Irish Republic	–	–	5	10	6	13	12	7	10	10
Netherlands	–	11	8	6	4	9	7	7	6	9
FR Germany	–	22	28	18	15	27	21	15	14	16
Egypt	–	–	4	- -	1	3	25	16	11	4
Yugoslavia	–	–	5	9	3	5	1	- -	- -	- -
Other countries	6	18	18	29	24	41	43	37	55[1]	50[1]
Total	10	115	152	137	118	186	191	171	166	176

[1] of which Brazil 1986 22 000 tonnes; 1987 15 000 tonnes.
- - Negligible.
Source. *Customs and Excise.*

Table 17.15. Beef and veal consumption per head per annum

Year	kg	Year	kg	Year	kg
1905–1909	30.6	1958	23.4	1982	18.1
1929	30.8	1959	20.5	1983	18.4
1930	29.9	1960	21.8	1984	18.5
1935	30.8	1961	22.4	1985	19.0
1938	25.1	1962	23.4	1986[1]	19.3
1939		1963	24.2	1987[2]	19.4
1940	22.1	1964	22.0		
1941	20.6	1965	20.8		
1942	20.4	1966	21.2		
1943	16.3	1967	22.1		
1944	17.8	1968	20.9		
1945	15.4	1969	22.0		
1946	21.0	1970	22.2		
1947	20.6	1971	22.6		
1948	18.7	1972	21.0		
1949	17.7	1973	19.3		
1950	21.7	1974	22.4		
1951	15.4	1975	23.6		
1952	14.9	1976	21.0		
1953	16.7	1977	21.1		
1954	20.2	1978	22.0		
1955	21.5	1979	22.5		
1956	24.5	1980	20.9		
1957	24.8	1981	19.7		

[1] Provisional. [2] Forecast.
Source. MAFF: *Food Facts*
Annual Abstracts of Statistics.

Table 17.16. Slaughter cattle prices (p per kg live weight)[1]

	At current prices	In 1986 money values
1900	3.55	142.9
1910	3.66	132.6
1915	5.35	150.7
1920	9.74	135.7
1925	6.09	119.9
1930	5.29	116.0
1935	3.67	89.0
1938	4.35	96.4
1940	6.10	111.8
1945	7.40	98.2
1948	10.03	114.5
1950	10.65	115.4
1955	15.66	137.0
1960	15.22	118.4
1965	17.76	117.3
1970	19.88	104.9
1975	38.56	110.4
1980	77.10	112.8
1981	89.45	117.0
1982	99.11	119.4
1983	96.49	111.1
1984	96.56	105.9
1985	95.11	98.3
1986	95.18	95.2
1987	97.21	93.2

[1]Certified cattle only since 1955.

Table 17.17. Producers' total returns for certified cattle[1] (p per kg live weight)

	At current prices	In 1986 money values
1955–1956	15.42	122.2
1960–1961	17.66	118.4
1965–1966	22.90	114.5
1970	22.18	120.9
1975	44.68	127.8
1980	81.22	118.6
1981	90.79	118.9
1982	100.22	120.3
1983	105.33	121.1
1984	105.28	115.8
1985	103.75	106.9
1986	104.00	104.0
1987	106.95	102.6

[1]Including any deficiency or variable premium payments; certified cattle only. Steers and heifers which have been certified as meeting certain quality standards are eligible for these payments.

Table 17.18. Retail beef prices 1939–66 (p per lb)[1]

	At current prices	In 1986 money values
1939	6.0[2]	130.4[2]
1940	6.5[2]	119.1[2]
1941	6.5[2]	98.7[2]
1942	6.5[2]	92.4[2]
1943	6.5[2]	89.5[2]
1944	6.5[2]	87.9[2]
1945	6.5[2]	86.3[2]
1946	6.5[2]	85.3[2]
1947	8.5	104.5
1948	8.5	97.0
1949	11.0	122.7
1950	11.0	119.2
1951	12.5	124.3
1952	15.0	140.4
1953	16.0	147.4
1954	19.0	172.1
1955	22.0	192.5
1956	21.0	176.2
1957	22.0	178.6
1958	26.5	209.6
1959	27.0	212.2
1960	27.0	210.0
1961	26.0	196.8
1962	27.5	200.2
1963	28.5	203.5
1964	34.0	234.9
1965	33.5	221.4
1966	34.5	219.4

[1]Sirloin (without bone). Not converted to p per kg as retail prices are still recorded as p per lb. [2]First quality ribs.

Table 17.19. Retail beef prices 1967–87 (p per lb)[1]

	At current prices	In 1986 money values
1967	29.6	183.2
1968	32.8	194.2
1969	34.9	196.1
1970	37.2	196.4
1971	42.9	206.8
1972	49.4	222.3
1973	62.6	258.5
1974	63.7	226.8
1975	74.8	213.9
1976	93.8	241.0
1977	105.7	224.1
1978	121.1	237.4
1979	142.3	246.2
1980	157.2	229.5
1981	174.8	229.0
1982	195.2	234.2
1983	200.4	230.5
1984	204.4	224.8
1985	204.7	210.8
1986	206.5	206.5
1987	207.8	199.3

[1]All cuts. Not converted to p per kg as retail prices are still officially recorded as p per lb.

Appendix 18: Sheepmeat

Table 18.1. Value of output of slaughter sheep and lambs (£ million)

Year	Value	Year	Value	Year	Value
1937–38	16	1954–55	58	1971–72	103
1938–39	16	1955–56	57	1972	187
1939–40	18	1956–57	63	1973	156
1940–41	29	1957–58	71	1974	164
1941–42	25	1958–59	68	1975	187
1942–43	27	1959–60	78	1976	240
1943–44	24	1960–61	79	1977	267
1944–45	23	1961–62	87	1978	300
1945–46	23	1962–63	84	1979	319
1946–47	26	1963–64	84	1980	405
1947–48	26	1964–65	86	1981	465
1948–49	32	1965–66	85	1982	515
1949–50	36	1966–67	88	1983	572
1950–51	38	1967–68	88	1984	561
1951–52	41	1968–69	87	1985	608
1952–53	51	1969–70	84	1986	602
1953–54	54	1970–71	95	1987[1]	659

[1]Forecast.
Source. MAFF: *Departmental Net Income Calculation.*

Table 18.2. Sheep numbers (millions)

	England and Wales	Scotland	Great Britain
1866	16.8	5.3	22.1
1867	22.0	6.9	28.9
1868	23.6	7.1	30.7
1869	22.5	7.0	29.5
1870	21.6	6.8	28.4
1871	20.2	6.9	27.1
1872	20.8	7.1	27.9
1873	22.1	7.3	29.4
1874	22.9	7.4	30.3
1875	22.1	7.1	29.2
1876	21.2	7.0	28.2
1877	21.2	7.0	28.2
1878	21.4	7.0	28.4
1879	21.3	6.8	28.2
1880	19.5	7.1	26.6
1881	17.9	6.7	24.6
1882	17.5	6.9	24.3
1883	18.2	6.9	25.1
1884	19.1	7.0	26.1
1885	19.6	7.0	26.5
1886	18.9	6.6	25.5
1887	19.2	6.8	26.0
1888	18.5	6.7	25.3
1889	18.7	7.0	25.6
1890	19.9	7.4	27.3
1891	21.1	7.6	28.7
1892	21.2	7.5	28.7
1893	19.9	7.4	27.3
1894	18.6	7.3	25.9
1895	18.6	7.2	25.8
1896	19.2	7.5	26.7
1897	18.9	7.4	26.3
1898	19.2	7.6	26.7
1899	19.7	7.6	27.2
1900	19.3	7.3	26.6
1901	19.0	7.4	26.4
1902	18.5	7.3	25.8
1903	18.4	7.2	25.6
1904	18.2	7.0	25.2
1905	18.2	7.0	25.3
1906	18.4	7.0	25.4
1907	18.8	7.3	26.1
1908	19.7	7.4	27.1
1909	20.3	7.3	27.6
1910	20.0	7.1	27.1
1911	19.3	7.2	26.5
1912	18.1	7.0	25.1
1913	17.1	6.8	23.9
1914	17.3	7.0	24.3
1915	17.5	7.1	24.6
1916	18.0	7.1	25.0
1917	17.2	6.9	24.0
1918	16.5	6.9	23.4
1919	15.1	6.4	21.5
1920	13.4	6.4	19.7
1921	13.8	6.7	20.5

continued opposite

[1]Provisional.
Source. Agricultural Departments: *Agricultural Census.*

Table 18.2. continued

	England and Wales	Scotland	Great Britain	Northern Ireland	United Kingdom
1922	13.4	6.7	20.1	0.4	20.5
1923	13.8	6.8	20.6	0.5	21.1
1924	14.8	6.9	21.7	0.5	22.2
1925	16.0	7.1	23.1	0.5	23.6
1926	16.9	7.2	24.1	0.5	24.6
1927	17.1	7.5	24.6	0.6	25.2
1928	16.4	7.6	24.0	0.6	24.6
1929	16.1	7.6	23.7	0.7	24.4
1930	16.3	7.7	24.0	0.7	24.7
1931	17.7	7.8	25.6	0.8	26.4
1932	18.5	7.9	26.4	0.8	27.2
1933	18.1	7.8	25.9	0.8	26.7
1934	16.5	7.7	24.2	0.7	24.9
1935	16.5	7.8	24.2	0.8	25.1
1936	16.6	7.6	24.2	0.8	25.0
1937	17.2	7.5	24.7	0.8	25.5
1938	17.9	8.0	25.9	0.9	26.8
1939	18.0	8.0	26.0	0.9	26.9
1940	17.7	7.8	25.5	0.9	26.3
1941	14.7	6.8	21.4	0.8	22.3
1942	13.9	6.8	20.8	0.7	21.5
1943	12.9	6.8	19.7	0.7	20.4
1944	12.6	6.8	19.4	0.7	20.1
1945	12.6	6.9	19.5	0.7	20.2
1946	12.8	7.0	19.7	0.6	20.4
1947	10.2	6.0	16.2	0.5	16.7
1948	10.9	6.7	17.6	0.6	18.2
1949	11.7	7.1	18.8	0.6	19.5
1950	12.4	7.3	19.7	0.7	20.4
1951	12.5	6.9	19.3	0.7	20.0
1952	13.6	7.3	20.9	0.8	21.7
1953	14.1	7.5	21.6	0.9	22.5
1954	14.5	7.4	21.9	0.9	22.9
1955	14.7	7.3	22.1	0.9	22.9
1956	15.2	7.5	22.7	0.9	23.6
1957	16.0	7.9	23.9	0.9	24.8
1958	17.2	7.9	25.1	1.0	26.1
1959	18.2	8.4	26.6	1.0	27.6
1960	18.4	8.4	26.8	1.1	27.9
1961	19.1	8.7	27.8	1.2	29.0
1962	19.7	8.6	28.3	1.2	29.5
1963	19.7	8.5	28.2	1.1	29.3
1964	20.0	8.5	28.6	1.1	29.7
1965	20.3	8.6	28.9	1.1	29.9
1966	20.5	8.4	28.9	1.1	30.0
1967	19.7	8.2	27.9	1.0	28.9
1968	19.2	7.8	27.0	1.0	28.0
1969	18.1	7.6	25.7	0.9	26.6
1970	17.6	7.5	25.1	1.0	26.1
1971	17.6	7.5	25.1	1.0	26.0
1972	18.3	7.6	25.9	1.0	26.9
1973	19.4	7.6	27.0	1.0	27.9
1974	20.0	7.6	27.6	0.9	28.5
1975	19.8	7.5	27.3	0.9	28.3
1976	19.9	7.5	27.4	0.9	28.3
1977	19.9	7.2	27.1	1.0	28.1
1978	21.4	7.4	28.8	1.0	29.8
1979	21.6	7.3	28.9	1.0	29.9
1980	22.7	7.7	30.4	1.1	31.4
1981	23.2	7.8	31.0	1.1	32.1
1982	23.9	8.0	31.9	1.2	33.1
1983	24.7	8.0	32.7	1.3	34.1
1984	25.2	8.1	33.3	1.5	34.8
1985	25.7	8.4	34.1	1.6	35.6
1986	26.8	8.5	35.3	1.7	37.0
1987	28.1	8.6	36.7	1.9	38.7
1988[1]					41.0

Table 18.3. Holdings by size of total sheep flock (England and Wales)

No. of sheep	1964	1975	1986
1–24	10 622	6384	8323
25–49	9741	5150	5321
50–99	16 158	8667	7635
100–199	21 300	11 731	10 130
200–299	12 068	7805	7122
300–399	6820	5140	4990
400–499	4250	3468	3673
500–699	4455	4451	5251
700–999	2631	3308	4638
1000–1499	1568	2319	3725
1500–1999	428	898	1616
2000 and over	401	776	1673
Total	90 442	60 097	64 097
Total No. of sheep	20 031 823	19 800 251	26 633 379

Source. MAFF: *Agricultural Statistics, England and Wales.*
Agricultural Statistics, United Kingdom.

Table 18.4. Sheep slaughterings (million)

	Ewes and rams	Other sheep and lambs	Total
1931			10.0
1935			10.7
1938			10.7
1942			8.2
1946			7.4
1950			6.9
1955			8.3
1960	1.1	10.3	11.4
1965	1.2	10.8	12.0
1970	1.3	10.1	11.5
1975	1.5	11.6	13.1
1980	1.5	12.8	14.3
1981	1.4	12.6	14.0
1982	1.3	12.6	13.9
1983	1.4	13.6	15.1
1984	1.6	13.4	15.0
1985	1.6	14.3	15.9
1986	1.4	14.1	15.5
1987	1.5	14.2	15.8

Source. MAFF: *Output and Utilisation of Farm Produce in the United Kingdom.*
Meat and Livestock Commission: *United Kingdom Weekly Market Survey.*

Table 18.6. Mutton and lamb supplies 1905–65 ('000 tonnnes)

	Production	Imports	Supplies[1]	Production as % of supplies
1905–09[2]	261	246	507	52
1924–27[2]	231	292	523	44
1931	250	386	636	39
1935	266	365	631	42
1938	214	351	565	38
1942	174	377	551	32
1946	153	418	571	27
1950	151	400	551	27
1955	177	358	535	33
1960	227	371	598	38
1965	245	342	587	42

[1]Production plus imports.   [2]Average.
Source. MAFF: *Agricultural Statistics.*

Table 18.5. Average sheep slaughter weights[1] (kg)

1963–64	19.3	1975	18.6
1964–65	19.3	1976	18.6
1965–66	19.0	1977	18.6
1966–67	18.8	1978	18.6
1967–68	18.9	1979	18.6
1968–69	18.5	1980	18.3
1969–70	18.9	1981	17.7
1970–71	18.6	1982	18.0
1971–72	18.9	1983	18.0
1972	19.0	1984	18.1
1973	19.1	1985	18.2
1974	18.4	1986[2]	17.9

[1]Clean sheep and lambs, i.e. excluding ewes and rams in kilogrammes dressed carcase weight.   [2]Provisional.
Source. MAFF: *Output and Utilisation of Farm Produce in the United Kingdom.*

Table 18.7. Mutton and lamb supplies 1970–87 ('000 tonnes)

	Production	Imports	Exports	Total[1] new supply	Production as % of new supply
1970–72[2]	229	339	22	546	42
1973	236	266	30	472	50
1974	253	213	28	438	58
1975	264	244	38	470	56
1976	248	226	37	437	57
1977	229	219	50	398	58
1978	238	226	51	413	58
1979	239	208	48	399	60
1980	286	191	47	430	67
1981	269	158	52	375	72
1982	276	222	49	449	61
1983	298	166	54	410	73
1984	298	146	58	386	77
1985	315	157	59	413	76
1986	303	125	72	356	85
1987[3]	325	125	88	362	90

[1]New supply: production plus imports less exports (including supplies to Channel Islands).   [2]Average.   [3]Forecast.
Source. MAFF: *Output and Utilisation of Farm Produce in the United Kingdom.*
HMSO: *Annual Review of Agriculture 1988.*

Table 18.8. Imports of live sheep and lambs ('000)[1]

1871	917
1872	810
1873	851
1874	759
1875	986
1876	1041
1877	874
1878	892
1879	945
1880	941
1881	935
1882	1124
1883	1116
1884	945
1885	751

[1]Including imports into the whole of Ireland.
Source. *Statistical Abstract for the United Kingdom 1871–1885.*

Table 18.9. Imports of mutton and lamb ('000 tonnes)

	1938	1942	1945	1950	1955	1960	1965	1970	1975	1980	1981	1982	1983	1984	1985	1986	1987
Mutton: fresh chilled and frozen																	
Argentina	5.0	12.6	9.0	10.8	–	–	0.6	–	–	–	–	–	–	–	–	–	–
Australia	18.7	2.7	7.7	24.0	10.0	7.7	9.0	14.6	4.9	1.5	–	0.1	- -	–	–	–	–
New Zealand	51.5	35.4	77.9	75.4	47.3	47.8	28.3	18.2	5.5	3.7	4.1	6.8	1.5	3.4	4.4	3.0	1.1
Other countries	6.2	5.0	12.1	10.0	0.2	0.1	1.0	0.7	0.4	- -	- -	- -	- -	- -	- -	–	–
Total	81.4	55.7	106.7	120.2	57.5	55.6	38.9	33.5	10.8	5.2	4.1	6.9	1.5	3.4	4.4	3.0	1.1
Lamb: fresh chilled and frozen																	
Argentina	40.3	57.2	32.6	29.8	52.4	31.0	14.4	–	–	–	–	–	–	–	–	–	–
Australia	77.8	71.2	45.9	40.6	43.2	23.7	14.3	17.5	2.6	0.9	1.3	4.0	1.5	1.8	4.5	5.5	5.5
Chile	5.1	3.7	3.7	3.9	0.2	1.8	0.8	–	–	–	–	–	—	–	–	–	–
New Zealand	135.1	181.9	171.9	199.4	203.5	257.0	271.1	277.4	228.6	185.0	151.7	210.4	162.3	139.9	146.5	115.3	123.3
Other countries	11.3	7.7	7.1	6.4	1.0	2.9	2.8	2.8	1.8	0.4	1.2	1.0	0.9	1.1	1.6	1.5	1.1
Total	269.6	321.7	261.2	280.1	300.3	316.4	303.4	297.7	233.0	186.3	154.2	215.4	164.7	142.8	152.6	122.3	129.9
Total mutton and lamb	351.0	377.4	367.9	400.3	357.8	372.0	342.3	331.2	243.8	191.5	158.3	222.3	166.2	146.2	157.0	125.3	131.0

- - Negligible.
Source: *Customs and Excise.*

Table 18.10. Exports of mutton and lamb ('000 tonnes)

	1970	1975	1980	1981	1982	1983	1984	1985	1986	1987
Belgium/ Luxembourg	1.1	2.4	13.7	6.1	5.6	4.1	4.1	6.0	7.0	7.9
France	7.7	25.9	3.5	19.8	22.2	30.0	35.5	34.6	43.9	53.9
FR Germany	–	2.6	13.6	5.1	5.5	4.5	3.0	2.5	2.9	2.5
Other countries	1.8	2.3	6.1	6.5	3.7	4.8	4.6	5.6	6.2	6.9
Total	10.6	33.2	36.9	37.5	37.0	43.4	47.2	48.7	60.0	71.2

Source. *Customs and Excise.*

Table 18.11. Trade in live sheep ('000)

	Imports	Exports
1938	298	–
1945	76	–
1950	91	–
1955	161	–
1960	313	–
1965	213	411
1970	71	268
1975	78	235
1980	91	393
1981	104	172
1982	44	147
1983	47	93
1984	64	102
1985	89	85
1986	65	196
1987	92	374

Source. *Customs and Excise.*

Table 18.12. Mutton and lamb consumption (kg per head per annum)

1931	14.1	1975	8.3
1935	14.1	1980	7.5
1938	11.4	1981	6.7
1942	10.9	1982	7.3
1946	11.0	1983	7.1
1950	11.4	1984	6.8
1955	11.1	1985	6.9
1960	11.1	1986	6.4
1965	10.5	1987[1]	6.3
1970	9.6		

[1]Forecast.
Source. MAFF: *Food Facts.*
Annual Abstract of Statistics.

Table 18.13. United Kingdom: market prices and producers' total returns for slaughter sheep (p per kg estimated dressed carcase weight)

	Market prices		Total returns	
	At current prices	In 1986 money values	At current prices	In 1986 money values
1955–1956	29.8	260.7	33.1	289.6
1956–1957	30.9	259.2	35.3	296.1
1957–1958	30.9	251.0	36.4	295.7
1958–1959	29.8	235.6	36.4	287.8
1959–1960	24.2	190.2	35.3	277.4
1960–1961	28.7	223.2	35.3	274.6
1961–1962	23.1	174.8	35.3	267.0
1962–1963	26.4	192.2	35.3	257.0
1963–1964	29.8	212.9	35.3	252.2
1964–1965	33.1	228.9	35.3	244.1
1965–1966	33.1	218.7	35.3	233.2
1966–1967	31.3	199.0	35.5	225.6
1967–1968	31.3	193.8	36.6	226.7
1968–1969	36.1	213.6	39.2	232.0
1969–1970	39.0	219.0	41.0	230.3
1970–1971	38.6	203.7	44.3	233.8
1971–1972	40.6	195.8	48.7	234.9
1972–1973	56.0	252.1	57.1	257.1
1973	70.5	290.9	70.5	290.9
1974	64.6	229.7	65.2	231.8
1975	75.4	215.8	76.7	219.5
1976	103.9	255.2	104.0	255.4
1977	124.5	263.9	124.7	264.4
1978	137.4	269.0	137.5	269.2
1979	139.2	240.3	142.8	247.0
1980	125.7	183.5	148.6	217.0
1981	153.3	200.8	184.3	241.4
1982[1]	152.7	183.2	193.7	232.4
1983[1]	146.5	168.5	209.2	240.6
1984[1]	166.5	183.2	213.7	235.1
1985[1]	167.1	172.1	226.2	233.0
1986[1]	175.3	175.3	226.9	226.9
1987[2]	180.6	173.0	233.7	223.9

[1]Great Britain only from 1982 onwards. [2]Forecast.
Source. *HMSO Annual Review of Agriculture.*

Table 18.14. Retail mutton prices (p per lb)[1]

	At current prices	In 1986 money values
1939	6.0	130.4
1940	7.0	128.3
1941	7.5	113.9
1942	7.5	106.6
1943	7.5	103.3
1944	7.5	101.4
1945	7.5	99.6
1946	7.5	98.4
1947	7.5	92.2
1948	7.5	85.6
1949	10.0	111.5
1950	10.0	108.4
1951	11.5	114.3
1952	14.0	131.0
1953	14.0	128.9
1954	16.0	145.0
1955	17.5	153.1
1956	17.0	142.6
1957	18.0	146.2
1958	19.0	150.3
1959	15.5	121.8
1960	17.5	136.2
1961	17.0	128.7
1962	18.5	134.7
1963	16.0	114.2
1964	18.5	127.8
1965	19.0	125.6
1966	20.5	130.4

[1]Legs with bone. Statistics for retail prices continue to use p per lb not p per kg.
Source. *Based on Department of Employment data.*

Table 18.15. Retail lamb prices (p per lb)[1]

	Home killed		Imported	
	At current prices	In 1986 money values	At current prices	In 1986 money values
1967	21.9	135.6	18.3	113.3
1968	24.0	142.1	19.0	123.7
1969	26.4	148.4	20.9	117.5
1970	28.0	147.8	21.9	115.6
1971	30.2	145.6	23.2	111.8
1972	35.7	160.7	28.4	127.8
1973	46.7	192.9	38.4	158.6
1974	50.4	179.4	42.3	150.6
1975	56.2	160.7	46.1	131.8
1976	69.9	172.0	57.6	141.7
1977	83.4	176.8	68.7	145.6
1978	96.3	188.7	77.5	151.9
1979	108.8	188.2	83.9	145.1
1980	110.1	160.7	89.0	129.9
1981	122.3	160.2	99.5	130.3
1982	132.8	159.4	109.0	130.8
1983	132.2	152.0	100.6	115.7
1984	131.1	144.2	106.7	117.4
1985	139.0	143.2	111.7	115.1
1986	144.3	144.3	114.4	114.4
1987	145.5	139.5	117.0	112.2

[1]All cuts.
Source. *Based on Department of Employment data.*

Appendix 19: Pigmeat

Table 19.1. Value of output of slaughter pigs (£ million)

1937–38	27	1954–55	186	1971–72	292
1938–39	28	1955–56	168	1972	308
1939–40	34	1956–57	167	1973	421
1940–41	39	1957–58	162	1974	468
1941–42	18	1958–59	172	1975	494
1942–43	18	1959–60	158	1976	557
1943–44	17	1960–61	150	1977	642
1944–45	23	1961–62	164	1978	689
1945–46	28	1962–63	186	1979	744
1946–47	26	1963–64	184	1980	790
1947–48	25	1964–65	203	1981	862
1948–49	43	1965–66	216	1982	923
1949–50	67	1966–67	208	1983	911
1950–51	87	1967–68	209	1984	995
1951–52	123	1968–69	220	1985	975
1952–53	162	1969–70	249	1986	955
1953–54	171	1970–71	281	1987[1]	951

[1]Forecast.
Source. MAFF: *Departmental Net Income Calculation.*

Table 19.2. Pig population (millions)

	England and Wales	Scotland	Great Britain
1866	2.3	0.2	2.5
1867	2.8	0.2	3.0
1868	2.2	0.1	2.3
1869	1.8	0.1	1.9
1870	2.0	0.2	2.2
1871	2.3	0.2	2.5
1872	2.6	0.2	2.8
1873	2.4	0.1	2.5
1874	2.3	0.2	2.4
1875	2.1	0.2	2.2
1876	2.1	0.2	2.3
1877	2.3	0.2	2.5
1878	2.3	0.1	2.5
1879	2.0	0.1	2.1
1880	1.9	0.1	2.0
1881	1.9	0.1	2.0
1882	2.4	0.2	2.5
1883	2.5	0.2	2.6
1884	2.4	0.2	2.6
1885	2.3	0.2	2.4
1886	2.1	0.1	2.2
1887	2.2	0.1	2.3
1888	2.3	0.2	2.4
1889	2.4	0.2	2.5
1890	2.6	0.2	2.8
1891	2.7	0.2	2.9
1892	2.0	0.1	2.1
1893	2.0	0.1	2.1
1894	2.2	0.2	2.4
1895	2.7	0.2	2.9
1896	2.7	0.1	2.9
1897	2.2	0.1	2.3
1898	2.3	0.1	2.5
1899	2.5	0.1	2.6
1900	2.3	0.1	2.4
1901	2.1	0.1	2.2
1902	2.2	0.1	2.3
1903	2.6	0.1	2.7
1904	2.7	0.1	2.9
1905	2.3	0.1	2.4
1906	2.2	0.1	2.3
1907	2.5	0.1	2.6
1908	2.7	0.1	2.8
1909	2.3	0.1	2.4
1910	2.2	0.1	2.4
1911	2.7	0.2	2.8
1912	2.5	0.2	2.7
1913	2.1	0.1	2.2
1914	2.5	0.2	2.6
1915	2.4	0.2	2.6
1916	2.2	0.1	2.3
1917	1.9	0.1	2.1
1918	1.7	0.1	1.8
1919	1.8	0.1	1.9
1920	2.0	0.1	2.1

continued opposite

Source. Agricultural Departments: *Agricultural Census.*

Table 19.2 continued

	England and Wales	Scotland	Great Britain	Northern Ireland	United Kingdom
1921	2.5	2.9	2.7	0.1	2.8
1922	2.3	0.2	2.5	0.1	2.6
1923	2.6	0.2	2.8	0.2	3.0
1924	3.2	0.2	3.4	0.1	3.5
1925	2.6	0.2	2.8	0.1	2.9
1926	2.2	0.1	2.3	0.2	2.5
1927	2.7	0.2	2.9	0.2	3.1
1928	3.0	0.2	3.2	0.2	3.4
1929	2.4	0.1	2.5	0.2	2.7
1930	2.3	0.1	2.5	0.2	2.7
1931	2.8	0.2	2.9	0.3	3.2
1932	3.2	0.2	3.4	0.2	3.6
1933	3.1	0.2	3.2	0.3	3.5
1934	3.3	0.2	3.5	0.4	3.9
1935	3.8	0.3	4.1	0.4	4.5
1936	3.8	0.2	4.0	0.6	4.6
1937	3.6	0.3	3.9	0.6	4.5
1938	3.6	0.2	3.8	0.6	4.4
1939	3.5	0.3	3.8	0.6	4.4
1940	3.4	0.3	3.6	0.5	4.1
1941	2.0	0.2	2.2	0.4	2.6
1942	1.7	0.2	1.9	0.3	2.1
1943	1.4	0.2	1.6	0.3	1.8
1944	1.2	0.2	1.6	0.3	1.9
1945	1.7	0.2	1.9	0.2	2.2
1946	1.5	0.2	1.6	0.3	2.0
1947	1.1	0.1	1.3	0.3	1.6
1948	1.6	0.2	1.8	0.3	2.2
1949	2.1	0.2	2.4	0.5	2.8
1950	2.2	0.3	2.5	0.5	3.0
1951	3.0	0.3	3.3	0.6	3.9
1952	3.8	0.2	4.0	0.7	5.0
1953	3.9	0.5	4.4	0.8	5.2
1954	4.9	0.6	5.5	0.8	6.3
1955	4.7	0.5	5.2	0.7	5.8
1956	4.4	0.4	4.8	0.7	5.5
1957	4.8	0.5	5.3	0.7	6.0
1958	5.2	0.5	5.7	0.8	6.5
1959	4.7	0.4	5.1	0.8	6.0
1960	4.3	0.4	4.7	1.0	5.7
1961	4.6	0.4	5.0	1.0	6.0
1962	5.1	0.5	5.6	1.2	6.7
1963	5.2	0.4	5.6	1.2	6.9
1964	5.7	0.5	6.2	1.2	7.4
1965	6.2	0.6	6.8	1.3	8.0
1966	5.8	0.5	6.3	1.2	7.3
1967	5.6	0.5	6.1	1.0	7.1
1968	5.8	0.6	6.4	1.0	7.4
1969	6.2	0.6	6.8	1.0	7.8
1970	6.4	0.6	7.0	1.1	8.1
1971	6.9	0.7	7.6	1.2	8.7
1972	6.9	0.7	7.6	1.0	8.6
1973	7.3	0.7	8.0	1.0	9.0
1974	7.1	0.6	7.7	0.8	8.5
1975	6.3	0.5	6.8	0.6	7.5
1976	6.7	0.7	7.4	0.6	7.9
1977	6.6	0.6	7.2	0.6	7.7
1978	6.5	0.5	7.0	0.7	7.7
1979	6.6	0.5	7.1	0.7	7.9
1980	6.7	0.5	7.2	0.7	7.8
1981	6.7	0.5	7.2	0.6	7.8
1982	6.9	0.5	7.4	0.6	8.0
1983	7.1	0.4	7.5	0.6	8.2
1984	6.7	0.4	7.1	0.6	7.7
1985	6.8	0.4	7.2	0.6	7.9
1986	6.9	0.4	7.3	0.6	7.9
1987	6.9	0.4	7.3	0.6	7.9

Table 19.3. Holdings by size of herds of breeding pigs
(England and Wales)

No. of breeding pigs per holding	1964	1975	1986
1	12 193	3418	1482
2–4	25 609	5439	2337
5–9	16 926	4154	1542
10–14	8232	2346	930
15–19	3834	1408	576
20–29	4093	1987	846
30–49	2820	2121	1072
50–99	1560	2401	1512
100–199		1141	1322
200–499	430	372	684
500 and over		54	151
Total	75 697	24 841	12 454
Total No. of breeding pigs	719 316	686 159	714 539

Source. MAFF: *Agricultural Statistics, England and Wales.*
Agricultural Statistics, United Kingdom.

Table 19.4. Holdings by size of total pig herd (England and Wales)

No. of pigs per holding	1964	No. of pigs per holding	1975	1986
1–4	18 157	1–2	3628	1975
5–9	11 480	3–9	4267	2429
10–29	29 150	10–19	3968	1701
30–49	12 357	20–29	2391	1020
50–99	13 870	30–49	3163	1208
100–199	7921	50–69	2186	811
200–499	4987	70–99	2201	840
500–999	1167	100–199	3942	1693
1000 and over	316	200–399	3317	1726
		400–999	2950	2169
		1000–4999	1233	1738
		5000 and over	45	136
Total	99 405		33 291	17 446
Total No of pigs	5 738 997		6 337 197	6 868 512

Source. MAFF: *Agricultural Statistics, England and Wales.*
Agricultural Statistics, United Kingdom.

Table 19.5. Pig slaughterings ('000)

England and Wales			Total
1928–29			4378
1930–31			3481
1931–32			3477
1932–33			4152
1933–34			4681
1934–35			4457
1935–36			4699
1936–37			5388
1937–38			5331

United Kingdom	For bacon	Not for bacon	Total
Pre-war	3336	2824	6160
1946–47	2025	168	2193
1947–48	1534	76	1610
1948–49	2431	199	2630
1949–50	2986	445	3431
1950–51	3380	692	4072
1951–52	4565	1226	5791
1952–53	5257	2144	7401
1953–54	4747	3912	8659
1954–55	5059	6084	11 143
1955–56	4113	5639	9752
1956–57	3901	5657	9558
1957–58	3737	6657	10 394

	Sows and boars	For bacon	Not for bacon	Total
1958–59	390	4169	7386	11 945
1959–60	335	3796	6819	10 950
1960–61	321	3767	6683	10 771

	Sows and boars	Used wholly for bacon	Used partly for bacon	Others	Total
1961	298	3307	1163	5959	10 727
1962	333	3533	1430	6786	12 082
1963	355	3371	1648	6828	12 202
1964	357	3276	1762	7410	12 805
1965	367	3549	1895	8519	14 330
1966	395	2903	2586	7601	13 485
1967	317	2542	2747	6730	12 337
1968	318	2684	3034	6940	12 977
1969	386	2896	3307	7439	14 028
1970	323	3076	3542	7450	14 391
1971	360	3524	4411	7669	15 964
1972	354	3287	4335	7430	15 406
1973	413	2877	4059	7742	15 091
1974	469	2726	4154	7925	15 274
1975	334	2260	3697	6477	12 768
1976	346	2487	3861	6816	13 510
1977	391	2450	3626	7727	14 195
1978	341	2127	4001	7299	13 768
1979	371	1990	4053	8258	14 672
1980	328	2043	4045	8210	14 626
1981	329	1814	4055	8669	14 867
1982	353	1786	3686	9230	15 055
1983	440	1866	3966	9717	15 989
1984	319	1788	4040	8790	14 938
1985	327	1720	4095	9163	15 305
1986	342	1726	4087	9455	15 610
1987	339	1496	4237	9735	15 807

Source. *Annual Abstract of Statistics.*

217

Table 19.6. Pigmeat production ('000 tonnes)

	For bacon	Not for bacon	Total[1]
1905–1909			273[2]
1924–1927			299[2]
Pre-war	249	174	423
1946–47	156	14	170
1947–48	128	7	135
1948–49	196	17	213
1949–50	248	45	293
1950–51	275	60	335
1951–52	333	100	433
1952–53	380	166	546
1953–54	316	253	569
1954–55	356	371	727
1955–56	291	341	632
1956–57	273	338	611
1957–58	260	401	661
1958–59	259	465	724
1959–60	232	431	663
1960–61	229	428	657
1961–62	254	460	714
1962–63			795

	Clean pigmeat[3]	Sow and boar meat[3]	Total[3]
1963–64	763	61	824
1964–65	818	57	875
1965–66	867	68	935
1966–67	785	57	842
1967–68	780	49	829
1968–69	817	57	874
1969–70	878	62	940
1970–71	941	53	994
1971–72	962	59	1021
1972	922	59	981
1973	930	65	995
1974	934	63	997
1975	782	44	826
1976	810	46	856
1977	865	53	918
1978	845	48	893
1979	902	49	951
1980	904	46	950
1981	909	45	954
1982	939	48	987
1983	974	62	1036
1984	920	45	965
1985	944	45	989
1986	963	47	1010
1987[4]	973	44	1017

[1]Pork only.   [2]Including Lard.   [3]Excluding offal.   [4]Forecast.
Note: Clean meat i.e. other than sow and boar meat.
Source. MAFF: *Output and Utilisation of Farm Produce in the United Kingdom.*
        Agricultural Statistics.

Table 19.7. Total pigmeat supplies ('000 tonnes)

	Home production	Retained imports	Total supplies	Home produced %
1926	283	491	774	37
1927	298	521	819	36
1928	339	549	888	38
1929	309	521	830	37
1930	279	578	857	33
1931	311	677	988	31
1932	357	675	1032	35
1933	365	570	935	39
1934	371	517	888	42
1935	414	467	881	47
1936	434	450	884	49
1937	415	469	884	47

Source. MAFF: *Agricultural Statistics.*

Table 19.8. Bacon and ham supplies 1938–65 ('000 tonnes)

	Home-killed pigs	Imported carcases	Retained imports	Total supplies	Home produced %
1938	197	21	376	594	33
1942	110	14	331	455	24
1946	117	24	181	322	36
1950	217	10	247	474	46
1955	246	–	311	557	44
1960	183	–	411	594	31
1965	236	–	402	638	37

Source. HMSO: *Annual Review of Agriculture and Determination of Guarantees.*

Table 19.9. Bacon and ham supplies 1970–87 ('000 tonnes)

	Production	Imports	Exports	Total new supply[1]	Production as % of new supply
1970–1972[2]	271	370	2	637	42
1973	252	314	1	564	45
1974	243	288	2	527	46
1975	210	273	1	482	44
1976	222	256	2	475	47
1977	221	287	2	505	44
1978	217	304	2	517	42
1979	212	307	2	516	41
1980	210	303	4	507	41
1981	200	301	5	495	40
1982	197	286	6	476	41
1983	212	271	6	477	44
1984	208	266	7	467	45
1985	203	264	6	462	44
1986	206	258	6	459	45
1987[3]	197	260	5	452	44

[1]New supply: production plus imports less exports (including supplies to Channel Islands).   [2]Average.   [3]Forecast.
Source. MAFF: *Output and Utilisation of Farm Produce in the United Kingdom.*
HMSO: *Annual Review of Agriculture 1988.*

Table 19.10. Pork supplies ('000 tonnes)

	Home produced	Retained imports	Total supplies	Home produced %
1938	181	38	219	99
1942	30	85	115	103
1946	25	54	79	99
1950	66	20	86	100
1955	374	32	406	92
1960	448	21	469	96
1965	637	17	654	97

Source. HMSO: *Annual Review and Determination of Guarantees.*

Table 19.11. Pork supplies ('000 tonnes)

	Production	Imports	Exports	Total new supply[1]	Production as % of new supply
1970–1972	646	29	13	660	98
1973	683	20	16	689	99
1974	695	7	24	675	103
1975	572	17	7	579	99
1976	584	13	11	583	100
1977	651	17	16	649	100
1978	634	39	13	658	96
1979	696	38	19	712	98
1980	693	39	25	705	98
1981	711	36	30	718	99
1982	745	27	41	731	102
1983	776	29	58	747	104
1984	713	37	41	710	100
1985	743	34	50	727	102
1986	760	32	57	736	103
1987[2]	791	46	51	786	101

[1]New supply: production plus imports less exports (including supplies to Channel Islands). [2]Forecast.
Source. MAFF: *Output and Utilisation of Farm Produce in the United Kingdom.*
HMSO: *Annual Review of Agriculture 1988.*

Table 19.13. Trade in live pigs ('000)

	Imports	Exports
1926	235	–
1930	415	–
1935	128	–
1938	48	–
1942	4	–
1945	106	–
1950	20	–
1955	–	–
1960	–	–
1965	–	–
1970	–	65
1975	62	31
1980	11	298
1981	52	606
1982	46	619
1983	44	571
1984	47	346
1985	60	234
1986	65	134
1987	60	61

Source. *Customs and Excise.*

Table 19.12. Estimated average pig slaughter weights[1] (kg dressed weight)

1963–64	62.0	1975	61.8
1964–65	61.8	1976	61.8
1965–66	61.0	1977	61.7
1966–67	61.9	1978	61.7
1967–68	62.4	1979	61.8
1968–69	61.3	1980	61.7
1969–70	61.3	1981	61.8
1970–71	61.3	1982	61.8
1971–72	60.7	1983	61.0
1972	61.1	1984	61.8
1973	62.1	1985	61.9
1974	61.5	1986	61.9

[1]Clean pigs only. i.e. other than sows and boars.
Note. Prior to 1973 derived from information supplied by slaughter houses and certification records. Since August 1975 the only figures for the average weight of pigs are based on the pig subsidy scheme which operated during part of 1977. That there has been little change since then is confirmed by the Cambridge University Pig Management Scheme.
Source. MAFF: *Output and Utilisation of Farm Produce in the United Kingdom.*

Table 19.14. Imports of bacon and ham 1871–85 ('000 tonnes)[1]

1871	56	1879	250
1872	102	1880	271
1873	152	1881	235
1874	129	1882	148
1875	134	1883	188
1876	162	1884	174
1877	143	1885	206
1878	218		

[1]Including imports into the whole of Ireland.
Source. *Statistical Abstract for the United Kingdom 1871–1885.*

Table 19.15. Imports of bacon and ham by country of origin ('000 tonnes)

	1926	1930	1935	1938	1942	1946	1950	1955	1960	1965	1970	1975	1980	1981	1982	1983	1984	1985	1986	1987
Belgium/Luxembourg	–	–	–	–	–	–	–	–	–	–	–	–	4	4	2	1	2	4	5	5
Canada	52	9	56	65	209	131	37	–	–	–	–	–	–	–	–	–	–	–	–	–
Denmark	185	311	194	172	–	41	146	232	286	304	287	232	208	204	196	187	170	152	139	129
Irish Republic	22	18	24	27	1	–	3	3	23	26	28	9	28	28	26	18	13	11	11	13
Netherlands	31	42	26	26	–	–	21	36	35	6	7	21	47	56	50	54	68	85	89	100
Poland	9	27	23	23	–	–	38	40	48	52	47	18	12	5	3	2	2	2	1	1
Sweden	13	27	13	13	–	–	- -	1	11	11	11	4	–	–	–	–	–	–	1	–
U.S.A.	111	66	22	2	81	6	–	–	–	–	–	–	–	–	–	–	–	–	–	–
FR Germany	–	–	–	–	–	–	–	–	–	–	–	–	3	3	9	9	9	9	10	10
Other countries	17	17	28	55[1]	40[1]	3[1]	3	1	9	5	4	3	1	1	- -	- -	2	1	2	2
Total	440	517	386	383	331	181	248	313	412	404	384	287	303	301	286	271	266	264	258	260

[1]Including hams from the countries listed.
- -Negligible.
Source. *Customs and Excise.*

Table 19.16. Trade in pork ('000 tonnes)

	Imports	Exports
1926	46	–
1930	33	–
1935	55	–
1938	62	–
1942	101	–
1946	81	–
1950	31	–
1955	38	–
1960	22	–
1965	21	–
1970	11	–
1975	17	7
1980	39	25
1981	36	30
1982	27	41
1983	29	58
1984	37	41
1985	34	50
1986	32	57
1987	46	51

Source. *Customs and Excise.*

Table 19.17. Pigmeat consumption (kg per head per annum)

	Pork	Bacon
1926	17.6[1]	
1930	19.2[1]	
1935	19.3[1]	
1934–38[2]	5.6	12.0
1942	2.2	8.8
1946	1.6	6.8
1950	2.0	9.7
1955	8.1	11.2
1960	8.7	11.3
1965	11.7	11.7
1970	11.1	11.4
1975	10.3	8.7
1980	12.6	9.1
1981	12.9	8.8
1982	13.2	8.4
1983	13.3	8.4
1984	12.5	8.3
1985	12.7	8.1
1986[3]	12.8	8.1
1987[4]	13.2	8.0

[1]All pig meats. [2]Average. [3]Provisional. [4]Forecast.
Source. MAFF: *Food Facts.*
Annual Abstracts of Statistics.

Table 19.18. Market prices and producers' total returns for slaughter pigs (p per kg dressed weight)

	Market prices		Total returns[2]	
	At current prices	In 1986 money values	At current prices	In 1986 money values
1955–56	21.0	183.8	28.4	248.5
1956–57	23.6	198.0	29.1	244.1
1957–58	20.4	165.6	26.3	213.6
1958–59	22.0	174.0	25.3	200.1
1959–60	21.5	169.0	25.0	196.5
1960–61	21.7	168.8	25.2	196.1
1961–62	19.2	145.3	24.9	188.5
1962–63	20.1	146.3	25.2	183.5
1963–64	20.6	147.1	24.0	171.4
1964–65	20.3	140.3	24.5	169.3
1965–66	19.7	130.2	24.3	160.6
1966–67	24.8	157.7	25.5	162.2
1967–68	24.7	152.9	26.3	162.8
1968–69	24.5	145.0	26.3	155.7
1969–70	25.7	144.4	27.8	156.2
1970–71	28.3	149.4	29.4	155.2
1971–72	28.0	135.0	30.7	148.0
1972–73	34.5	155.3	34.7	156.2
1973	43.8	180.9	43.8	180.9
1974	46.0	163.8	46.0	163.8
1975	61.9	177.0	61.9	177.0
1976	67.3	165.6	67.3	165.6
1977	72.6	153.9	74.0[1]	156.9
1978	80.1	157.0	80.1	157.0
1979	81.4	140.8	81.4	140.8
1980	86.6	126.4	86.6	126.4
1981	93.7	122.7	93.7	122.7
1982	97.1	116.5	97.1	116.5
1983	92.6	106.5	92.6	106.5
1984	107.7	118.5	107.7	118.5
1985	102.8	105.9	102.8	105.9
1986	98.8	98.8	98.8	98.8
1987	98.3	94.3	98.3	94.3

[1]Estimated payments of 5.5 p per kg dressed weight. 31 January–11 June 1977. [2]There were no deficiency payments from 1973 onwards with the exception of 1977 when there was a temporary payment for about four months.
Source. HMSO: *Annual Review of Agriculture*

Table 19.19. Changes in profitability and efficiency of pig production

	Margin per £100 output	No. of weaners reared per sow p.a.	Quantity of feed used per weaner (kg)	Feed conversion ratio
1946	7.0	10.8	135	4.95
1947	20.5	10.8	131	4.65
1948	19.0	11.4	123	5.04
1949	27.7	12.8	108	4.63
1950	30.4	12.8	111	4.51
1951	19.8	12.5	112	4.95
1952	16.1	12.5	111	4.80
1953	19.4	13.3	111	4.58
1954	12.9	13.4	111	4.30
1955	15.7	13.9	114	4.18
1956	13.0	14.0	114	4.24
1957	15.9	14.5	107	4.07
1958	11.2	13.5	116	3.99
1959	11.2	14.3	113	4.10
1960	14.1	13.7	120	3.96
1961	18.5	14.1	118	3.89
1962	13.2	13.9	118	3.96
1963	13.8	14.4	113	3.92
1914	11.8	14.3	116	3.95
1965	11.1	15.5	104	3.79
1966	11.5	15.7	105	3.90
1967	16.5	16.4	97	3.84
1968	16.5	17.1	95	3.82
1969	12.5	16.9	96	3.88
1970	16.3	16.8	95	3.85
1971	10.6	17.2	91	3.68
1972	16.6	17.3	92	3.72
1973	20.3	17.7	87	3.72
1974	2.7	17.5	88	3.74
1975	22.1	17.5	89	3.63
1976	16.6	17.8	88	3.51
1977	0.7	18.1	83	3.49
1978	15.4	18.6	83	3.47
1979	3.6	18.6	84	3.45
1980	9.7	18.9	82	3.25
1981	7.1	19.3	81	3.18
1982	9.7	19.5	79	3.07
1983	−5.7	20.1	78	3.06
1984	10.5	20.2	79	2.94
1985	10.4	20.6	78	2.90
1986	7.7	20.3	80	2.88
1987	7.4	21.0	79	2.77

Source. *University of Cambridge, Agricultural Economics Unit, Department of Land Economy, Pig Management Scheme results.*

Table 19.20. Retail bacon prices (p per lb)[1]

	At current prices	In 1986 values
1939	6.5	141.3
1940	7.5	137.5
1941	8.5	129.1
1942	8.5	120.8
1943	9.0	123.9
1944	9.0	121.7
1945	9.0	119.5
1946	9.0	118.1
1947	9.0	110.6
1948	10.0	114.1
1949	10.0	111.5
1950	10.5	113.8
1951	10.5	104.4
1952	16.0	149.8
1953	12.5	115.1
1954	15.5	140.4
1955	17.5	153.1
1956	17.5	146.8
1957	13.5	109.6
1958	15.5	122.6
1959	15.0	117.9
1960	14.5	112.8
1961	12.5	94.6
1962	14.0	101.9
1963	15.5	110.7
1964	14.5	100.2
1965	13.5	89.2
1966	13.5	85.9

[1]Streaky, thick smoked. Retail prices continue to be recorded as p per lb not per kg.
Source. *Based on Department of Employment data.*

Table 19.22. Retail pork prices (p per lb)[1]

	At current prices	In 1986 money values
1947	7.5	92.2
1948	7.5	85.6
1949	10.0	111.5
1950	10.0	108.4
1951	11.5	114.3
1952	14.0	131.0
1953	14.0	128.9
1954	15.0	135.9
1955	21.0	183.8
1956	20.0	167.8
1957	19.5	158.3
1958	20.0	158.2
1959	21.5	169.0
1960	21.0	163.4
1961	21.0	159.0
1962	19.5	142.0
1963	21.0	149.9
1964	21.5	148.6
1965	21.0	138.8
1966	24.0	152.6

[1]Leg (foot off). Retail prices continue to be recorded as p per lb not per kg.
Source. *Based on Department of Employment data.*

Table 19.21. Retail bacon prices (p per lb)[1]

	At current prices	In 1986 money values
1967	25.1	155.4
1968	25.5	151.0
1969	27.2	152.9
1970	29.5	155.8
1971	30.2	145.6
1972	34.6	155.7
1973	48.8	201.5
1974	57.0	202.9
1975	68.0	194.5
1976	79.7	196.1
1977	82.2	174.3
1978	88.9	174.2
1979	98.2	169.9
1980	101.0	147.5
1981	115.1	150.8
1982	127.9	153.5
1983	127.8	147.0
1984	135.3	148.8
1985	140.8	145.0
1986	140.7	140.7
1987	148.2	142.1

[1]All cuts. Retail prices continue to be recorded as p per lb not per kg.
Source. *Based on Department of Employment data.*

Table 19.23. Retail pork prices (p per lb)[1]

	At current prices	In 1986 money values
1967	24.0	148.6
1968	24.6	145.6
1969	25.4	142.7
1970	27.7	146.3
1971	29.3	141.2
1972	32.9	148.1
1973	42.6	175.9
1974	47.7	169.8
1975	58.7	167.9
1976	67.9	167.0
1977	71.8	152.2
1978	79.0	154.8
1979	86.2	149.1
1980	93.3	136.2
1981	98.1	128.5
1982	104.0	124.8
1983	102.9	118.3
1984	112.2	123.4
1985	114.3	117.7
1986	114.5	114.5
1987	117.2	112.4

[1]All cuts. Retail prices continue to be recorded as p per lb not per kg.
Source. *Based on Department of Employment data.*

Appendix 20: Poultry meat

Table 20.1. Value of output of poultry (£ million)

1937–38	6	1954–55	29	1971–72	152
1938–39	6	1955–56	35	1972	164
1939–40	8	1956–57	38	1973	211
1940–41	11	1957–58	46	1974	256
1941–42	11	1958–59	57	1975	296
1942–43	11	1959–60	69	1976	360
1943–44	9	1960–61	73	1977	445
1944–45	10	1961–62	75	1978	444
1945–46	11	1962–63	75	1979	488
1946–47	16	1963–64	76	1980	508
1947–48	17	1964–65	90	1981	515
1948–49	21	1965–66	93	1982	604
1949–50	21	1966–67	100	1983	626
1950–51	25	1967–68	107	1984	674
1951–52	25	1968–69	118	1985	702
1952–53	27	1969–70	127	1986	757
1953–54	24	1970–71	138	1987[1]	785

[1]Forecast.
Source. MAFF: *Departmental Net Income Calculation.*

Table 20.2. Poultry numbers (million)

	England and Wales	Scotland	Great Britain	Northern Ireland	United Kingdom
1884	10.8	1.9	12.7		
1885	10.8	2.0	12.8		
1908	28.9	4.2	33.1		
1913	29.7	4.1	33.8		
1921	25.3	4.3	29.5		
1924	31.4			6.8	
1925	34.3[2]	5.4[2]	39.8	6.8	46.5
1926	37.2	5.1	42.3	7.9	50.2
1927	40.1	5.4	45.5	7.9	53.4
1928	40.5	5.5	46.0	8.0	54.0
1929	43.5	5.7	49.2	8.3	57.5
1930	48.6	6.4	55.0	8.8	63.8
1931	53.1	7.2	60.3	8.7	69.0
1932	58.3	7.5	65.8	9.4	75.2
1933	62.0	8.2	70.2	10.2	80.4
1934	62.1	8.2	70.3	10.3	80.6
1935	59.0	7.8	66.8	10.1	76.9
1936	58.5	8.0	66.5	10.6	77.1
1937	53.3	7.3	60.6	10.2	70.8
1938	53.3	7.5	60.9	10.2	71.1
1939	53.6	7.5	61.1	10.2	71.3
1940	51.8	7.5	59.3	9.1	68.4
1941	40.5	6.2	46.7	12.9	59.6
1942	34.3	6.3	40.6	14.6	55.2
1943	26.8	5.9	32.7	15.4	48.1
1944	29.2	6.3	35.5	16.6	52.1
1945	34.3	7.0	41.3	17.5	58.8
1946	36.7	7.3	44.0	19.8	63.8
1947	38.4	7.6	45.9	21.0	66.9
1948	48.6	8.9	57.5	24.2	81.7
1949	57.8	9.6	67.4	24.2	91.6
1950	62.3	9.8	72.0	20.7	92.7
1951	64.2	9.7	73.9	17.8	91.7
1952	66.0	9.8	75.8	16.5	77.4
1953	65.2	9.7	74.9	14.6	89.5
1954	61.5	8.8	70.3	11.4	81.7
1955	65.2	8.8	74.0	11.3	85.3
1956	70.3	9.1	79.4	11.5	90.9
1957	72.4	9.1	81.5	11.7	93.2
1958	77.1	8.9	86.0	12.3	98.3
1959	84.4	9.0	93.3	11.9	105.2
1960	82.7	8.4	91.1	10.4	101.5
1961	93.2	9.1	102.3	10.2	112.5

continued opposite

Table 20.2 continued

	England and Wales	Scotland	Great Britain	Northern Ireland	United Kingdom
1962	89.2	8.8	97.9	9.6	107.5
1963	93.1	8.4	101.5	9.3	110.8
1964	97.4	8.9	106.4	10.6	117.0
1965	97.2	9.1	106.3	10.4	116.6
1966	97.9	8.8	106.7	10.8	117.5
1967	103.4	8.9	112.3	11.9	124.2
1968	105.3	8.8	114.1	12.0	126.1
1969	102.7	9.5	112.2	12.9	125.1
1970	115.3	12.7	128.1	13.9	142.0
1971	109.5	13.3	122.9	14.6	137.5
1972	109.6	14.1	123.7	14.8	138.5
1973	115.2	14.6	129.8	12.7	142.4
1974	112.9	13.5	126.4	11.8	138.2
1975	110.2	13.0	123.2	12.0	135.3
1976	114.6	14.1	128.7	12.1	140.8
1977	108.8	13.1	121.9	11.0	133.0
1978	111.2	12.8	124.0	11.9	135.9
1979	108.6	12.7	121.3	11.9	133.2
1980	108.9	13.3	122.2	11.4	133.7
1981	107.6	11.6	119.2	11.5	130.9
1982	110.2	12.6	122.8	11.0	133.9
1983	103.2	12.4	115.6	10.5	126.2
1984	102.5	12.7	115.2	10.8	126.0
1985	104.1	13.1	117.2	10.1	127.3
1986	98.6[3]	12.5[3]	111.0[3]	9.7	120.7[3]
1987	104.7[3]	13.8[3]	118.5[3]	10.1[3]	128.6[3]
1988[4]					129.0

[1]Fowls and turkeys.   [2]Estimate.   [3]Fowls only.   [4]Provisional.
Note. Because of changes in definition figures may not be comparable from year to year.
Source. Agricultural Departments: *Agricultural Census.*

Table 20.3. The poultry population (million)

	Laying fowls	Table fowls	Total fowls	Turkeys
1935			75.1	1.2
1938			69.1	1.4
1944			50.2	1.0
1951			90.1	1.2
1956			88.3	2.3
1960	86.7	16.3	103.0	3.0
1965	74.1	31.2	112.1[1]	4.4
1970	79.8	49.8	137.2[1]	4.8
1975	49.4	56.7	130.3[1]	5.0
1980	46.0	59.9	127.1[1]	6.5
1981	44.5	57.8	122.6[1]	8.2
1982	44.8	60.1	126.1[1]	7.7
1983	41.1	58.9	117.9[1]	8.2
1984	40.6	59.3	118.8[1]	7.1
1985	39.5	61.3	119.5[1]	7.9
1986	38.1	63.8	120.7[1]	
1987	38.5	70.6	128.6[1]	
1988[2]	36.9	73.6	129.0[1]	

[1]Including growing pullets.   [2]Provisional.
Note. Because of changes in coverage of poultry holdings, data for 1983 and subsequent years cannot be directly compared with data for earlier years.
Source. Agricultural Departments: *Agricultural Census.*

Table 20.4. Number of holdings by size of broiler flock
(England and Wales)

Number of Broilers	1976	1981	1986
1–999	595	400	467
1000–1999	64	50	43
2000–4999	84	67	64
5000–9999	160	125	105
10 000–19 999	202	200	166
20 000–49 999	240	268	295
50 000–99 999	129	126	180
100 000–249 999	72	87	103
250 000–499 999	8	12	10
500 000–999 999	11	4 ⎫	
1 000 000 and over	6	3 ⎬	10
Total number of holdings	1571	1341	1443
Number of fowls (million)	49.9	46.5	50.9
(United Kingdom)			
Average size of flock ('000)	25.0	27.4	31.4
% of broilers in flocks of 100 000 and over	59.4	54.9	53.8

Source. MAFF: *Agricultural Statistics England and Wales.*
Agricultural Statistics United Kingdom.

Table 20.5. Estimated slaughterings and poultry meat production

	Pre-war	1946-47	1950-51	1955-56	1960-61	1965-66	1970-71	1975	1980	1981	1982	1983	1984	1985	1986	1987[1]
Slaughterings (million)																
Fowls																
over 6 months							48.8	44.0	39.8	36.5	38.3	38.6	36.2	37.1	37.2	34.0
under 6 months							287.2	324.2	370.9	375.9	401.7	387.7	413.3	428.6	454.1	492.0
Total fowls	42.4	27.2	42.0	72.6	195.8	236.0	336.0	368.2	410.7	412.4	440.0	426.3	449.6	465.7	491.3	526.0
Ducks	2.8	2.8	3.0	4.2	4.3	4.4	6.0	5.9	7.1	7.1	7.6	7.7	7.6	7.9	8.5	8.1
Geese	0.6	0.8	0.8	0.5	0.4	0.3	0.2	0.1	0.2	0.2	0.2	0.2	0.2	0.2	0.2	0.2
Turkeys	1.1	1.0	1.1	1.9	4.6	7.5	14.1	16.9	23.4	22.2	24.7	26.0	26.3	26.7	30.2	31.9
Total poultry	46.9	31.9	46.7	79.2	205.1	248.2	356.3	391.2	441.4	441.9	472.6	460.2	483.7	500.5	530.2	566.2
Poultry meat production ('000 tonnes)																
Fowls																
over 6 months							72.8	66.5	60.6	57.0	59.1	59.9	57.0	57.9	57.6	52.9
under 6 months							419.6	483.8	554.8	555.7	604.7	589.5	632.7	657.6	698.5	772.0
Total fowls	65.5	40.8	63.5	94.0	280.5	337.4	492.4	550.3	615.4	612.7	663.8	649.4	689.7	715.5	756.1	824.9
Ducks	6.2	6.1	6.1	7.6	8.0	8.0	12.8	0.8	15.4	15.3	16.5	16.7	16.4	17.1	18.4	17.6
Geese	2.8	3.8	3.8	2.2	2.1	1.4	0.7	0.5	0.8	0.8	0.9	0.9	0.8	0.8	0.9	1.1
Turkeys	6.0	5.6	5.9	10.3	21.7	32.4	69.3	76.6	122.1	116.7	130.3	136.6	138.5	140.4	158.7	167.3
Total poultry meat	80.6	56.3	79.2	114.0	312.4	379.2	575.3	628.2	753.7	745.5	811.5	803.6	845.4	873.8	934.1	1010.9

[1]Forecast.
Source. MAFF: *Output and Utilisation of Farm Produce in the United Kingdom.*

Table 20.6. Poultry meat supplies, pre-war–1965 ('000 tonnes)

	Production	Supplies	Production as % of supplies
Pre-war[1]	79	100	79
1941–42[1]	56	60	85
1945	52	61	85
1950	84	130	65
1955	112	148	76
1960	312	297	105
1965	407	405	100

[1]Average.
Source. MAFF: *Agricultural Statistics.*

Table 20.7. Poultry meat supplies, 1970–87 ('000 tonnes)

	Production	Imports	Exports	Total new supply[1]	Production as % of new supply
1970–1972[2]	613	9	1	619	99
1973	664	10	5	669	99
1974	652	7	4	654	100
1975	628	8	4	633	99
1976	663	6	17	652	102
1977	717	8	30	693	103
1978	727	19	32	712	102
1979	752	32	27	756	99
1980	754	28	22	760	99
1981	745	24	20	749	99
1982	812	27	20	819	99
1983	804	51	23	832	97
1984	846	53	28	871	97
1985	874	61	31	904	97
1986	922	89	38	973	95
1987[3]	1010	85	41	1054	96

[1]New supplies: production plus imports less exports (including supplies to Channel Islands). [2]Average. [3]Forecast.
Source. HMSO: *Annual Review of Agriculture.*

Table 20.8. Imports of poultry meat ('000 tonnes)

	1938	1942	1945	1950	1955	1960	1965	1970	1975	1980	1981	1982	1983	1984	1985	1986	1987
Denmark	0.1	–	–	1.4	3.1	2.3	11.9	5.7	2.8	–	2.5	21.1	18.4	10.4	10.0	8.4	6.1
France	0.4	–	–	1.3	0.1	–	–	–	–	4.6	1.5	–	6.1	13.6	22.5	47.3	38.3
Irish Republic	5.2	10.2	8.0	10.8	7.2	2.9	0.5	0.5	1.9	5.0	3.2	3.9	2.8	–	–	–	–
Netherlands	1.2	–	–	1.0	–	–	–	–	2.6	15.3	15.6	–	23.1	23.4	25.3	28.1	31.5
Poland	0.4	–	–	6.1	–	–	–	–	–	–	–	–	–	–	–	–	–
Other countries	13.7[1]	–	1.2	10.8	2.4	0.5	0.2	–	1.2	2.7	0.9	2.2	0.7	5.5	3.2	4.5	6.1
Total	21.0	10.2	9.2	31.4	12.8	5.7	12.6	6.3	8.5	27.6	23.7	27.2	51.1	52.9	61.0	88.3	82.0

[1]Of which 7400 tonnes imported from Hungary.
Source. *Customs and Excise.*

Table 20.9. Exports of poultry meat ('000 tonnes)

	1970	1975	1980	1981	1982	1983	1984	1985	1986	1987
Egypt			5.1							
France			0.8	1.1	1.8	2.1	2.3	2..5	1.9	
Irish Republic			5.3	5.8	6.7	6.5	7.4	8.4	8.3
Italy							1.1	3.0	2.4	
Netherlands				1.6	3.2	4.4	3.7	4.2	4.6	
FR Germany			1.8	3.8	5.9	7.5	9.8	8.4	10.1	10.8
USSR			4.0							
Other countries			7.7	5.2	2.9	2.1	3.9	5.0	10.0	29.2
Total	1.0	2.0	19.4	17.0	19.7	22.8	27.3	30.6	37.3	48.3

Source. *Customs and Excise.*

Table 20.10. Poultry meat consumption
(kg per head per annum)

Pre-war	2.3
1942	1.7
1945	1.3
1950	2.5
1955	2.9
1960	5.3
1965	7.6
1970	10.7
1975	11.4
1980	13.4
1981	13.3
1982	14.4
1983	14.7
1984	15.4
1985	16.0
1986	17.2
1987[1]	18.1

[1]Forecast.
Source. MAFF: *Food Facts. Annual Abstract of Statistics*.

Table 20.11. Wholesale poultry meat prices (p per kg)

	At current prices	In 1986 money values
Fowls		
1929	15.4	326.5
1930	14.3	313.5
1935	12.1	293.7
1938	13.2	292.6
1948	35.3	402.8
1950	28.7	311.1
1955	27.6	241.5
1960	23.7[1]	184.4
Broilers		
1970–71[2]	29.6	156.3
1972–73[2]	32.4	145.8
1973	42.9	177.2
1974	45.8	163.0
1975	55.0	157.3
1976	63.6	156.5
1977	76.0	161.1
1978	81.1	159.0
1979	82.1	142.0
1980	91.1	133.0
1981	91.6	120.0
1982	92.8	111.4
1983	99.5	114.4
1984	104.2	114.6
1985	98.9	101.9
1986	99.7	99.7
1987[3]	98.1	94.1

[1]Estimate.   [2]Average.   [3]Forecast.
Source. HMSO: *Annual Review of Agriculture*.

Table 20.12. Retail poultry meat prices (p per lb)

	At current prices	In 1986 money values
1967	16.1	99.7
1968	16.0	94.7
1969	16.2	91.0
1970	16.5	87.1
1971	18.2	87.7
1972	17.7	79.7
1973	23.2	95.8
1974	25.3	90.1
1975	30.1	86.1
1976	34.1	83.9
1977	41.0	86.9
1978	44.0	86.2
1979	49.5	85.6
1980	51.9	75.8
1981	52.7	69.0
1982	56.7	68.0
1983	57.7	66.4
1984	61.8	68.0
1985	61.6	63.4
1986	64.5	64.5
1987	64.6	62.0

Note. Retail price statistics are still recorded as p per lb not per kg.

Appendix 21: Milk and milk products

Table 21.1. Value of output of milk and milk products[1] (£ million)

Year	£ million
1937–38	80
1938–39	82
1939–40	91
1940–41	114
1941–42	129
1942–43	146
1943–44	156
1944–45	163
1945–46	176
1946–47	190
1947–48	210
1948–49	242
1949–50	274
1950–51	284
1951–52	299
1952–53	318
1953–54	340
1954–55	328
1955–56	339
1956–57	348
1957–58	344
1958–59	333
1959–60	341
1960–61	350
1961–62	359
1962–63	360
1963–64	371
1964–65	394
1965–66	406
1966–67	416
1967–68	438
1968–69	442
1969–70	455
1970–71	512
1971–72	584
1972	622
1973	695
1974	833
1975	1063
1976	1292
1977	1484
1978	1620
1979	1764
1980	1960
1981	2101
1982	2384
1983	2493
1984	2337
1985	2399
1986	2512
1987[2]	2411

[1]Farm manufactured milk products only. [2]Forecast.
Source. MAFF: *Departmental Net Income Calculation.*

Table 21.2. Cow population ('000)

Year	United Kingdom Total cows	United Kingdom Dairy cows	Great Britain Total cows	Great Britain Dairy cows
1866–70			2072	
1871–75			2204	
1876–80			2228	
1881–85			2353	
1886–90			2499	
1891–95			2562	
1896–1900			2585	
1901–05			2627	
1906–10			2765	
1911–15			2825	
1916–20			2921	
1921–25			3053	
1926–30			3187	
1931–35			3412	
1936–40			3605	
1929	2996		2410	
1930	2953		2384	
1935	3293		2602	
1938	3264		2606	
1939	3321		3075	
1942	3397		3132	
1946	3537		3241	
1947	3540		3233	
1948	3583		3273	
1949	3690		3379	
1950	3767		3462	
1951	3653		3367	
1952	3599		3334	
1953	3682		3425	
1954	3729		3467	
1955	3706		3451	2779
1956	3793		3540	2815
1957	3891		3623	2868
1958	3884		3618	2884
1959	3849		3595	2846
1960	4013	3165	3733	2953
1961	4154	3246	3846	3035
1962	4269	3291	3944	3089
1963	4260	3247	3933	3053
1964	4125	3144	3798	2948
1965	4208	3186	3866	2990
1966	4268	3162	3897	2963
1967	4356	3215	3974	3014
1968	4378	3225	3995	3025
1969	4485	3275	4089	3070
1970	4548	3244	4119	3035
1971	4611	3234	4142	3019
1972	4800	3325	4290	3101
1973	5114	3436	4554	3200
1974	5281	3393	4700	3153
1975	5140	3242	4573	3003
1976	4991	3228	4459	2986
1977	4945	3265	4408	3015
1978	4852	3274	4333	3014
1979	4823	3292	4314	3024
1980	4691	3224	4197	2954
1981	4594	3187	4118	2916
1982	4639	3250	4163	2970
1983	4690	3333	4202	3039
1984	4632	3281	4137	2982
1985	4483	3150	3989	2856
1986	4446	3138	3956	2846
1987	4385	3042	3901	2753
1988[3]	4282	2911		

[1]Cows and heifers in milk or in calf. [2]Cows and heifers in milk and cows in milk but not in calf. [3]Provisional. Source. Agricultural Departments: *Agricultural Census.*

Table 21.3. Dairy cow numbers by country ('000)

	England and Wales	Scotland	Northern Ireland	United Kingdom
1939		335		
1945		365		
1950		371		
1955	2415	363		
1960	2595	358	213	3165
1965	2650	340	196	3186
1970	2714	321	208	3244
1975	2701	302	239	3242
1980	2672	282	270	3224
1981	2638	278	271	3187
1982	2688	282	280	3250
1983	2750	289	294	3333
1984	2699	283	299	3281
1985	2583	273	294	3150
1986	2576	270	292	3138
1987	2489	264	289	3042

Source. Agricultural Departments: *Agricultural Census.*

Table 21.5. Average milk yields in the United Kingdom (litres per cow per annum)

	Gross yield per cow
Pre-war	2457
1940–41	2125
1946–47	2300
1953–54	2787

	Gross yield per dairy cow
1954–55	3144
1959–60	3381
1962–63	3576
1964–65	3626
1969–70	3737
1975	4102
1980	4714
1981	4728
1982	4913
1983	4967
1984	4749
1985	4848
1986[1]	4935

[1]Provisional.
Source. Milk Marketing Board: *Dairy Facts.*
     MAFF: *Output and Utilisation of Farm Produce in the United Kingdom.*

Table 21.4. Holdings with dairy cows (England and Wales)

No of cows	1955[1]	1960[1]	1976[2]	1981[2]	1986[2]
1–2			3597	3051	2060
3–4	45 110	28 011	1583	819	578
5–9			3574	1387	973
10–14	52 760	45 833	4003	1789	1323
15–19			4100	2282	1514
20–29	22 907	24 025	8441	5514	4004
30–39	10 102	11 377	7808	5629	4645
40–49	4971	6085	6481	5359	4692
50–59			4878	4331	3859
60–69			3922	3608	3395
70–99	5549	7635	6542	7101	7069
100–199			4099	5395	6006
200–299			503	904	937
300 and over			209		
Total	141 399	122 966	59 740	47 169	41 055
No of cows	2 475 610	2 552 857	2 688 075	2 637 869	2 573 222
Average herd size	17.5	20.8	45.0	55.9	62.7

[1]Milk Marketing Board estimates.   [2]MAFF: *Agricultural Census.*

Table 21.6. Milk production and utilisation (million litres)

	Great Britain	
	Liquid consumption	Manufactured milk
1905–09	3517	
1924–27	3977	
1936–37[1]	3096	1407

	United Kingdom							
	Gross production	Output for human consumption	Liquid milk and cream	Butter	Cheese	Condensed milk[2]	Full cream milk powder	Other[3]
Pre-war	8065	7074	4587	1232	464	350	59	18
1946–47	8137	7515	6574	436	209	123	168	5
1947–48	8337	7687	6596	400	227	173	291	–
1948–49	9306	8624	7378	496	355	223	173	–
1949–50	9792	9087	7528	564	473	323	186	14
1950–51	9819	9092	7742	436	496	236	150	18
1951–52	9806	9101	7719	368	518	286	182	14
1952–53	10 012	9274	7565	414	1208	350	159	14
1953–54	10 569	9806	7519	705	959	359	164	9
1954–55	10 483	9719	7483	696	1050	527	173	14
1955–56	10 792	10 028	7533	709	782	605	218	18
1956–57	11 160	10 506	7528	882	1146	664	259	27
1957–58	11 351	10 656	7555	1091	1182	577	209	41
1958–59	10 788	10 065	7678	641	905	586	209	41
1959–60	11 197	10 415	7796	723	1023	609	218	45
1960–61	11 892	11 115	7896	1173	1205	596	191	55
1961–62	12 338	11 533	8074	1427	1196	582	186	68
1962–63	12 392	11 570	8192	1396	1123	582	209	68
1963–64	12 024	11 188	8319	864	1086	600	232	86
1964–65	11 351	11 170	8315	1078	1214	641	209	91
1965–66	11 551	11 388	8387	905	1155	636	209	95
1966–67	11 506	11 365	8469	750	1168	672	209	95
1967–68	12 011	11 874	8574	1086	1255	632	214	109
1968–69	12 033	11 892	8496	1241	1218	623	214	105
1969–70	12 344	12 212	8539	1464	1298	600	203	107
1970–71	12 648	12 521	8528	1577	1464	623	211	116
1971–72[4]	13 058	12 926	8433	1835	1710	593	234	111
1972	13 593	12 459	8519	2205	1854	560	204	117
1973	13 830	13 699	8688	2248	1819	603	219	122
1974	13 431	13 309	8896	1259	2181	580	260	132
1975	13 407	13 332	9047	1112	2361	502	195	114
1976	13 877	13 807	8897	2070	2039	524	175	103
1977	14 645	14 583	8620	3055	2073	560	178	97
1978	15 340	15 262	8548	3667	2172	578	210	87
1979	15 354	15 271	8493	3602	2359	534	194	99
1980[4]	15 409	15 340	8363	3782	2381	472	249	93
1981[5]	15 305	15 238	8169	3822	2420	459	240	106
1982[5]	16 174	16 093	8037	4721	2440	506	270	102
1983[5]	16 729	16 590	8002	5294	2450	422	355	89
1984[4][5]	15 722	15 592	7821	4436	2451	428	367	84
1985[5]	15 560	15 420	7600	4366	2558	428	367	84
1986[5]	15 766	15 629	7453	4715	2562	432	354	101
1987[5][6]	14 914	14 798	7385	3716	2620	407	510	97

[1]England and Wales only.   [2]Including quantities manufactured into chocolate crumb.   [3]Including inter Board transfer   [4]366 days.   [5]From 1981 onwards includes measurement adjustment. Sales through schemes will therefore not add up to total utilisation of milk within the scheme.   [6]Forecast.

Source. *Output and Utilisation of Farm Produce in the United Kingdom.*

Table 21.7. United Kingdom supplies of butter ('000 tonnes)

	Production	Imports	Exports	New supplies	Production as % of new supply	Closing stocks	Consumption
1905–09[1]	37	246	–	283	13		
1924–27[1]	35	223	–	258	14		
Pre-war	48	488	–	536	9		
1940–41	25	233	–	258	10		
1946–47	18	208	–	226	8		
1953–54	29	293	–	322	9		
1959–60	30	410	–	440	7		
1964–65	31	469	–	500	6		
1969–70	61	436	2	495	12		
1975	48	496	3	541	9	83	517
1980	170	208	80	298	57	70	352
1981	172	207	72	307	56	43	337
1982	216	185	63	338	64	111	302
1983	242	185	54	373	65	177	307
1984	206	160	24	342	60	231	288
1985	202	141	25	318	64	264	285
1986	223	145	34	334	67	318	280
1987[2]	177	125	145	157	113	209	266

[1]Average. [2]Forecast.
Source. MAFF: *Output and Utilisation of Farm Produce in the United Kingdom.*
HMSO: *Annual Review of Agriculture.*

Table 21.8. Imports of butter ('000 tonnes)

	1935	1938	1942	1945	1950	1955	1960	1965[1]	1970	1975	1980	1981	1982	1983	1984	1985	1986	1987
Argentina	56.9	62.9	–	–	–	7.4	15.8	4.1	0.2	–	–	–	–	–	–	–	–	–
Australia	107.4	91.3	41.4	45.8	67.1	74.4	59.3	64.5	66.3	–	–	–	–	–	–	–	–	–
Belgium	–	–	–	–	–	–	–	–	–	8.8	2.6	- -	1.7	2.1	- -	0.2	0.7	–
Denmark	111.1	120.1	–	26.5	128.2	86.2	99.8	102.2	84.3	84.1	39.8	43.2	37.3	39.7	33.9	31.8	31.8	29.0
Finland	–	–	–	–	–	–	22.6	16.5	11.2	–	–	–	–	–	–	–	–	–
France	0.4	–	–	–	–	4.0	3.7	9.3	4.1	37.3	1.8	1.3	1.0	0.9	1.3	1.5	1.2	–
Irish Republic	24.8	16.6	- -	–	–	1.1	7.3	19.2	32.5	53.3	30.6	31.0	27.5	21.0	24.4	19.7	23.5	13.3
Netherlands	23.6	36.2	–	–	15.2	10.7	17.6	20.5	13.3	118.3	13.1	21.9	10.6	14.2	7.4	6.3	5.1	4.7
New Zealand	134.0	131.7	94.9	120.1	129.7	123.8	149.4	177.0	158.2	124.0	104.8	100.5	99.2	93.8	89.7	77.9	76.3	72.4
Poland	5.0	–	–	–	–	3.1	21.8	17.7	12.5	–	–	–	–	–	–	–	–	–
Federal Republic of Germany	–	–	–	–	–	–	–	–	–	58.3	11.6	9.0	6.1	1.9	0.6	0.7	0.4	–
Other countries	24.9	24.7	0.1	0.7	0.5	1.7	17.6	15.1	12.0	0.1	–	0.1	0.2	9.2	1.7	0.6	1.6	4.3
Total	488.1	483.5	136.4	193.1	340.7	312.4	414.9	446.1	394.6	484.2	204.3	207.0	183.6	182.8	159.0	138.7	140.6	123.7

[1]Including imports of butter oil. - - Negligible.
Source. *Customs and Excise.*

Table 21.9. United Kingdom supplies of cheese ('000 tonnes)

	Production	Imports	Exports	New supplies	Production as % of new supplies
1905–09[1]	38	118	–	156	24
1924–27[1]	44	145	–	189	23
Pre-War	46	144	–	190	24
1940–41	33	177	–	210	16
1946–47	20	194	–	214	9
1953–54	91	152	–	243	37
1959–60	98	145	–	243	40
1964–65	117	158	–	275	43
1969–70	123	155	3	275	45
1975	235	152	7	380	62
1980	238	116	16	338	70
1981	242	140	23	359	67
1982	244	130	34	340	72
1983	245	135	34	346	71
1984	246	145	32	359	68
1985	256	162	32	386	66
1986	257	173	34	396	64
1987[2]	263	160	30	393	66

[1]Average.   [2]Forecast.
Source. HMSO: *Annual Review of Agriculture.*

Table 21.10. Imports of cheese ('000 tonnes)

	1935	1938	1942	1945	1950	1955	1960	1965	1970	1975	1980	1981	1982	1983	1984	1985	1986	1987
Australia	6.8	12.0	5.0	3.6	16.5	20.1	15.4	12.3	11.2	[1]	2.5	2.8	2.7	[1]	2.5	2.8	2.6	2.5
Belgium	–	–	–	–	–	–	–	–	–	0.7	3.9	5.2	4.4	7.0	12.6	14.8	15.5	13.7
Canada	23.9	34.4	56.7	59.4	26.3	6.1	8.5	13.9	12.9	[1]	[1]	3.1	3.3	2.9	2.7	3.4	3.0	3.7
Denmark	0.5	–	–	–	7.2	10.7	10.6	9.5	9.2	17.6	19.8	21.7	21.3	16.8	13.8	11.9	11.6	12.1
France	0.4	[1]	–	–	2.9	0.8	1.2	5.2	7.4	13.8	13.1	14.2	11.9	10.4	11.2	12.6	13.8	16.8
Irish Republic	–	–	–	–	0.5	0.1	0.7	9.0	20.2	55.7	31.9	40.3	38.9	42.9	47.6	51.6	61.0	47.8
Italy	4.1	–	–	–	5.0	0.9	1.4	1.1	0.9	1.4	1.7	1.9	1.9	2.0	2.3	2.6	2.9	3.3
Netherlands	10.1	10.3	–	–	5.9	7.1	9.3	11.6	14.5	26.5	20.6	23.3	23.5	22.7	20.5	23.0	25.1	21.1
New Zealand	89.6	83.3	134.3	85.2	81.6	82.8	78.7	82.5	66.5	30.3	6.7	8.0	7.2	9.2	6.1	7.5	7.9	6.8
Switzerland	0.7	[1]	–	–	0.8	0.9	1.0	1.1	1.2	[1]	[1]	1.1	[1]	[1]	[1]	[1]	[1]	[1]
Federal Republic of Germany	–	–	–	–	–	–	–	–	–	3.2	11.5	16.6	11.9	15.8	22.7	28.0	25.5	27.1
Other countries	1.1	8.7	124.2[2]	46.1[3]	9.7	1.5	8.0	6.4	12.9	2.8	4.1	1.9	3.1	4.8	3.3	3.5	3.8	5.2
Total	137.2	148.7	320.2	194.3	156.4	131.0	134.8	152.6	156.9	152.0	115.8	140.1	130.1	134.5	145.3	161.7	172.7	160.1

[1]Included in other countries.   [2]of which United States 45.5.   [3]of which United States 12.4.
Source. *Customs and Excise.*

Table 21.11. UK production of condensed milk ('000 tonnes)

	Sweetened whole	Unsweetened whole	Skimmed
Pre-war	121.2[1]		
1942			
1946			
1950			
1956–57	51.9	102.4	25.8
1960	52.6	113.7	22.9
1965	44.7	140.7	20.8
1970	34.0	152.6	18.3
1975		195	48
1980		182	51
1981		177	47
1982		195	65
1983		188	60
1984		163	47
1985		165	46
1986		166	50
1987[2]		159	

[1]Estimate, whole sweetened and unsweetened skimmed milk as well as chcolate crumb.   [2]Forecast.
Source. MAFF: *Output and Utilisation of Farm Produce in the United Kingdom.*

Table 21.13. UK production of milk powder ('000 tonnes)

	Whole	Skimmed	Butter milk and whey powder
1938	41[1]		
1955	22.4	23.0	5.0
1960	26.3	58.7	12.2
1965	25.9	68.3	12.5
1970	21.3	93.6	12.5
1975	24	106	30.5
1980	31	251	34.1
1981	30	260	7.8
1982	34	322	36.4
1983	32	321	35.1
1984	44	246	60.3
1985	46	266	60.6
1986	44	268	63.1
1987[2]	58	202	54.8

[1]Production and imports of all types of milk powder.   [2]Forecast.
Source. MAFF: *Output and Utilisation of Farm Produce in the United Kingdom.*

Table 21.12. Trade in condensed milk ('000 tonnes)

	Imports	Exports
1935	90.8	14.5
1942	195.1	- -
1945	66.4	2.3
1950	27.4	8.8
1955	1.1	42.2
1960	9.7	41.8
1965	6.4	47.0
1970	12.7	36.0
1975	9.4	14.7
1980	2.2	38.3
1981	1.0	31.1[1]
1982	3.9	37.4
1983	5.8	36.9
1984	6.7	26.5
1985	3.9	34.1
1986	9.1	26.5

- -Negligible.
[1]Estimated.
Source. *Customs and Excise.*

Table 21.14. Trade in milk powder ('000 tonnes)

	Imports	Exports
1935	11.4	- -
1942	66.0	- -
1945	30.4	1.1
1950	38.5	1.6
1955	39.5	3.0
1960	64.1	8.6
1965	81.4	15.5
1970	54.8	31.9
1975	63.0	91.8
1980	10.6	182.0
1981	11.2	147.7
1982	11.4	159.8
1983	19.1	151.0
1984	21.4	212.8
1985	16.2	173.9
1986	11.2	214.3

- - Negligible.
Source. *Customs and Excise.*

Table 21.15. Consumption per head of milk and dairy products (kg per head per annum)

	Liquid milk[1]	Cream	Liquid skimmed milk[3]	Evaporated and condensed milk	Milk powder	Butter	Cheese
Pre-war	98.5	0.7		6.0	0.7	11.2	4.0
1942	128.7	–		2.4	1.3	3.5	6.4
1946	140.3	–		3.1	1.1	5.0	4.5
1950	156.3	–		3.7	1.1	7.7	4.6
1955	147.6	0.3		2.9	1.4	6.7	4.1
1960	144.8	0.6		3.3	2.0	8.3	4.5
1965	145.7	1.0		3.4	1.8	8.8	4.6
1970	141.1	1.5		3.9	2.0	8.8	5.4
1975	146.3	1.6		2.9	1.7	8.4	6.3
1980	152.8[2]		0.9	1.8	1.1	6.3	6.0
1981	149.2[2]		1.9	1.9	1.7	5.8	6.1
1982	146.7[2]		2.5	2.1	1.3	5.4	6.2
1983	146.2[2]		3.7	1.7	1.7	5.4	6.0
1984	141.9[2]		7.4	1.7	2.4	5.1	6.5
1985	137.6[2]		10.0	1.6	2.7	5.0	6.6
1986[4]	135.1[2]		12.2	1.6	1.9	4.2	6.5

[1]1 kg = approx. 0.97 litres.   [2]New series – including cream.   [3]Liquid skimmed milk (as such). This is a by product of cream and butter production.   [4]Provisional.
Source. MAFF: *Food Facts.*

Table 21.17. Net returns to milk producers
(p per litre)

	At current prices	In 1986 money values
1955–56	3.38	29.58
1956–57	3.26	27.35
1957–58	3.17	25.74
1958–59	3.24	25.63
1959–60	3.23	25.39
1960–61	3.07	23.88
1961–62	3.06	23.16
1962–63	3.02	21.99
1963–64	3.17	22.63
1964–65	3.42	23.63
1965–66	3.46	22.87
1966–67	3.56	22.64
1967–68	3.61	22.35
1968–69	3.61	21.37
1969–70	3.61	20.29
1970–71	3.89	20.54
1971–72	4.29	20.68
1972	4.44	19.98
1973	5.16	21.31
1974	6.34	22.57
1975	7.98	22.82
1976	9.36	23.03
1977	10.18	21.58
1978	10.61	20.80
1979	11.55	19.98
1980	12.77	18.64
1981	13.79	18.06
1982	14.81	17.77
1983	15.03	17.28
1984	14.99	16.49
1985	15.56	16.04
1986	16.07	16.07
1987[1]	16.36	15.69

[1]Forecast.
Source. 1955–56 to 1965–66: *United Kingdom Dairy Facts and Figures.*
1966–67 to date: HMSO: *Annual Review of Agriculture.*

Table 21.16. Production and consumption of margarine

	Production ('000 tonnes)	Total consumption ('000 tonnes)	Consumption per head (kg)
Pre-war			3.9
1942			7.9
1955	372	408	8.0
1960	374	369	5.9
1965	313	307	4.4
1970	314	308	5.0
1975	298	291	5.0
1980	382	398	6.9
1981	398	419	7.2
1982	399	424	7.4
1983	387	420	7.3
1984	382	422	7.3
1985	378	422	7.3
1986	384	432	7.4

Source. MAFF: *Food Facts.*
Annual Abstract of Statistics.

Table 21.18. Average retail prices of milk (p per pint)[1]

	At current prices	In 1986 money values
1938	1.41	31.26
1939	1.41	30.65
1940	1.51	27.68
1941	1.82	27.65
1942	1.82	25.86
1943	1.82	25.06
1944	1.88	25.42
1945	1.88	24.97
1946	1.88	24.67
1947	1.98	24.33
1948	2.08	23.73
1949	2.08	23.19
1950	2.08	22.55
1951	2.20	21.87
1952	2.60	24.34
1953	2.73	25.14
1954	2.74	24.82
1955	2.92	25.55
1956	3.02	25.34
1957	3.28	26.63
1958	3.25	25.71
1959	3.25	25.55
1960	3.23	25.13
1961	3.33	25.21
1962	3.40	24.75
1963	3.47	24.78
1964	3.70	25.57
1965	3.84	25.38
1966	3.96	25.19
1967	4.11	25.44
1968	4.27	25.28
1969	4.43	24.90
1970	4.72	24.92
1971	5.52	26.61
1972	5.34	24.03
1973	5.50	22.72
1974	5.88	20.93
1975	7.50	21.45
1976	8.74	21.50
1977	11.04	23.40
1978	12.49	24.48
1979	14.24	24.64
1980	16.39	23.92
1981	18.29	23.96
1982	19.79	23.74
1983	20.64	23.74
1984	21.09	23.20
1985	22.19	22.86
1986	23.24	23.24
1987	25.10	24.05

[1]Retail prices are recorded as p per pint not per litre.
Source: 1938–1974: *United Kingdom Dairy Facts and Figures.*
1975 to date: *Estimated using Department of Employment data.*

Table 21.19. Average retail prices of butter and cheese (p per lb.)

	Butter		Cheese[1]	
	At current prices	In 1986 money values	At current prices	In 1986 money values
1966	17.2	109.4		
1967	16.3	100.9	19.0	120.8
1968	16.8	99.5	19.3	119.5
1969	16.4	92.2	20.0	118.4
1970	16.4	86.6	19.8	111.3
1971	22.9	110.4	20.5	108.2
1972	25.5	114.8	25.5	114.8
1973	22.2	91.7	33.0	136.3
1974	23.8	84.7	33.4	118.9
1975	28.0	80.0	42.9	122.7
1976	38.7	95.2	49.9	122.8
1977	48.6	103.0	62.9	133.3
1978	54.8	107.4	70.8	138.8
1979	65.9	114.0	83.4	144.3
1980	71.0	103.7	97.1	141.8
1981	76.1	99.7	106.2	139.1
1982	82.9	99.5	113.3	136.0
1983	83.3	95.8	116.8	134.3
1984	85.7	94.3	119.6	131.6
1985	84.2	86.7	126.3	130.1
1986	90.7	90.7	128.9	128.9
1987	91.6	87.8	131.5	126.0

[1]Cheddar cheese 1966–74; cheese other than processed, 1975–87.
Source. *Based on Department of Employment data.*

Appendix 22: Eggs

Table 22.1. Value of egg output (£ million)

1937–38	39	1954–55	129	1971–72	194
1938–39	40	1955–56	140	1972	188
1939–40	44	1956–57	144	1973	304
1940–41	57	1957–58	154	1974	326
1941–42	48	1958–59	156	1975	294
1942–43	36	1959–60	164	1976	362
1943–44	35	1960–61	170	1977	412
1944–45	37	1961–62	165	1978	400
1945–46	46	1962–63	171	1979	462
1946–47	51	1963–64	167	1980	489
1947–48	63	1964–65	173	1981	522
1948–49	79	1965–66	186	1982	529
1949–50	103	1966–67	178	1983	496
1950–51	108	1967–68	180	1984	554
1951–52	117	1968–69	196	1985	522
1952–53	132	1969–70	192	1986	467
1953–54	128	1970–71	199	1987[1]	506

[1]Forecast.
Source. MAFF: *Departmental Net Income Calculation.*

Table 22.2. Poultry population for egg production (million)

Total fowls
Laying fowls

	Total fowls
Great Britain	
1885	12.4
1908	32.4
1913	33.1
1921	29.0
1925	39.0
United Kingdom	
1929	55.5
1930	61.9
1935	75.1
1938	69.1
1942	53.5
1945	62.1
1950	96.1
1955	86.9
1960	103.0
Laying fowls	
1966	50.8
1970	55.2
1975	49.4
1980	46.0[1]
1981	44.5[1]
1982	44.8[1]
1983	41.1[1]
1984	40.6[1]
1985	39.6[1]
1986	38.1[1]
1987	38.5[1]
1988[2]	36.9[1]

[1]Since 1980 average number of layers comprising pullets and hens on holdings of 40 standard man days or more.   [2]Provisional.
Note. Appendix Table 20.2 shows total poultry numbers for each year.
Source. Agricultural Departments: *Agricultural Census.*

Table 22.3. Number of holdings by size of laying flock
England and Wales

Size of laying flock	1964	1975	1981[1]	1986[1]
1–25	53 581	33 746	27 239	23 580
26–49	27 438	8348	5365	4444
50–99	31 145	5975	3264	2573
100–199	26 783	3462	1646	1263
200–499	25 582	2505	1176	892
500–999	8708	1085	502	374
1000–2499	5483	1322	724	546
2500–4999	1785	833	594	448
5000–9999	666	744	512	369
10 000–19 999	239	503	398	305
20 000–49 999	78	256	234	192
50 000 and over		95	128	124
Total holdings	181 488	58 874	41 782	35 110

[1]Since 1980 average number of layers comprising pullets and hens on holdings of 40 standard man days or more. The figures may therefore not be strictly comparable with earlier years.
Source. MAFF: *Agricultural Statistics, England and Wales; Agricultural Statistics, United Kingdom.*

Table 22.4. Egg yields per annum (number of eggs per laying bird)[1]

Pre-war	149	1967–68	211
1946–47	116	1968–69	214
1947–48	120	1969–70	218
1948–49	126	1970–71	220
1949–50	133	1971–72	226
1950–51	136	1972	230
1951–52	139	1973	228
1952–53	150	1974	229
1953–54	161	1975	229
1954–55	165	1976	238
1955–56	168	1977	240
1956–57	171	1978	242
1957–58	174	1979	247
1958–59	179	1980	248
1959–60	184	1981	250
1960–61	188	1982	251
1961–62	191	1983	258
1962–63	193	1984	256
1963–64	197	1985	258
1964–65	204	1986	258
1965–66	204	1987[2]	261
1966–67	207		

[1]Including breeding flocks.   [2]Forecast.
Source. MAFF: *Output and Utilisation of Farm Produce in the United Kingdom.*

Table 22.5. Egg production and output for human consumption (million dozen)

	Gross production	Output for human consumption
Pre-war	556.3	545.4
1946–47	460.3	451.1
1947–48	486.7	474.5
1948–49	579.5	566.2
1949–50	670.8	658.4
1950–51	704.3	691.8
1951–52	677.2	664.0
1952–53	717.9	705.0
1953–54	776.2	764.5
1954–55	809.4	793.0
1955–56	848.6	828.6
1956–57	929.7	908.5
1957–58	972.6	949.2
1958–59	1048.2	1020.1
1959–60	1100.0	1068.8
1960–61	1080.0	1043.4
1961–62	1131.7	1093.2
1962–63	1130.9	1091.9
1963–64	1197.4	1146.0
1964–65	1152.3	1105.3
1965–66	1104.4	1056.4
1966–67	1146.4	1089.2
1967–68	1182.2	1127.6
1968–69	1183.1	1124.8
1969–70	1212.0	1150.7
1970–71	1219.2	1157.8
1971–72[1]	1231.9	1167.8
1972	1237.4	1173.5
1973	1157.9	1095.6
1974	1176.4	1116.6
1975	1207.4	1147.6
1976[1]	1213.9	1148.9
1977	1220.8	1156.3
1978	1253.3	1187.7
1979	1246.8	1180.4
1980[1]	1165.9	1100.5
1981	1136.2	1069.4
1982	1146.2	1079.1
1983	1103.8	1038.6
1984[1]	1085.4	1018.0
1985	1088.8	1017.5
1986	1089.3	1015.4
1987[1,2]	1125.3	1043.9

[1] 366 days.　[2] Forecast.
Source. MAFF: *Output and Utilisation of Farm Produce in the United Kingdom.*

Table 22.6. Egg supplies (million dozen)

	Output	Imports	Exports	New supplies	Output as % of new supplies
1905–09	118	246			32[3]
1924–27	189	235			45[3]
Pre-war	545	346			61[3]
1946–47	451	436			51[3]
1953–54	765	188			80[3]
1959–60	1069	51			95[3]
1964–65	1105	47			96[3]
1966–67	1089	55			96[3]
1970–71	1158	34	34	1158	100
1971–72[1]	1168	26	11	1183	99
1972	1174	12	7	1178	100
1973	1096	43	7	1132	97
1974	1117	39	12	1144	98
1975	1148	42	9	1181	97
1976[1]	1149	20	16	1152	100
1977	1156	15	22	1150	101
1978	1188	14	40	1162	102
1979	1180	31	53	1158	102
1980[1]	1101	42	42	1100	100
1981	1069	46	39	1076	99
1982	1079	28	31	1075	100
1983	1039	39	30	1048	99
1984[1]	1018	54	22	1050	97
1985	1018	56	19	1055	96
1986[2]	1015	43	20	1038	98
1987[2]	1044	35	23	1056	99

[1] 366 days.　[2] Including output from commercially insignificant units and domestic egg production.　[3] As per cent of output plus imports (supplies).
Source. *Output and Utilisation of Farm Produce in the United Kingdom.*

Table 22.7. Imports of eggs and egg products

	1931	1938	1942	1945	1950	1955	1960	1965	1970	1975	1980	1981	1982	1983	1984	1985	1986	1987
Eggs (million dozen)																		
Australia	9.2	10.0	–	1.0	14.0	13.5	2.6	–	–	–	–	–	–	–	–	–	–	–
Denmark	75.5	95.0	–	6.0	102.0	47.6	10.0	3.0	6.2	1.0	–	1.3	5.7	1.7	1.6	–	–	–
France	1.0	–	–	–	–	–	–	–	–	17.4	16.7	15.0	1.6	7.7	10.2	3.9	2.3	0.2
Irish Republic	4.6	22.0	22.0	18.0	34.0	5.5	0.6	0.1	0.1	0.1	–	–	0.3	–	–	–	–	0.7
Netherlands	38.4	59.0	–	–	1.0	2.8	3.2	1.6	0.9	3.4	14.6	10.6	–	14.0	24.0	34.0	22.5	13.8
Poland	26.9	–	–	–	–	5.4	8.8	6.3	2.9	–	–	–	–	–	–	–	–	–
South Africa	5.9	–	–	–	15.0	4.3	5.1	4.1	0.3	–	–	–	–	–	–	–	–	–
Other countries	97.8	91.0	12.0	44.0[1]	2.0	4.8	4.8	7.4	6.7	1.3	1.4	1.7	0.6	0.3	0.5	1.0	3.8	1.6
Total	259.3	277.0	34.0	69.0	168.0	83.9	35.1	22.5	17.1	23.2	32.7	28.6	8.2	23.7	36.3	38.9	28.6	16.3
Egg products ('000 tonnes)	40.7	–	8.9	35.7	15.7	18.3	19.0	14.0	11.3	4.4	2.3	4.5	5.0	3.0	4.4	3.7	2.9	4.2

[1] Of which Canada 39.0.　Source. *Customs and Excise.*

Table 22.9. Producer egg prices[1] (p per dozen)

	At current prices	In 1986 money values
1954–55	20.9	189.4
1955–56	21.0	183.8
1956–57	20.9	175.4
1957–58	20.9	169.7
1958–59	18.7	147.9
1959–60	17.7	139.1
1960–61	18.3	137.7
1961–62	16.5	138.5
1962–63	17.4	126.7
1963–64	15.4	110.0
1964–65	14.6	100.9
1965–66	16.5	109.1
1966–67	14.4	91.6
1967–68	13.3	82.3
1968–69	14.6	86.4
1969–70	14.6	82.0
1970–71	14.4	76.0
1971–72	14.5	69.9
1972	13.0	58.5
1973	27.7	114.5
1974	24.6	87.5
1975	22.8	65.2
1976	27.7	68.1
1977	31.2	66.1
1978	27.0	52.9
1979	32.8	56.7
1980	37.4	54.6
1981	40.7	53.3
1982	38.8	46.6
1983	35.5	40.8
1984	44.7	49.2
1985	40.0	41.2
1986	32.6	32.6
1987	36.8	35.3

[1]Until 1970–71 average price paid by British Egg Marketing Board for 1st quality hen eggs (including subsidy). Since then average price paid for all class A eggs weighted according to the quantity in each grade.
Source. *Estimate pre-1966–67. Since then Annual Review of Agriculture.*

Table 22.8. Consumption of eggs (number per head per annum)

Year	Shell eggs	Egg products[1]	Total	Year	Shell eggs	Egg products[1]	Total
Pre-war	201	19	220	1966	246	24	270
1942	127	67	194	1967	249	26	275
1946	140	63	203	1968	250	23	273
1947	139	52	191	1969	248	23	271
1948	160	40	200	1970	251	24	275
1949	197	22	219	1971	254	19	273
1950	219	25	244	1972	253	20	273
1951	190	24	214	1973	244	18	262
1952	195	19	214	1974	240	16	256
1953	201	18	219	1975	232	14	246
1954	221	12	283	1976	236	12	248
1955	210	19	229	1977	236	12	248
1956	212	17	229	1978	239	12	251
1957	225	16	241	1979	238	11	249
1958	231	17	248	1980	227	8	235
1959	231	24	255	1981	219	8	227
1960	237	21	258	1982	216	12	228
1961	243	21	264	1983	211	13	224
1962	243	21	264	1984	211	13	224
1963	238	22	260	1985	211	13	224
1964	249	24	273	1986[2]	207	13	220
1965	250	21	271				

[1]Equivalent number of eggs.
Source. MAFF: *Food Facts.*

Table 22.10. Retail egg prices[1] (p per dozen)

Year	At current prices	In 1986 money values	Year	At current prices	In 1986 money values
1939	10.5	228	1964	13.5	93
1940	16.0	293	1965	21.5	142
1941	12.0	182	1966	18.5	118
1942	9.5	135	1967	19.9	123
1943	10.0	138	1968	18.5	110
1944	10.0	135	1969	20.2	114
1945	10.0	133	1970	20.1	106
1946	10.0	131	1971	22.7	109
1947	9.0	111	1972	19.1	86
1948	15.0	171	1973	32.7	135
1949	17.5	195	1974	35.7	127
1950	20.0	217	1975	35.7	102
1951	22.5	224	1976	42.0	103
1952	22.5	211	1977	48.0	102
1953	27.5	253	1978	46.5	91
1954	25.5	231	1979	56.0	97
1955	27.5	241	1980	63.8	93
1956	19.5	164	1981	69.7	91
1957	18.5	150	1982	72.6	87
1958	21.0	166	1983	67.8	78
1959	15.5	122	1984	82.6	91
1960	25.0	195	1985	83.8	86
1961	17.0	129	1986	89.4	89
1962	16.0	116	1987	95.0	91
1963	20.5	146			

[1]Approximate due to changes in classes of eggs.
Source. *Based on data from the Department of Employment.*

Appendix 23: Wool

Table 23.1. Value of clip wool output (£ million)[1]

1937–38	4	1954–55	16	1971–72	14
1938–39	4	1955–56	15	1972	15
1939–40	3	1956–57	15	1973	16
1940–41	4	1957–58	16	1974	17
1941–42	4	1958–59	17	1975	20
1942–43	4	1959–60	17	1976	24
1943–44	4	1960–61	16	1977	30
1944–45	4	1961–62	17	1978	33
1945–46	4	1962–63	17	1979	35
1946–47	4	1963–64	16	1980	36
1947–48	4	1964–65	17	1981	35
1948–49	5	1965–66	16	1982	34
1949–50	6	1966–67	16	1983	37
1950–51	7	1967–68	16	1984	37
1951–52	20	1968–69	14	1985	41
1952–53	15	1969–70	14	1986	41
1953–54	16	1970–71	13	1987[2]	44

[1]After allocation of marketing costs. [2]Forecast.
Source. MAFF: *Departmental Net Income Calculation.*

Table 23.2. Sheep population (million)

	Breeding ewes	Total sheep		Breeding ewes	Total sheep
Great Britain			1948	7.5	18.2
1866–70	18.2	27.9	1949	7.7	19.5
1871–75	18.5	28.8	1950	8.1	20.4
1876–80	18.0	27.9	1951	8.1	20.0
1881–85	16.1	25.3	1952	8.5	21.7
1886–90	16.1	25.9	1953	8.7	22.5
1891–95[1]	9.8	27.3	1954	8.9	22.9
1896–1900	10.2	26.7	1955	9.2	22.9
1901–05	10.0	25.6	1956	9.6	23.6
1906–10	10.5	26.7	1957	9.8	24.8
1911–15	10.0	24.9	1958	10.3	26.1
1916–20	9.2		1959	10.7	27.7
			1960	11.2	27.9
United Kingdom			1961	11.5	29.0
1922	8.4[2]	20.5	1962	11.8	29.5
1923	8.4[2]	21.2	1963	11.8	29.3
1924	9.2[2]	22.2	1964	11.9	29.7
1925	9.7[2]	23.6	1965	11.9	29.9
1926	10.2[2]	24.6	1966	12.0	30.0
1927	10.5[2]	25.2	1967	11.8	28.9
1928	10.6[2]	24.6	1968	11.4	28.0
1929	10.3	24.4	1969	10.9	26.6
1930	10.4	24.7	1970	10.5	26.1
1931	11.0	26.4	1971	10.4	26.0
1932	11.4	27.2	1972	10.7	26.9
1933	11.5	26.6	1973	10.9	27.9
1934	11.0	24.9	1974	11.2	28.5
1935	10.8	25.1	1975	11.3	28.3
1936	10.9	25.0	1976	11.3	28.3
1937	11.0	25.5	1977	11.2	28.2
1938	10.8	26.8	1978	11.5	29.8
1939	11.0	26.9	1979	11.7	29.9
1940	10.7	26.3	1980	12.2	31.4
1941	9.2	22.3	1981	12.5	32.1
1942	8.9	21.5	1982	12.9	33.1
1943	8.2	20.4	1983	13.3	34.1
1944	8.1	20.1	1984	13.6	34.8
1945	8.2	20.2	1985	13.9	35.6
1946	8.3	20.4	1986	14.2	37.0
1947	7.1	16.7	1987	14.8	38.7
			1988[3]	15.5	41.0

[1]Three year average (1893–95). [2]Estimated. [3]Provisional.
Source. Agricultural Departments: *Agricultural Census.*

Table 23.3. Number of registered wool producers

Year	Producers ('000)	Year	Producers ('000)
1950–51	97.4	1970–71	100.3
1951–52	102.4	1971–72	96.0
1952–53	111.4	1972–73	93.1
1953–54	116.0	1973–74	91.7
1954–55	117.3	1974–75	90.4
1955–56	119.6	1975–76	89.0
1956–57	120.3	1976–77	87.5
1957–58	121.1	1977–78	86.6
1958–59	124.4	1978–79	87.7
New series		1979–80	84.9
1959–60	130.3	1980–81	86.0
1960–61	130.8	1981–82	86.5
1961–62	131.6	1982–83	87.5
1962–63	131.9	1983–84	88.8
1963–64	131.0	1984–85	90.3
1964–65	129.3	1985–86	93.5
1965–66	126.4	1986–87	95.2
1966–67	123.5	1987–88	97.2
1967–68	119.2		
1968–69	113.6		
1969–70	106.1		

Source. *British Wool Marketing Board.*

Table 23.4. Wool production ('000 tonnes)

	1925	Pre-war	1946–47	1950–51	1955–56	1960–61	1965–66	1970–71	1973	1975	1980	1981	1982	1983	1984	1985	1986[1]	1987[2]
Clip wool																		
Greasy			22.5	22.2	26.3	32.1	34.2	30.2	33.4	33.9	39.0	38.9	38.4	40.8	39.5	41.3	42.5	
Washed			4.1	4.2	4.5	3.8	3.4	1.6	1.1	0.8	–	–	–	–	–	–	–	
Washed or greasy equivalent			5.0	4.9	5.3	4.4	3.6	1.9	1.3	1.2	–	–	–	–	–	–	–	
Total as greasy	31	34.6	27.5	27.1	31.6	36.5	37.8	32.1	34.7	35.1	39.0	38.9	38.4	40.8	39.5	41.3	42.5	
Skin wool																		
As produced		14.3	12.0	10.8	12.8	16.4	18.0	12.5	12.2	12.5	11.2	10.2	10.4	8.6	11.0	12.4	12.5	
As greasy equivalent	9	16.9	14.1	12.5	14.6	18.5	20.8	14.2	13.8	14.3	12.8	11.6	11.8	11.4	14.6	16.6	16.7	
Total wool production (as greasy)	40	51.5	41.6	39.6	46.2	55.0	58.6	46.3	48.5	49.3	51.8	50.5	50.2	52.2	54.1	57.9	59.2	61.0

[1]Provisional. [2]Forecast.
Source. MAFF: *Output and Utilisation of Farm Produce in the United Kingdom.*

Table 23.5. Wool supplies ('000 tonnes)

	Production[1]	Imports[2]	Exports[2]	New supply	Production as % of total new supply
Pre-war	52	400	13	439	12
1946–47	42	215	5[3]	252[2]	17
1950–51	40	319	11	348	11
1955–56	46	328	16[3]	358[2]	13
1960	55	293	19	329	17
1965	59	253	22	290	20
1970	46	206	25	226	20
1975	49	132	29	152	32
1980	52	96	31	117	44
New series					
1981	51	120	44	127	40
1982	50	110	38	122	41
1983	52	121	41	132	39
1984	54	131	45	140	39
1985	58	145	45	158	37
1986	59	145[4]	74[4]	131	45
1987[5]	61	152[4]	73[4]	140	44

[1]Greasy weight.   [2]Greasy weight from 1981 onwards therefore not comparable with earlier years.   [3]Estimated.   [4]Provisional.   [5]Forecast.
Source. MAFF: *Output and Utilisation of Farm Produce in the United Kingdom.*

Table 23.6. Imports of raw wool ('000 tonnes)

	1938	1942	1945	1950	1955	1960	1965	1970	1975	1980	1981	1982	1983	1984	1985	1986	1987
Argentina	36.0	–	–	0.1	1.5	24.9	20.4	12.2	6.9	4.2	6.8	0.8	–	–	0.1	0.2	–
Australia	165.8	63.0	159.0	174.2	153.5	120.8	82.8	58.9	21.1	16.0	10.3	10.5	7.5	13.5	24.2	24.1	26.7
India and Pakistan	20.9	9.2	7.2	4.4	9.3	11.6	7.3	3.6	0.7	2.3	3.0	2.9	5.0	7.3	8.3	5.7	2.5
New Zealand	89.8	71.1	29.4	81.6	84.4	73.5	61.4	62.1	50.3	28.1	30.4	35.2	37.7	37.4	43.8	32.8	29.1
South Africa	48.4	41.1	30.1	27.2	29.4	22.0	20.7	13.3	11.9	15.3	16.6	12.0	14.3	16.4	15.3	10.7	9.0
Other countries	38.8	2.2	3.2	32.0	50.1	40.6	60.7	55.5	41.6	30.1	40.4	39.9	44.7	41.8	36.1	44.8	71.6
Total	399.7	186.6	228.9	319.5	328.2	293.4	253.3	205.6	132.5	96.0	107.5	101.3	109.2	116.4	127.8	118.3	138.9

Source. *Customs and Excise.*

Table 23.7. Guaranteed and budgeted wool prices (p per kg)

Clip	Guaranteed price to producers	Guaranteed marketing allowance	Total outgoings
1950–51	24.85 (+ bonus 4.14)	3.44	28.29 (+ bonus 4.14)
1951–52	66.14	3.44	69.58
1952–53	49.60	3.44	53.05
1953–54	49.60	4.36	53.97
1954–55	49.60	4.36	53.97

Beginning with the 1955–56 clip, the Guarantee has been to the Board. From the Guarantee, the Board deducts its estimated marketing costs; the remainder forms the basis of the Price Schedule calculated and is paid to producers.

continued opposite

Table 23.7 continued

	Budgeted average price to producers	Marketing cost deduction	Guaranteed price
1955–56	49.60 (+0.17)[1]	3.90 (+.17)[2]	53.51 (+0.33)
1956–57	47.77	3.90 (+0.17)[2]	51.67 (+0.17)
1957–58	47.17	4.50	51.67
1958–59	46.71	4.96	51.67
1959–60	45.70	4.13	49.83
1960–61	44.61	4.32	48.92
1961–62	44.55	4.36	48.92
1962–63	44.32	4.59	48.92
1963–64	44.17	4.75	48.92
1964–65	46.00	4.75	50.75
1965–66	45.46	5.29	50.75
1966–67	43.48	5.44	48.92
1967–68	42.98	5.93	48.92
1968–69	42.58	6.34	48.92
1969–70	42.50	6.41	48.92
1970–71	41.64	7.28	48.92
1971–72	42.49	7.55	50.04
1972–73	43.09	7.62	50.71
1973–74	46.96	8.16	55.12
1974–75	48.72	8.60	57.32
1975–76	57.54	10.80	68.34
1976–77	70.47	13.23	83.70
1977–78	95.45	14.55	110.00
1978–79	95.45	14.55	110.00
1979–80	99.00[3]	16.50	112.00
1980–81	93.00	22.00	115.00
1981–82	91.25	23.75	115.00
1982–83	89.44	25.56	115.00
1983–84	89.94	25.06	115.00
1984–85	94.43	25.57	120.00
1985–86	102.10[4]	28.25	129.00
1986–87	99.06	29.94	129.00
1987–88	98.56	30.44	129.00

[1]From 1954 underpayment. [2]Special Review Award. [3]3.5 p per kg was added in view of the small increases in the Guarantee; it came out of the Savings Element of the Special Account. [4]1.35 p per kg was added.

Table 23.8. Producer prices for clip wool[1] (p per kg)

	At current prices	In 1986 money values		At current prices	In 1986 money values
1950–51	29.06	315.00	1970–71	41.37	209.10
1951–52	64.32	639.30	1971–72	42.79	206.30
1952–53	48.98	458.50	1972–73	42.75	192.40
1953–54	49.24	453.50	1973–74	46.72	192.70
1954–55	49.45	448.00	1974–75	48.19	171.40
1955–56	49.58	433.80	1975–76	57.54	164.60
1956–57	48.76	409.10	1976–77	69.51	170.70
1957–58	47.79	388.10	1977–78	93.20	197.60
1958–59	45.58	359.60	1978–79	93.78	183.60
1959–60	45.65	358.80	1979–80	97.66	168.70
1960–61	44.90	349.30	1980–81	91.25	133.60
1961–62	44.53	330.40	1981–82	89.46	117.00
1962–63	43.95	316.50	1982–83	89.21	107.40
1963–64	43.76	307.00	1983–84	90.00	103.60
1964–65	45.40	306.90	1984–85	94.06	103.20
1965–66	44.31	292.90	1985–86	101.52	104.55
1966–67	43.26	271.10	1986–87	98.69	98.69
1967–68	42.56	257.30	1987–88[2]	98.56	94.52
1968–69	42.03	242.90			
1969–70	43.27	235.40			

[1]Average price paid by British Wool Marketing Board including any stabilization payment.
[2]Forecast.   Source. *British Wool Marketing Board.*

Appendix 24: Forestry

Table 24.1. Forest Area ('000 hectares)

| | United Kingdom total[1] | Great Britain total[1] | Forestry Commission | | | Private | |
			total estates	productive woodland	New area planted	productive woodland	New area planted
1937–38	1252	1232	444	163	9.8		
1938–39	1261	1241	463	176	11.4		
1939–40	1271	1250	490	183	11.0		
1940–41	1278	1258	497	191	10.9		
1941–42	1284	1263	501	196	6.8		
1942–43	1288	1267	507	200	5.4		
1943–44	1290	1269	514	200	3.7		
1944–45	1291	1270	552	202	2.6		
1945–46	1294	1273	573	205	4.2		
1946–47	1301	1280	583	216	10.7		
1947–48	1481	1459	598	230	14.7		
1948–49	1506	1484	631	248	17.8		
1949–50	1524	1500	675	273	21.7		
1950–51	1543	1518	721	298	23.1		
1951–52	1560	1535	751	324	24.9		
1952–53	1579	1553	773	351	27.4		
1953–54	1596	1569	825	379	28.5		
1954–55	1613	1585	851	407	27.5		
1955–56	1629	1600	881	430	25.3		
1956–57	1644	1614	912	454	23.4		
1957–58	1666	1634	955	474	21.2		
1958–59	1681	1649	972	495	22.2		
1959–60	1700	1667	1002	519	25.0		
1960–61	1719	1685	1030	544	25.8		
1961–62	1738	1702	1046	566	25.1		
1962–63	1756	1718	1033	586	22.5		
1963–64	1776	1736	1055	606	22.0		
1964–65	1802	1760	1074	627	21.7		
1965–66	1829	1785	1104	646	21.8		
1966–67	1849	1801	1134	666	21.2		
1967–68 } 1968–69 }	1858	1807[2]	1172	688	27.7		
1969–70	1882	1828	1187	706	22.5		
1970–71	1908	1853	1212	727	28.5		
1971–72	1951	1893	1214	749	26.3		
1972–73	1984	1924	1212	768	23.2		
1973–74	1981	1920	1207	789	21.7		
1974–75	2007	1956	1212	809	23.2		
1975–76	2043	1980	1231	826	20.5	846	12.2
1976–77	2057	1994	1251	841	18.7	848	9.2
1977–78	2061	1997	1253	856	17.2	851	8.3
1978–79	2079	2014	1256	868	15.4	858	10.8
1979–80	2102	2036	1263	884	21.5	865	11.2
1980–81	2121	2054	1264	896	16.6	873	11.4
1981–82	2142	2075	1259	905	16.5	886	15.9
1982–83	2233	2165[3]	1251	909	14.8	1084[2]	15.6
1983–84	2258	2189	1209	902	15.1	1116	19.7
1984–85	2277	2207	1181	892	11.1	1145	19.1
1985–86	2301	2230	1166	889	11.4	1171	23.4
1986–87	2328	2256	1157	890	13.3	1195	23.6

[1] Including unproductive woodland. Year ended 30 September.   [2] Year ended 31 March.   [3] Based on new information derived from 1980 census of woodlands and trees.
Source. *United Kingdom Annual Abstract of Statistics.*

Table 24.2. Woodland on agricultural holdings ('000 hectares)[1]

1968	105	1978	260
1969	105	1979	264
1970	153	1980	271
1971	153	1981	277
1972	162	1982	285
1973	164	1983	292
1974	212	1984	299
1975	225	1985	312
1976	239	1986	316
1977	250		

[1]The statistics need to be interpreted with caution.
Source. MAFF: *Agricultural census.*

Table 24.3. Apparent consumption of wood (million m^3)[1]

	UK production	Imports	Apparent consumption[2]	Production as % of apparent consumption
1965	3.0	39.1	41.3	7.3
1970	3.2	40.3	42.3	7.6
1971	3.2			
1972	3.3	40.2	42.6	7.5
1973	3.3	45.5	47.6	6.9
1974	3.3	42.3	44.0	7.5
1975	3.2	30.9	33.1	10.2
1976	3.5	37.0	39.3	8.9
1977	3.7	36.1	38.5	9.8
1978	3.8	37.1	39.7	9.6
1979	4.1	41.3	43.9	9.3
1980	3.9	34.7	36.3	10.7
1981	4.3	34.5	36.3	11.8
1982	4.1	35.9	37.8	10.8
1983	3.9	36.4	38.0	10.3
1984	3.8	38.7	39.7	9.6
1985	4.7	37.5	39.9	11.8
1986	5.2	40.6	43.0	12.1

[1]Raw material equivalent.   [2]Apparent consumption: imports, plus UK round wood production less exports.
Source. Forestry Commission: *Forestry Facts and Figures.*

Appendix 25: Purchased feeding stuffs

Table 25.1. Expenditure on purchased feed (£ million)

1937–38	78	1954–55	334	1971–72	606
1938–39	68	1955–56	324	1972	661
1939–40	67	1956–57	348	1973	977
1940–41	61	1957–58	328	1974	1157
1941–42	41	1958–59	359	1975	1180
1942–43	28	1959–60	355	1976	1567
1943–44	31	1960–61	354	1977	1827
1944–45	32	1961–62	382	1978	1774
1945–46	42	1962–63	404	1979	2089
1946–47	34	1963–64	401	1980	2188
1947–48	43	1964–65	465	1981	2282
1948–49	62	1965–66	499	1982	2615
1949–50	144	1966–67	463	1983	2864
1950–51	142	1967–68	499	1984	2858
1951–52	178	1968–69	513	1985	2690
1952–53	187	1969–70	545	1986	2749
1953–54	276	1970–71	637	1987[1]	2667

[1]Forecast.
Source. MAFF: *Departmental Net Income Calculation.*

Table 25.2. Breakdown of expenditure on purchased feeding stuffs (£ million)

Concentrates	1972	1975	1980	1981	1982	1983	1984	1985	1986	1987[2]
Compounds[3]										
Cattle	159.2	328.9	611.5	641.1	745.2	855.3	744.4	657.2	668.5	578.8
Calf	24.5	37.2	70.6	75.8	89.3	98.3	90.0	80.8	78.9	71.7
Pig	108.8	175.4	332.8	349.0	391.4	421.2	407.0	398.8	390.9	395.5
Poultry	171.9	281.6	525.2	575.0	633.2	679.5	662.0	622.1	626.4	666.0
Sheep	3.1	5.3	17.7	48.2	55.8	64.5	80.7	76.8	87.4	97.9
Other	6.4	11.2	30.7							
Total compounds	473.9	839.6	1588.3	1689.1	1915.8	2118.8	1984.0	1835.7	1852.1	1810.1
Straights	149.5	294.2	505.2	496.4	590.0	634.1	744.7	770.6	721.9	683.3
Total concentrates	623.4	1133.8	2093.5	2185.5	2505.9	2752.9	2728.2	2606.3	2574.0	2496.3
Non-concentrates[1]	17.1	29.3	48.2	52.3	53.4	54.8	65.1	55.5	54.5	54.6
Other costs	20.2	16.9	45.8	44.4	55.4	56.4	64.5	27.7	120.9	116.3
Total purchased feed	660.8	1180.0	2187.5	2282.3	2614.7	2864.1	2858.4	2689.5	2749.4	2667.2

[1]In terms of concentrate equivalent.   [2]Forecast.   [3]Compounds include protein concentrates and cereal livestock mixtures.
Source. MAFF: *Departmental Net Income Calculation.*

Table 25.3. Farmers' purchases of feeding stuffs (million tonnes)

Compounds	1967–69	1975	1980	1981	1982	1983	1984	1985	1986[2]
Cattle	3.3	4.0	4.5	4.5	5.0	5.4	4.4	4.1	4.5
Calf	0.4	0.4	0.4	0.4	0.5	0.5	0.4	0.4	0.4
Pig	2.2	2.4	2.2	2.2	2.3	2.3	2.1	2.1	2.2
Poultry	3.6	3.2	3.5	3.5	3.6	3.5	3.3	3.2	3.5
Other	0.2	0.1	0.4	0.4	0.4	0.4	0.5	0.5	0.6
Total compounds	9.6	10.1	11.1	10.9	11.8	12.1	10.8	10.4	11.2
Straights	3.7	3.9	3.9	3.7	4.2	4.2	4.8	5.1	5.2
Total concentrates	13.3	14.0	15.0	14.6	16.0	16.3	15.6	15.5	16.3
Non-concentrates[1]	0.4	0.4	0.7	0.7	0.7	0.7	0.8	0.8	0.7
All purchased feed	13.7	14.5	15.7	15.4	16.7	17.0	16.4	16.3	17.1
of which purchased commercially			15.3	15.1	16.4	16.7	16.0	15.9	16.7

[1]In terms of concentrate equivalent.   [2]Provisional.
Source. MAFF: *Output and Utilisation of Farm Produce in the United Kingdom.*

Table 25.4. Production of compound feeding stuffs ('000 tonnes)

	1964	1965	1970	1975	1980	1981	1982	1983	1984	1985	1986
Cattle feed	2740	2954	3689	4076	4556	4538	5012	5456	4382	3652	3940
Calf feed	393	424	400	357	428	436	478	504	422	357	356
Pig feed	2076	2252	2588	2162	2267	2169	2317	2292	2099	1931	1986
Poultry feed	4088	4095	4109	3320	3492	3445	3640	3532	3331	2898	3127
Other compounds	169	173	227	222	365	355	408	450	509	509	600
Total	9466	9898	11013	10137	11108	10943	11855	12234	10743	9347	10009

Source. *Annual Abstract of Statistics.*

Table 25.5. Concentrated feeding stuffs: Estimated raw material content of all deliveries ('000 tonnes)

	1964–65	1967–68	1970–71	1975	1980	1981	1982	1983	1984	1985	1986[1]
Wheat	2270	2087	3673	2962	3634	3036	3763	3819	4454	4509	5305
Barley	3141	3867	3911	2980	2682	2706	2378	2903	2875	2852	2125
Oats	192	194	169	99	91	119	114	114	135	161	227
Mixed corn	6	8	8	133	58	48	39	27	39	33	25
Rye	–	5	8	5	13	14	23	16	10	20	20
Maize	2246	2270	1495	1564	1040	771	629	331	329	331	121
Sorghum	306	124	76	368	6	8	–	3	3	3	3
Total cereals	8162	8555	9338	8111	7524	6702	6946	7213	7845	7909	7826
Wheat offals	1518	1459	1326	1335	1271	1216	1232	1169	1120	1020	1264
Other cereal offals	364	320	424	372	481	264	320	354	270	307	315
Total offals	1882	1779	1750	1707	1752	1480	1552	1523	1390	1327	1579
Peas and beans	7	39	40	83	72	155	157	137	130	102	183
Oilseed and meal	1604	1231	1258	1428	2244	2363	2440	2446	2410	2383	2951
Fish meal	448	545	385	312	260	232	260	274	268	318	336
Meat, blood, bone and feather meals	148	205	217	310	323	256	219	174	178	212	224
Milk and whey products	30	41	29	33	90	21	23	33	24	24	56
Grass and hay meal	72	59	63	124	120	65	67	148	65	60	52
Maize gluten					265	644	733	512	638	606	703
Other protein				115	42	42	42	42	42	42	42
Total protein	2309	2120	1992	2405	3312	3778	3941	3765	3755	3747	4547
Molasses	376	397	414	430	420	475	529	537	499	450	508
Locust beans	61	36	26	13	1	36	50	38	28	52	44
Brewers' and distillers' dried grains				81	83	57	138	112	112	102	91
Brewers', distillers' and maltsters' by products	143	136	237	421	337	306	231	306	248	254	186
Dried sugar beet pulp	485	567	569	440	644	590	577	497	595	690	680
Oil and fats					162	188	205	206	189	187	201
Grain screenings					242	252	273	294	256	248	254
Manioc					28	394	778	336	126	94	60
Miscellaneous	123	234	166	322	204	254	348	422	360	336	324
Total other	1188	1370	1412	1708	2121	2552	3129	2748	2413	2413	2348
Grand total	13541	13824	14492	13931	14813	14512	15568	15249	15403	15396	16300

[1]Provisional.
Source. MAFF: *Output and Utilisation of Farm Produce in the United Kingdom.*

Table 25.6. Imports of animal feeding stuffs ('000 tonnes)

	1964–65	1967–68	1970–71	1973	1975	1980	1981	1982	1983	1984	1985	1986[1]
Maize and maize meal	2225	2727	1509	1845	1610	1070	794	570	374	357	247	273
Wheat	588	508	1546	860	520	245	120	100	187	186	167	216
Barley	190	49	909	210	340	175	105	35	99	9	66	187
Others	399	130	104	105	400	2	9	2	14	16	17	18
Total cereals	3403	3414	4068	3020	2870	1492	1028	707	674	568	497	694
Cereal offals	309	201	265	235	270	340	365	440	398	308	524	464
Cotton seed cake and meals	211	192	168	180	35	50	5	40	79	37	107	204
Ground nut cake and meals	498	318	334	320	210	80	10	–	3	3	–	–
Soya bean meals	247	190	322	200	250	625	719	1081	1165	1154	1241	1168
Sunflower seed cakes and meals	66	150	59	30	10	25	40	64	163	200	254	297
Linseed cake and meal	25	9	3									
Rapeseed meal				90	50	30	80	80	82	41	76	220
Other oilcakes	72	117	112	45	25	220	374	416	442	425	436	388
Total oil cakes and meals	1119	976	998	865	580	1030	1228	1681	1933	1859	2115	2277
Fish meals	397	470	314	235	240	215	174	214	193	174	236	236
Meat and bone meals	20	18	21	45	35	35	28	29	30	33	28	31
Molasses	364	375	390	370	380	440	510	700	589	493	490	494
Other feeds	155	166	199	160	305	675	1134	1535	1367	1182	1331	1278
Total other	936	1029	924	810	960	1365	1846	2478	2179	1882	2085	2039
Grand total	5768	5621	6256	4930	4680	4227	4467	5306	5184	4617	5221	5474
Value £ million	155	156	210	289	306	427	481	576	619	575	593	612

[1]Provisional.
Source. MAFF: *Output and Utilisation of Farm Produce in the United Kingdom.*

Table 25.7. Feeding wheat price index (1986 = 100)

	At current prices	In 1986 money values		At current prices	In 1986 money values
1948	15.9	182	1968	19.5	115
1949	17.3	193	1969	20.4	115
1950	18.9	205	1970	22.4	118
1951	21.1	210	1971	23.7	114
1952	21.9	205	1972	24.6	111
1953	23.6	217	1973	38.5	159
1954	19.9	180	1974	51.3	182
1955	20.3	178	1975	48.3	138
1956	20.7	174	1976	62.3	153
1957	19.3	157	1977	72.1	153
1958	18.3	145	1978	75.6	148
1959	18.6	146	1979	85.1	147
1960	17.8	139	1980	89.4	131
1961	18.3	138	1981	98.4	129
1962	18.0	131	1982	103.3	124
1963	17.9	128	1983	114.7	132
1964	19.2	133	1984	104.2	114
1965	19.0	126	1985	99.8	103
1966	19.4	123	1986	100.0	100
1967	19.3	120	1987	106.5	102

Source. Based on MAFF price indices for agricultural materials.

Table 25.8. Barley meal price index (1986 = 100)

	At current prices	In 1986 money values		At current prices	In 1986 money values
1929	7.2	153	1959	16.3	128
1930	3.9	86	1960	15.6	121
1931	3.8	89	1961	15.9	120
1932	4.4	106	1962	16.5	120
1933	3.6	89	1963	16.3	117
1934	3.9	96	1964	16.6	115
1935	3.9	95	1965	16.9	112
1936	4.2	99	1966	16.8	107
1937	5.5	123	1967	16.7	103
1938	4.7	104	1968	16.8	99
1939	4.0	87	1969	17.0	96
1940	7.8	143	1970	19.3	102
1941	9.9	150	1971	21.3	103
1942	9.7	138	1972	21.0	95
1943	10.1	139	1973	31.6	130
1944	10.1	137	1974	44.2	157
1945	10.1	134	1975	43.6	125
1946	10.1	133	1976	54.9	135
1947	10.2	125	1977	62.7	133
1948	10.3	118	1978	62.7	123
1949	12.7	142	1979	74.3	128
1950	14.9	162	1980	76.3	112
1951	19.4	193	1981	81.1	106
1952	20.3	190	1982	87.3	105
1953	20.2	186	1983	94.2	109
1954	17.5	159	1984	96.3	106
1955	17.4	152	1985	95.7	99
1956	17.3	145	1986	100.0	100
1957	16.1	131	1987	100.0	96
1958	16.1	127			

Source. Based on MAFF price indices for agricultural materials.

Table 25.9. Maize meal price index (1986 = 100)

	At current prices	In 1986 money values		At current prices	In 1986 money values
1929	5.5	117	1960	13.6	106
1930	4.0	88	1961	13.5	102
1931	2.9	68	1962	13.7	100
1932	3.1	75	1963	14.2	102
1933	2.8	69	1964	14.9	103
1934	3.2	79	1965	15.2	100
1935	2.8	68	1966	15.2	97
1936	3.1	73	1967	15.2	94
1937	3.9	88	1968	15.4	91
1938	4.0	89	1969	16.5	93
1939	3.7	80	1970	18.8	99
1940	5.6	103	1971	19.0	92
1941	6.0	91	1972	19.9	90
1942	6.0	85	1973	29.6	122
1943	6.0	83	1974	41.3	147
1944	6.0	81	1975	37.8	108
1945	6.0	80	1976	45.0	111
1946	6.0	79	1977	53.8	114
1947	6.2	76	1978	62.2	122
1948	6.5	74	1979	69.8	121
1949	10.1	113	1980	78.1	114
1950	14.2	155	1981	83.3	109
1951	16.8	167	1982	90.0	108
1952	17.6	165	1983	93.8	108
1953	17.6	162	1984	95.4	105
1954	16.5	149	1985	95.9	99
1955	16.5	144	1986	100.0	100
1956	16.7	140	1987	106.4	102
1957	15.5	126			
1958	13.9	110			
1959	13.8	108			

Source. Based on MAFF price indices for agricultural materials.

Table 25.10. White fish meal price index (1986 = 100)

	At current prices	In 1986 money values		At current prices	In 1986 money values
1929	6.0	127	1960	17.5	136
1930	6.0	132	1961	17.1	129
1931	5.4	127	1962	18.5	135
1932	4.7	113	1963	18.6	133
1933	4.8	119	1964	19.4	134
1934	5.0	123	1965	21.6	143
1935	4.8	117	1966	22.7	144
1936	4.6	108	1967	21.2	131
1937	4.8	108	1968	20.9	124
1938	4.8	106	1969	24.4	137
1939	4.9	107	1970	28.0	148
1940	6.7	123	1971	27.7	134
1941	6.6	100	1972	30.6	138
1942	6.7	95	1973	65.2	269
1943	6.8	94	1974	59.0	210
1944	6.8	92	1975	41.6	119
1945	6.8	90	1976	69.6	171
1946	6.8	89	1977	91.7	194
1947	6.8	84	1978	80.6	158
1948	7.8	89	1979	72.3	125
1949	12.1	135	1980	78.1	114
1950	17.0	184	1981	85.5	112
1951	11.8	117	1982	84.0	101
1952	12.3	115	1983	94.8	109
1953	13.0	120	1984	98.4	108
1954	19.3	175	1985	94.6	98
1955	19.7	172	1986	100.0	100
1956	20.1	169	1987	97.7	94
1957	20.5	167			
1958	20.7	164			
1959	20.0	157			

Source. Based on MAFF price indices for agricultural materials.

Table 25.11. Compound feed price indices (1986 = 100)

	Cattle	Calves	Pigs	Poultry
1954–55	21.0	23.0	18.3	19.2
1955–56	21.4	23.2	18.6	19.3
1956–57	22.1	23.5	19.1	19.7
1957–58	19.6	21.5	16.9	17.2
1958–59	19.4	21.0	17.0	17.1
1959–60	20.2	21.8	17.0	17.2
1960–61	19.4	21.0	16.5	16.6
1961–62	19.7	21.1	16.9	16.8
1962–63	20.3	21.8	17.4	17.3
1963–64	21.3	22.5	17.7	18.1
1964–65	21.3	23.1	18.1	18.7
1965–66	21.8	23.5	18.6	19.2
1966–67	21.6	23.1	18.6	19.3
1967–68	22.5	23.8	18.9	19.8
1968–69	23.1	23.8	19.2	20.3
1969–70	23.8	24.2	20.2	21.5
1970	25.4	25.9	21.8	23.1
1971	28.0	27.5	24.3	25.4
1972	27.2	26.8	23.4	24.3
1973	37.8	37.6	34.8	36.4
1974	50.0	50.9	45.6	46.1
1975	50.4	52.5	45.2	45.0
1976	61.5	61.8	57.1	56.6
1977	72.7	72.3	67.7	67.8
1978	70.0	69.5	65.1	67.1
1979	80.0	78.9	73.3	74.3
1980	86.5	85.6	79.9	77.7
1981	91.3	90.6	87.8	85.4
1982	96.7	98.6	92.4	90.6
1983	105.2	105.1	99.7	98.8
1984	107.5	105.3	103.8	102.6
1985	101.2	101.0	100.4	99.8
1986	100.0	100.0	100.0	100.0
1987	98.8	101.6	100.4	99.1

Source. Based on MAFF price indices for agricultural materials.

Table 25.12. Compound feed prices at current and in 1986 money values[1] (1986 = 100)

	At current prices	In 1986 money values
1954–55	19.8	179
1955–56	20.1	176
1956–57	20.6	173
1957–58	18.2	148
1958–59	18.1	143
1959–60	18.4	145
1960–61	17.8	138
1961–62	18.1	137
1962–63	18.6	135
1963–64	19.3	138
1964–65	19.7	136
1965–66	20.2	134
1966–67	20.2	128
1967–68	20.8	129
1968–69	21.3	126
1969–70	22.2	125
1970	23.8	126
1971	26.3	127
1972	25.3	114
1973	36.8	152
1974	47.9	171
1975	47.7	136
1976	59.0	145
1977	70.0	148
1978	68.0	133
1979	76.6	133
1980	82.1	120
1981	88.6	116
1982	93.8	113
1983	101.8	117
1984	105.0	116
1985	100.6	107
1986	100.0	100
1987	99.6	95

[1] All compound feeds.
Source. Based on MAFF price indices for agricultural materials, *Agricultural Statistics*.

Appendix 26: Seeds

Table 26.1. Value of output of seeds (£ million)

Year	Value	Year	Value
1937–38	5	1963–64	32
1938–39	5	1964–65	42
1939–40	7	1965–66	43
1940–41	8	1966–67	47
1941–42	14	1967–68	47
1942–43	15	1968–69	48
1943–44	17	1969–70	51
1944–45	18	1970–71	54
1945–46	17	1971–72	49
1946–47	19	1972	27
1947–48	20	1973	39
1948–49	22	1974	50
1949–50	22	1975	58
1950–51	24	1976	88
1951–52	23	1977	101
1952–53	24	1978	91
1953–54	27	1979	99
1954–55	29	1980	94
1955–56	26	1981	102
1956–57	28	1982	111
1957–58	28	1983	129
1958–59	30	1984	122
1959–60	30	1985	120
1960–61	32	1986	128
1961–62	32	1987[1]	132
1962–63	32		

[1]Forecast.
Source. MAFF: *Departmental Net Income Calculation.*

Table 26.2. Total expenditure on seeds (£ million)

Year	Value	Year	Value	Year	Value
1937–38	5	1954–55	29	1971–72	49
1938–39	5	1955–56	26	1972	61
1939–40	7	1956–57	28	1973	84
1940–41	8	1957–58	28	1974	103
1941–42	14	1958–59	30	1975	124
1942–43	15	1959–60	30	1976	188
1943–44	17	1960–61	32	1977	216
1944–45	18	1961–62	32	1978	193
1945–46	17	1962–63	32	1979	212
1946–47	19	1963–64	32	1980	200
1947–48	20	1964–65	42	1981	217
1948–49	22	1965–66	43	1982	236
1949–50	22	1966–67	47	1983	275
1950–51	24	1967–68	47	1984	260
1951–52	23	1968–69	48	1985	255
1952–53	24	1969–70	51	1986	272
1953–54	27	1970–71	54	1987[1]	282

[1]Forecast.
Source. MAFF: *Departmental Net Income Calculation.*

Table 26.3. Expenditure on seeds by crop (£ million)

	1972	1975	1980	1981	1982	1983	1984	1985	1986	1987
Grass	10.4	15.2 ⎫	32.9	28.8	34.9	65.7[1]	29.5	16.5	19.4	20.7
Clover	1.7	2.6 ⎭								
Root and fodder crops	4.4	9.2	19.5	22.2	20.4	23.3	39.1	39.3	39.7	46.0
Cereals	21.1	41.8	85.7	106.6	109.8	119.1	125.7	124.8	134.8	129.8
Potatoes	7.3	22.5	26.7	28.5	44.4	37.1	26.0	19.4	20.4	23.6
Vegetables and other horticultural seeds[2]	16.2	32.8	35.4	30.5	35.0	38.8	48.9	54.6	57.2	61.5
Total	61.1	124.1	200.2	216.6	244.5	284.0	269.2	254.6	271.5	281.6

[1]Due to exceptionally bad weather during the winter 1982–83, a heavy reseeding programme was necessary.   [2]Includes mushroom spawn, hardy nursery stock, flower seed.
Source. MAFF: *Departmental Net Income Calculation.*

Table 26.4. Supplies of herbage and legume seeds ('000 tonnes)

	Area ('000 hectares)	Production All	Production Certified	Imports	Exports	Total supply
1961–64	13.6	24	10	19	5	37
1968–69	14.8	13	9	20	1	31
1970–71	17.8	17	14	17	2	33
1975–76	22.6	16	16	16	3	30
1980–81	21.8	18	18	11	5	23
1981–82	19.0	18	18	13	6	25
1982–83	14.2	14	14	18	3	28
1983–84	14.5	16	16	13	2	26
1984–85	15.0	19	19	13	2	30
1985–86	15.7	14	13	12	2	24
1986–87	15.7	16	16	12	2	26
1987–88	17.0	15	15			

Source. HMSO: *Annual Review of Agriculture.*

Table 26.5. Seed price indices

	Farm gate selling prices At current prices	Farm gate selling prices In 1986 money values	Purchase prices At current prices	Purchase prices In 1986 money values
1973	43.3	178.8	43.8	180.9
1974	53.8	191.5	57.9	206.1
1975	67.2	192.2	58.6	167.6
1976	142.8	351.3	101.7	250.2
1977	127.4	270.1	103.3	219.0
1978	88.2	172.9	84.0	164.6
1979	95.0	164.4	90.3	156.2
1980	100.4	146.5	94.0	137.2
1981	101.4	132.8	94.9	124.3
1982	109.5	131.4	102.1	122.5
1983	109.7	126.2	109.5	125.9
1984	125.3	137.8	114.8	126.3
1985	92.6	95.4	93.9	97.7
1986	100.0	100.0	100.0	100.0
1987	113.2	108.6	106.2	101.8

Source. MAFF: *Agricultural Statistics, United Kingdom.*

Appendix 27: Fertilisers and lime

Table 27.1. Expenditure on fertilisers and lime[1] (£ million)

1937–38	8	1954–55	66	1971–72	225
1938–39	9	1955–56	82	1972	203
1939–40	11	1956–57	85	1973	213
1940–41	16	1957–58	102	1974	296
1941–42	21	1958–59	100	1975	325
1942–43	24	1959–60	118	1976	376
1943–44	27	1960–61	111	1977	426
1944–45	27	1961–62	120	1978	491
1945–46	27	1962–63	108	1979	548
1946–47	28	1963–64	120	1980	651
1947–48	33	1964–65	122	1981	762
1948–49	37	1965–66	120	1982	777
1949–50	41	1966–67	132	1983	868
1950–51	51	1967–68	144	1984	954
1951–52	50	1968–69	150	1985	901
1952–53	66	1969–70	140	1986	815
1953–54	66	1970–71	169	1987[2]	737

[1]Before subsidy. The fertiliser subsidy was discontinued in 1975 and the lime subsidy in 1977.   [2]Forecast.
Source. MAFF: *Departmental Net Income Calculation.*

Table 27.2. Breakdown of expenditure on fertilisers and lime[1] (£ million)

	1972	1975	1980	1981	1982	1983	1984	1985	1986	1987[3]
Straights										
Nitrogen	52.0	82.6	208.1	255.8	282.0	332.2	388.3	357.1	305.8	277.7
Phosphate	8.8	14.5	14.5	13.1	14.0	13.3	11.4	12.6	12.5	12.3
Potash	2.1	2.0	1.6	2.0	2.4	2.9	2.6	2.0	3.8	2.6
Compounds	123.5	200.2	379.6	437.4	419.2	456.2	478.2	461.7	426.4	377.0
Other[2]	4.9	9.4	16.8	17.6	18.8	21.0	22.5	26.0	24.0	25.0
Total fertilisers	191.3	308.7	620.6	725.9	736.4	825.6	903.0	859.4	772.5	694.6
Lime	11.4	15.7	27.5	32.3	37.0	38.4	46.8	37.6	38.5	39.5
VAT	–	0.9	2.9	3.4	3.5	3.9	4.3	4.0	3.6	3.3
Total fertilisers and lime	202.7	325.3	651.0	761.6	776.9	867.9	954.1	901.0	814.6	737.4

[1]Before subsidy. The fertiliser subsidy was discontinued in 1975 and the lime subsidy in 1977.   [2]Includes organics and deliveries of fertilisers to very small holdings.   [3]Forecast.
Source. MAFF: *Departmental Net Income Calculation.*

Table 27.3. Quantity of inorganic fertilisers purchased

	1976	1980	1981	1982	1983	1984	1985	1986	1987[3]
Straights[1]									
Nitrogen	576	733	891	882	974	1181	1039	1094	1122
Phosphate	64	56	43	45	43	35	35	35	35
Potash	11	11	13	16	18	16	11	23	15
Compounds[2]	3060	3239	3454	3298	3505	3578	3369	3439	3481

[1]'000 tonnes nutrient.   [2]'000 tonnes product weight.   [3]Forecast.
Source. MAFF: *Departmental Net Income Calculation.*

Table 27.4. Index of fertiliser prices[1]

	At current prices	In 1986 money values		At current prices	In 1986 money values
1938	7.7	170.7	1965–66	18.6	122.9
1939	7.7	167.4	1966–67	19.2	122.1
1940	10.0	183.3	1967–68	21.7	134.3
1941	10.2	154.9	1968–69	22.2	131.4
1942	10.1	143.5	1969–70	22.1	124.2
1943	10.2	140.5	1970–71	24.3	128.3
1944	10.2	137.9	1971–72	29.5	142.2
1945	10.2	135.5	1972–73	34.3	154.4
1946	10.4	136.4	1973	36.9	152.4
1947	10.4	127.8	1974	46.8	166.6
1948	10.7	122.1	1975	55.5	158.7
1949	10.7	123.1	1976	59.4	146.1
1950	12.3	133.3	1977	68.4	145.0
1951	15.1	150.1	1978	79.2	155.2
1952	19.2	179.7	1979	85.5	147.9
1953	19.5	179.6	1980	100.0	146.0
1954	19.5	176.7	1981	110.2	144.4
1954–55	20.0	181.2	1982	115.5	138.6
1955–56	20.4	178.5	1983	116.8	134.3
1956–57	20.3	170.3	1984	120.2	132.2
1957–58	19.5	158.3	1985	127.7	131.5
1958–59	18.7	147.9	1986	115.1	115.1
1959–60	18.2	143.1	1987[3]	105.1	110.4
1960–61	17.7	137.7			
1961–62	17.8	134.7			
1962–63	17.5	127.4			
1963–64	17.8	127.1			
1964–65	18.1	125.1			

[1]Fertilisers and soil improvers net of subsidy where appropriate; the fertiliser subsidy was discontinued in 1975 and the lime subsidy in 1977. [2]Estimated prior to 1954–55.
[3]Forecast.
Source. MAFF: *Agricultural Statistics.*

Table 27.5. Fertiliser use on some major tillage crops (kg per hectare)

	1975	1980	1981	1982	1983	1984	1985	1986
Nitrogen (N)								
Winter wheat	93	145	162	166	183	186	192	186
Winter barley	90	129	143	145	150	149	150	148
Spring barley	77	87	98	94	108	98	102	103
Potatoes (main crop)	169	185	194	199	203	214	198	195
Sugar beet	149	146	152	144	154	148	126	128
Oil seed rape	193	254	260	265	274	279	272	261
Phosphates (P_2O_5)								
Winter wheat	39	46	49	51	51	56	54	56
Winter barley	43	48	50	51	52	57	55	54
Spring barley	36	37	37	38	39	39	38	37
Potatoes (main crop)	174	185	192	199	207	228	209	203
Sugar beet	86	71	67	67	72	74	56	61
Oil seed rape	53	51	46	59	61	63	58	62
Potash (K_2O)								
Winter wheat	33	39	42	45	46	53	52	52
Winter barley	41	45	47	54	54	59	58	59
Spring barley	36	40	40	41	44	44	44	44
Potatoes (main crop)	239	259	259	267	268	278	278	264
Sugar beet	168	158	152	159	160	160	137	139
Oil seed rape	49	38	36	50	58	60	55	56

Source. ADAS, Rothamsted Experimental Station, Fertilisers Manufacturers' Association: *Survey of Fertiliser Practice – Fertiliser Use on Farms.*

Table 27.6. Proportion of nitrogen applied in compound form (per cent)

	1975	1981	1985	1986
Winter wheat	19	11	6	4
Winter barley	31	16	10	8
Spring barley	75	62	48	44
Potatoes (main crop)	98	94	92	90
Sugar beet	89	66	46	36
Oilseed rape	26	18	15	13

Source. ADAS, Rothamsted Experimental Station; Fertilisers Manufacturers' Association: *Survey of Fertiliser Practice – Fertiliser Use on Farms.*

Table 27.7. Fertiliser usage on tillage and grass (kg per hectare)

	1970	1975	1980	1981	1982	1983	1984	1985	1986
Straight nitrogen (N)									
Tillage		36	77	92	99	117	128	134	133
Leys (seeded down 7 years or less)		67	69	74	71	68	71	70	77
Permanent grass									
All crops and grass		54	73	83	85	92	99	102	106
Compound nitrogen (N)									
Tillage		50	44	43	42	37	34	27	24
Leys (seeded down 7 years or less)		32	50	51	52	57	61	62	57
Permanent grass									
All crops and grass		40	47	47	47	47	48	44	40
Total nitrogen (N)									
Tillage	88	86	121	135	141	154	162	161	156
Leys (seeded down 7 years or less)	110	99	119	125	123	125	132	131	135
Permanent grass	55								
All crops and grass	81	94	120	130	132	139	147	146	146
Phosphates (P$_2$O$_5$)									
Tillage	56	46	49	51	55	54	61	56	56
Leys (seeded down 7 years or less)	44	24	27	25	24	26	25	24	22
Permanent grass	25								
All crops and grass	43	34	37	38	39	39	42	40	40
Potash (K$_2$O)									
Tillage	61	51	54	56	61	60	68	63	62
Leys (seeded down 7 years or less)	32	20	26	26	28	28	33	32	33
Permanent grass	18								
All crops and grass	42	34	40	41	44	44	50	48	48

Source. ADAS, Rothamsted Experimental Station, Fertilisers Manufacturers' Association: *Survey of Fertiliser Practice – Fertiliser Use on Farms.*

Table 27.8. Percentage of total crop area receiving lime

	1975	1980	1981	1982	1983	1984	1985
Winter wheat			4.5	5.2	4.6	6.5	5.7
Winter barley			7.1	7.1	9.2	8.5	6.1
Spring barley			10.3	8.9	9.7	10.1	9.3
Potatoes (main crop)			1.6	2.8	0.5	3.7	0.9
Sugar beet			34.2	27.5	22.9	28.0	28.1
Oil seed rape			6.8	10.4	10.1	10.6	8.3
All tillage	7.2		8.4	8.1	7.8	9.0	7.5
All grass	5.6[1]		4.1	4.4	4.3	6.0	3.5
All crops and grass	5.5	5.5	6.2	6.2	6.0	7.5	5.5

[1]Leys, permanent grass 3.3%.
Source. ADAS, Rothamsted Experimental Station, Fertilisers Manufacturers' Association: *Survey of Fertiliser Practice – Fertiliser Use on Farms.*

Appendix 28: Machinery expenses

Table 28.1. Total machinery expenses (£ million)

1937–38	15	1954–55	123	1971–72	199
1938–39	16	1955–56	128	1972	199
1939–40	19	1956–57	135	1973	224
1940–41	30	1957–58	134	1974	278
1941–42	36	1958–59	139	1975	330
1942–43	44	1959–60	137	1976	380
1943–44	49	1960–61	132	1977	453
1944–45	51	1961–62	139	1978	493
1945–46	55	1962–63	140	1979	593
1946–47	60	1963–64	139	1980	668
1947–48	71	1964–65	136	1981	743
1948–49	75	1965–66	136	1982	833
1949–50	84	1966–67	137	1983	906
1950–51	101	1967–68	145	1984	944
1951–52	114	1968–69	153	1985	1035
1952–53	125	1969–70	161	1986	969
1953–54	124	1970–71	181	1987[1]	997

[1]Forecast.
Source. MAFF: *Departmental Net Income Calculation.*

Table 28.2. Expenditure on machinery and farm car repairs (£ million)

1937–38	6	1954–55	55	1971–72	95
1938–39	7	1955–56	59	1972	98
1939–40	8	1956–57	62	1973	114
1940–41	11	1957–58	64	1974	131
1941–42	15	1958–59	67	1975	159
1942–43	18	1959–60	69	1976	180
1943–44	20	1960–61	66	1977	209
1944–45	20	1961–62	69	1978	244
1945–46	22	1962–63	70	1979	274
1946–47	25	1963–64	69	1980	307
1947–48	30	1964–65	61	1981	336
1948–49	32	1965–66	63	1982	370
1949–50	36	1966–67	66	1983	398
1950–51	43	1967–68	69	1984	430
1951–52	47	1968–69	73	1985	470
1952–53	52	1969–70	78	1986	500
1953–54	54	1970–71	87	1987[1]	534

[1]Forecast.
Source. MAFF: *Departmental Net Income Calculation.*

Table 28.3. Maintenance and repair of plant purchase price index (1986 = 100)

	At current prices	In 1986 money values
1970	17.5	92.4
1971	19.4	93.5
1972	20.8	93.6
1973	23.6	97.5
1974	29.6	105.4
1975	37.7	107.8
1976	43.0	105.6
1977	50.8	107.7
1978	55.4	108.6
1979	62.2	107.6
1980	72.5	105.9
1981	77.4	101.4
1982	81.9	98.3
1983	85.6	98.4
1984	90.7	99.8
1985	94.6	97.4
1986	100.0	100.0
1987	105.3	101.0

Source. MAFF: *Agricultural Statistics, United Kingdom.*

Table 28.4. Expenditure on fuel and oil (£ million)

1937–38	5	1954–55	48	1971–72	72
1938–39	5	1955–56	48	1972	78
1939–40	7	1956–57	52	1973	85
1940–41	11	1957–58	49	1974	122
1941–42	12	1958–59	50	1975	139
1942–43	14	1959–60	47	1976	163
1943–44	15	1960–61	46	1977	200
1944–45	17	1961–62	49	1978	202
1945–46	18	1962–63	48	1979	265
1946–47	20	1963–64	48	1980	299
1947–48	24	1964–65	49	1981	337
1948–49	25	1965–66	50	1982	388
1949–50	30	1966–67	49	1983	430
1950–51	40	1967–68	54	1984	432
1951–52	49	1968–69	56	1985	475
1952–53	53	1969–70	57	1986	372
1953–54	50	1970–71	66	1987[1]	364

[1]Forecast.
Source. MAFF: *Departmental Net Income Calculation.*

Table 28.5. Energy and lubricants purchase price indices (1986 = 100)

	Lubricants		Fuel and oil for heating		Motor fuel		All energy and lubricants	
	At current prices	In 1986 money values	At current prices	In 1986 money values	At current prices	In 1986 money values	At current prices	In 1986 money values
1955							8.9	77.9
1956							9.1	76.3
1957							10.2	82.8
1958							9.7	76.7
1959							9.7	76.2
1960							9.8	76.2
1961							9.9	74.9
1962							10.6	77.2
1963							10.6	75.7
1964							10.8	74.6
1965							11.0	72.7
1966							11.4	72.5
1967							12.1	74.8
1968							12.6	74.6
1969							12.9	72.5
1970							13.8	72.9
1971							14.8	71.3
1972							15.7	70.7
1973	20.2	83.4	17.5	72.3	17.8	73.5	19.4	80.1
1974	27.5	97.9	23.8	84.7	25.0	89.0	25.4	90.4
1975	31.4	89.8	28.0	80.1	27.8	79.5	29.8	85.2
1976	36.7	90.3	35.1	86.3	34.4	84.6	36.8	90.5
1977	42.9	90.9	46.2	97.9	41.8	88.6	44.0	93.3
1978	44.1	86.4	47.3	92.7	42.1	82.5	45.6	89.4
1979	53.3	92.2	57.3	99.1	52.1	90.1	54.3	93.9
1980	71.5	104.4	75.9	110.8	69.4	101.3	71.0	103.7
1981	79.5	104.1	92.4	121.0	85.9	112.5	85.7	112.3
1982	84.0	100.1	106.7	128.0	98.3	118.0	97.5	117.0
1983	88.2	101.4	121.5	139.7	110.2	126.7	107.4	123.5
1984	94.4	103.8	129.8	142.8	113.5	124.9	110.1	121.1
1985	104.6	111.0	140.7	144.9	127.8	131.6	120.2	123.8
1986	100.0	100.0	100.0	100.0	100.0	100.0	100.0	100.0
1987	99.5	95.4	109.1	104.6	101.1	97.0	101.1	97.0

[1]Estimated prior to 1973.
Source. MAFF: *Agricultural Statistics, United Kingdom.*

Table 28.6. Other machinery expenses (£ million)

1937–38	4	1954–55	20	1971–72	32
1938–39	4	1955–56	21	1972	23
1939–40	4	1956–57	21	1973	25
1940–41	8	1957–58	21	1974	25
1941–42	9	1958–59	22	1975	32
1942–43	12	1959–60	21	1976	37
1943–44	14	1960–61	20	1977	44
1944–45	14	1961–62	21	1978	47
1945–46	15	1962–63	22	1979	54
1946–47	15	1963–64	22	1980	62
1947–48	17	1964–65	26	1981	70
1948–49	18	1965–66	23	1982	76
1949–50	18	1966–67	22	1983	77
1950–51	18	1967–68	22	1984	82
1951–52	18	1968–69	24	1985	89
1952–53	20	1969–70	26	1986	97
1953–54	20	1970–71	28	1987[1]	99

[1]Forecast.
Source. MAFF: *Departmental Net Income Calculation.*

Table 28.7. Details of expenditure on machinery (£ million)

	1972	1975	1980	1981	1982	1983	1984	1985	1986	1987[1]
Repairs										
Machinery repairs	80.3	128.3	247.4	272.8	301.2	326.1	353.4	388.8	413.4	442.7
Farm car repairs	5.8	10.4	21.1	23.3	25.7	27.8	30.1	33.1	35.2	37.7
Tyres and tubes	12.0	20.1	38.7	39.6	42.9	44.4	46.3	48.5	51.5	53.8
Total repairs	98.1	158.8	307.2	335.7	369.8	398.3	429.8	470.4	500.1	534.2
Fuel and oil										
Petrol	27.0	47.1	88.0	105.3	116.1	122.2	124.6	131.4	118.4	112.6
Gas and diesel: agriculture	24.8	53.0	134.7	152.8	189.5	223.9	224.3	262.2	183.1	185.0
horticulture	3.1	5.1	10.3	13.6	13.0	10.1	11.0	13.1	9.5	10.1
Derv	3.7	5.8	19.6	18.7	20.6	22.6	22.9	23.4	20.7	19.0
TVO	1.2	1.2	0.5							
Fuel oil: agriculture	0.3	2.2	2.0	1.0	0.8	0.6	1.2	0.8	0.7	0.7
horticulture	5.1	12.1	24.9	25.2	25.3	27.0	22.8	16.5	13.4	11.5
Lubricating oil	11.4	10.4	15.7	16.4	18.3	19.5	20.8	23.1	21.7	21.2
Grease	1.1	0.7	1.1	1.1	1.3	1.5	1.5	1.7	1.6	1.6
Anti freeze	0.3	1.0	1.1	1.1	1.0	1.0	1.0	1.1	1.1	0.9
VAT		0.3	1.3	1.5	1.7	1.9	1.9	2.1	1.7	1.6
Total fuel and oil	78.0	138.9	299.2	336.7	387.6	430.3	432.0	475.4	371.9	364.2
Other expenses										
Licences:	8.8	11.0	19.0	22.1	25.5	26.6	27.9	31.3	33.0	33.5
of which										
tractors and combines	2.1	2.4	3.9	4.3	5.0	5.3	5.7	6.1	6.1	6.1
lorries and vans	2.3	2.8	5.4	6.4	7.5	7.2	7.4	9.0	10.3	11.0
farm vans	4.3	5.8	9.7	11.3	13.0	14.1	14.8	16.2	16.6	16.4
Insurance:	11.0	16.3	33.7	39.0	40.4	40.4	42.2	44.3	50.3	50.5
of which										
tractors	2.9	3.7	9.6	11.4	11.7	11.8	12.0	12.6	14.4	16.0
combines	0.3	0.4	1.0	1.1	1.3	1.3	1.4	1.4	1.5	1.5
lorries, vans, unlicensed cars	2.2	3.3	6.8	8.1	9.0	8.9	9.3	9.8	10.8	7.0
farm cars	5.6	8.9	16.3	18.4	18.4	18.4	19.5	20.5	23.6	26.0
Other incl. second-hand machinery transport	3.3	4.7	8.9	9.3	9.9	10.4	12.0	13.1	13.9	14.5
Total other expenses	23.0	32.0	61.6	70.4	75.8	77.4	82.1	88.7	97.2	98.5
Total expenditure on machinery	199.1	329.7	668.0	742.8	833.2	906.0	943.9	1034.5	969.2	996.9

[1]Forecast.
Source. MAFF: *Departmental Net Income Calculation.*

Appendix 29: Farm maintenance and depreciation

Table 29.1. Farm maintenance (£ million)

Year	Value	Year	Value
1937–38	5	1963–64	60
1938–39	5	1964–65	70
1939–40	5	1965–66	74
1940–41	8	1966–67	78
1941–42	11	1967–68	83
1942–43	13	1968–69	88
1943–44	13	1969–70	93
1944–45	13	1970–71	100
1945–46	16	1971–72	100
1946–47	16	1972	66
1947–48	19	1973	71
1948–49	19	1974	83
1949–50	22	1975	103
1950–51	24	1976	122
1951–52	27	1977	134
1952–53	27	1978	147
1953–54	27	1979	166
1954–55	30	1980	179
1955–56	30	1981	190
1956–57	30	1982	215
1957–58	31	1983	230
1958–59	31	1984	255
1959–60	36	1985	271
1960–61	43	1986	287
1961–62	50	1987[1]	308
1962–63	58		

[1]Forecast.
Source. MAFF: *Departmental Net Income Calculation.*

Table 29.2. Farm maintenance in detail (£ million)

	Occupier	Landlord	Total
1974	66.6	16.8	83.4
1975	84.0	19.0	103.0
1976	100.7	21.4	122.1
1977	109.2	24.3	133.5
1978	119.4	27.4	146.8
1979	134.8	30.9	165.7
1980	142.9	36.2	179.1
1981	147.6	42.5	190.1
1982	169.0	46.1	215.1
1983	178.3	51.2	229.5
1984	200.2	55.2	255.4
1985	211.8	59.6	271.4
1986	223.2	63.3	286.6
1987[1]	245.0	63.0	308.0

[1]Forecast.
Source. MAFF: *Departmental Net Income Calculation.*

Table 29.3. Maintenance and repair of buildings purchase price index (1986 = 100)

	At current prices	In 1986 money values
1970	14.5	76.6
1971	16.0	77.1
1972	17.6	79.2
1973	20.9	86.3
1974	26.1	92.9
1975	32.4	92.7
1976	38.3	94.2
1977	44.8	95.0
1978	48.7	95.5
1979	55.7	96.4
1980	65.9	96.2
1981	72.2	94.6
1982	78.5	94.2
1983	84.0	96.6
1984	89.4	98.3
1985	95.5	98.4
1986	100.0	100.0
1987	106.1	101.7

Source. MAFF: *Agricultural Statistics.*

Table 29.4. Depreciation (£ million)

1937–1938	9
1938–39	10
1939–40	12
1940–41	16
1941–42	19
1942–43	20
1943–44	23
1944–45	24
1945–46	27
1946–47	29
1947–48	36
1948–49	36
1949–50	44
1950–51	56
1951–52	65
1952–53	74
1953–54	80
1954–55	80
1955–56	85
1956–57	89
1957–58	94
1958–59	97
1959–60	103
1960–61	102
1961–62	107
1962–63	108
1963–64	110
1964–65	126
1965–66	133
1966–67	145
1967–68	150
1968–69	164
1969–70	178
1970–71	195
1971–72	226
1972	252
1973	298
1974	402
1975	518
1976	607
1977	721
1978	821
1979	957
1980	1133
1981	1203
1982	1269
1983	1312
1984	1356
1985	1428
1986	1450
1987[1]	1486

[1]Forecast.
Source. MAFF: *Departmental Net Income Calculation.*

Table 29.5. Depreciation of plant, vehicles, buildings and works (£ million)

	Plant and machinery	Farm cars	Buildings and works	Total
1972	161.9	18.4	71.6	251.9
1973	181.0	19.1	97.7	297.8
1974	238.6	22.0	140.9	401.5
1975	322.6	27.6	167.4	517.6
1976	389.2	32.4	185.7	607.3
1977	470.9	40.4	209.2	720.5
1978	534.7	46.5	239.9	821.1
1979	605.5	52.2	299.7	957.4
1980	668.1	57.6	407.1	1132.8
1981	690.4	62.0	450.4	1202.8
1982	754.5	65.4	448.9	1268.8
1983	786.8	69.0	456.3	1312.1
1984	813.1	72.4	470.3	1355.8
1985	844.2	77.2	507.0	1428.4
1986	834.7	81.5	533.4	1449.6
1987[1]	841.3	85.8	558.5	1485.6

[1]Forecast.
Source. MAFF: *Departmental Net Income Calculation.*

Table 29.6. Farm machinery purchase price indices: cultivation and harvesting equipment (1986 = 100)

	Machinery and plant for cultivation		Machinery and plant for harvesting	
	At current prices	In 1986 money values	At current prices	In 1986 money values
1970	21.4	113.0	14.0	73.9
1971	23.7	114.2	15.2	73.3
1972	25.7	115.7	17.0	76.5
1973	28.2	116.5	18.8	77.6
1974	28.9	102.9	21.8	77.6
1975	35.6	101.8	29.3	83.8
1976	41.3	101.6	35.5	87.3
1977	50.5	107.1	44.2	93.7
1978	58.1	113.9	49.2	96.4
1979	64.8	112.1	54.4	94.1
1980	75.8	110.7	66.5	97.1
1981	79.3	103.9	72.4	94.8
1982	81.9	98.3	79.2	95.0
1983	84.0	96.6	86.4	99.4
1984	87.8	96.6	91.5	100.7
1985	92.8	95.5	94.3	97.1
1986	100.0	100.0	100.0	100.0
1987	102.5	98.3	103.7	99.4

Source. MAFF: *Agricultural Statistics, United Kingdom.*

Table 29.7. Farm machinery purchase price indices:
installations and tractors (1986 = 100)

	Farm machinery and installations		Tractors	
	At current prices	In 1986 money values	At current prices	In 1986 money values
1968	14.5	85.8		
1969	15.4	86.5		
1970	16.9	89.2	13.3	70.2
1971	18.5	89.2	15.3	73.7
1972	20.0	90.0	16.9	76.1
1973	23.0	95.0	18.1	74.8
1974	28.1	100.0	21.6	76.9
1975	34.0	97.2	29.7	84.9
1976	40.7	100.1	38.0	93.5
1977	48.4	102.6	47.4	100.5
1978	55.8	109.4	53.8	105.4
1979	64.0	110.7	59.5	102.9
1980	72.7	106.1	66.5	97.1
1981	78.8	103.2	71.4	93.5
1982	86.5	103.8	75.7	90.8
1983	86.3	99.2	81.8	94.1
1984	90.0	99.0	89.2	98.1
1985	95.1	98.0	95.7	98.6
1986	100.0	100.0	100.0	100.0
1987	104.3	100.0	100.6	96.5

Source. MAFF: *Agricultural Statistics, United Kingdom.*

Table 29.8. Farm machinery purchase price indices:
other vehicles and machinery (1986 = 100)

	Other vehicles		Machinery and other equipment in total	
	At current prices	In 1986 money values	At current prices	In 1986 money values
1970	15.2	80.3	15.8	83.4
1971	16.3	78.6	17.4	83.9
1972	17.1	77.0	18.9	85.1
1973	19.7	81.4	20.7	85.5
1974	24.3	86.5	24.3	86.5
1975	31.8	90.9	31.5	90.1
1976	37.5	92.3	38.5	94.7
1977	46.6	98.8	47.3	100.3
1978	53.7	105.3	53.8	105.4
1979	60.4	104.5	60.3	104.3
1980	67.8	99.0	69.2	101.0
1981	73.8	96.7	74.5	97.6
1982	78.3	94.0	80.2	96.2
1983	81.8	94.1	84.2	96.8
1984	87.1	95.8	89.6	98.6
1985	93.5	96.3	94.9	97.7
1986	100.0	100.0	100.0	100.0
1987	107.8	103.4	102.8	98.6

Source. MAFF: *Agricultural Statistics, United Kingdom.*

Table 29.9. Farm buildings, engineering and soil improvement operations
purchase price indices (1986 = 100)

	Farm buildings		Engineering and soil improvement operations		Building group	
	At current prices	In 1986 money values	At current prices	In 1986 money values	At current prices	In 1986 money values
1970	14.7	77.6	14.0	73.9	14.4	76.0
1971	16.2	78.1	15.4	74.2	15.8	76.2
1972	17.7	80.0	17.3	77.9	17.3	77.9
1973	20.9	86.3	19.3	79.7	20.3	83.3
1974	26.1	92.9	24.2	86.2	25.3	90.1
1975	32.4	92.7	29.6	84.7	31.3	89.5
1976	38.3	94.2	34.4	84.6	36.7	90.3
1977	44.8	95.0	38.4	81.4	42.2	89.5
1978	48.7	95.5	43.6	85.5	46.6	91.3
1979	55.7	96.4	50.5	87.4	53.6	92.7
1980	65.9	96.2	62.3	91.0	64.5	94.2
1981	72.2	94.6	67.1	87.9	70.1	91.8
1982	78.5	94.2	73.0	87.6	76.3	91.6
1983	84.0	96.6	78.4	90.2	81.7	94.0
1984	89.4	98.3	83.7	92.1	87.1	95.8
1985	95.5	98.4	86.0	88.6	91.6	94.3
1986	100.0	100.0	100.0	100.0	100.0	100.0
1987	106.1	101.7	116.0	111.2	110.2	105.7

Source. MAFF: *Agricultural Statistics, United Kingdom.*

263

Appendix 30: Commercial interest

Table 30.1. Interest charges (£ million)

1937–38	4	1954–55	15	1971–72	37
1938–39	4	1955–56	16	1972	54
1939–40	4	1956–57	17	1973	88
1940–41	3	1957–58	19	1974	124
1941–42	3	1958–59	18	1975	121
1942–43	3	1959–60	20	1976	136
1943–44	2	1960–61	23	1977	147
1944–45	3	1961–62	24	1978	184
1945–46	4	1962–63	20	1979	318
1946–47	5	1963–64	20	1980	464
1947–48	6	1964–65	24	1981	468
1948–49	8	1965–66	25	1982	501
1949–50	9	1966–67	28	1983	494
1950–51	12	1967–68	32	1984	569
1951–52	12	1968–69	35	1985	704
1952–53	13	1969–70	41	1986	700
1953–54	14	1970–71	39	1987[1]	646

[1]Forecast.
Source. MAFF: *Departmental Net Income Calculation.*

Table 30.2. Interest charges in detail at current prices (£ million)

	1971	1972	1975	1980	1981	1982	1983	1984	1985	1986	1987[4]
Total bank advances to agriculture	565	647	986	2844	3380	3997	4718	5275	5543	5909	5962
Estimated rates of interest on advances[1] (%)	7.8	8.0	13.0	18.7	15.6	14.3	12.2	12.2	14.7	13.4	12.2
Total bank interest on advances for current farming purposes and building/works	40.8	48.1	118.7	475.2	472.0	494.2	462.0	537.7	676.9	656.5	605.0
Instalment credit	4.0	4.1	6.3	22.8	20.8	20.8	22.2	24.3	33.1	30.4	28.7
Agricultural Mortgage Corporation	2.9	3.1	2.9	5.1	4.7	4.8	4.7	5.7	5.9	6.2	6.1
Other credit[2]	1.8	1.9	3.4	17.2	20.7	29.1	43.1	45.1	54.9	61.1	46.9
Less interest on deposits[3]	3.1	3.6	10.1	55.9	50.0	48.3	38.4	44.1	67.0	54.5	41.0
Total interest charges	46.5	53.5	121.2	464.4	468.2	500.6	493.5	568.7	703.8	699.7	645.7

[1] Weighted average of the rates of interest in England and Wales, Scotland and Northern Ireland. [2] Including Department of Agriculture for Northern Ireland loans fund, Agricultural Credit Corporation charges, leasing charges and borrowings from private services. [3] Interest earned by money temporarily not in the farm business on short term deposits. [4]Forecast.
Source. MAFF: *Departmental Net Income Calculation.*

Table 30.3. Total bank advances to agriculture (£ million: annual averages)

	At current prices	In 1986 money values
1972	647	2912
1973	778	3213
1974	926	3297
1975	986	2820
1976	1042	2563
1977	1297	2750
1978	1705	3342
1979	2234	3865
1980	2844	4152
1981	3380	4428
1982	3997	4796
1983	4718	5426
1984	5275	5803
1985	5543	5709
1986	5909	5909
1987[1]	5962	5724

[1]Forecast.
Source. MAFF: *Departmental Net Income Calculation.*

Table 30.4. Estimated rates of interest on bank advances

	Per cent		Per cent
1944	3.5	1969	7.2
1949	4.0	1970	7.9
1951	4.5	1971	7.1
1952	5.5	1972	8.0
1953	5.0	1973	12.1
1954	4.5	1974	14.7
1955	5.5	1975	13.0
1956	5.7	1976	13.6
1957	6.1	1977	11.4
1958	5.8	1978	11.6
1959	5.0	1979	16.1
1960	6.0	1980	18.7
1961	7.0	1981	15.6
1962	6.5	1982	14.3
1963	5.5	1983	12.2
1964	5.8	1984	12.2
1965	6.2	1985	14.7
1966	6.8	1986	13.4
1967	7.4	1987[1]	12.1
1968	6.8		

[1]Forecast.
Source. Prior to 1971, author's estimate. From 1971 onwards, MAFF: *Departmental Net Income Calculation.*

Appendix 31: Rent

Table 31.1. Net rent (£ million)[1]

1937–38	34	1954–55	22	1971–72	52
1938–39	35	1955–56	23	1972[1]	32
1939–40	35	1956–57	24	1973	29
1940–41	33	1957–58	26	1974	20
1941–42	32	1958–59	26	1975	24
1942–43	31	1959–60	28	1976	33
1943–44	30	1960–61	30	1977	43
1944–45	30	1961–62	33	1978	55
1945–46	28	1962–63	36	1979	66
1946–47	28	1963–64	39	1980	69
1947–48	25	1964–65	43	1981	88
1948–49	26	1965–66	46	1982	105
1949–50	23	1966–67	49	1983	126
1950–51	21	1967–68	51	1984	141
1951–52	20	1968–69	53	1985	156
1952–53	21	1969–70	56	1986	168
1953–54	21	1970–71	56	1987[1]	167

[1]Change in definition from 1972 onwards: landlords' expenses are included within farm maintenance, miscellaneous expenditure and depreciation on buildings and works. Net rent is the rent paid on tenanted land less these landlords' expenses and the benefit value of dwellings on that land. [2]Forecast.
Source. MAFF: *Departmental Net Income Calculation.*

Table 31.2. Rent bill for the tenanted sector (£ million)

	1973	1974	1975	1976	1977	1978	1979	1980	1981	1982	1983	1984	1985	1986[1]	1987[2]
Gross rent[3]	87	94	109	129	151	177	206	240	277	311	342	371	395	417	417
Less															
Benefit value of farm houses (private use and cottages)	16	17	18	21	23	25	25	29	29	40	44	46	46	47	49
Adjusted gross rent	71	77	91	108	128	152	181	212	248	271	298	325	349	370	368
of which:															
Net rent	25	20	23	32	43	55	66	69	88	105	125	142	155	168	167
Landowners' current expenses[4]	27	29	34	39	46	53	61	71	84	92	100	111	117	124	124
Landowners' depreciation[5]	20	28	34	36	40	44	54	71	77	74	73	73	76	77	78

[1]Provisional. [2]Forecast. [3]Total rent paid on all tenanted land. [4]Items included are repairs and maintenance, management costs, insurance and statutory charges. [5]Depreciation on buildings and works at replacement cost and assuming a 30 year life.
Source. MAFF: *Departmental Net Income Calculation.*

Table 31.3. Number of holdings by tenure: England and Wales ('000)

	Rented	Owned	Part rented/ Part owned	Total[1]
1887	393.0	64.6	19.0	481.8
1891	404.6	68.9	21.4	494.9

	Rented or mainly rented		Owned or mainly owned	Total[1]
1908	375.2		54.9	430.1
1910	376.2		55.4	431.7
1914	385.9		49.2	435.1
1922	352.0		62.7	414.7

	Rented	Owned	Mainly rented	Mainly owned	Total
1950	185.0	138.7	← 56.3	→	380.0[3]
1960	123.7	157.7	20.6	31.2	333.2[4]

Great Britain

	Owned or mainly owned	Rented or part rented	Total
1971	159.6	107.0	266.7

[1]Excluding holdings comprising rough grazing only. [2]Including 5202 holdings which cannot be distributed between preceding columns. [3]Including 7219 holdings with only rough grazing. [4]Including 5990 holdings with rough grazing only, but excluding 17 751 statistically insignificant holdings.
Source. MAFF.

Table 31.4. Number of holdings by tenure: Great Britain ('000)

Size of holding (hectares)	Under 2	2–19.9	20–199.9	200 and over	Total
1971[1]					
Owned or mainly owned	17.3	60.6	75.0	6.7	159.6
Rented or mainly rented	7.9	35.8	56.9	6.4	107.0
Total	25.2	96.4	132.0	13.1	266.7
1975[1]					
Owned or mainly owned	12.4	53.2	72.1	6.9	144.7
Rented or mainly rented	5.1	28.9	52.8	6.7	93.5
Total	17.5	82.1	124.9	13.6	238.2
1980					
Owned or mainly owned	9.9	50.2	74.3	7.6	142.0
Rented or mainly rented	2.6	20.1	45.2	6.6	74.6
Total	12.6	70.2	119.5	14.3	216.6
1986					
Owned or mainly owned	12.0	57.2	76.6	8.2	153.9
Rented or mainly rented	2.2	15.6	37.9	6.5	62.2
Total	14.2	72.9	114.5	14.6	216.2

[1]In 1971 and 1975 the size groups were under 2.02 hectares; 2.02–20.13; 20.13–202.25; 202.25 hectares and above.
Source. MAFF: *Agricultural Statistics.*

Table 31.5. Area of holdings by tenure: Great Britain 1887 to 1960
(million hectares)

	Area rented	%	Area owned	%	Total area – crops and grass	%
1887[1]	11.2	85	2.0	15	13.2	100
1891[1]	11.3	85	2.0	15	13.3	100
1908[1]	11.4	88	1.6	12	13.0	100
1910[1]	11.4	88	1.6	12	13.0	100
1914[1]	11.5	89	1.4	11	12.9	100
1922[1]	10.2	82	2.2	18	12.4	100
1950[2]	8.3	62	5.0	38	13.3	100
1960[3]	6.7	50	6.6	50	13.3	100

[1]Area of crops and grass.   [2]Area of crops and grass and rough grazings in England and Wales, and crops and grass in Scotland.   [3]Total area of farms in England and Wales and crops and grass in Scotland.
Source. MAFF: *Based on A Century of Agricultural Statistics. 1866–1966.*

Table 31.6. Area of holdings by tenure: Great Britain 1970–86
(million hectares)

	Rented area	%	Owned area	%	Total area	%
1970	7.7	43	10.3	57	18.0	100
1971	7.7	43	10.3	57	18.0	100
1972	7.5	42	10.4	58	17.9	100
1973	7.5	42	10.4	58	17.9	100
1974	7.5	42	10.4	58	17.9	100
1975	7.5	42	10.4	58	17.9	100
1976	7.5	42	10.4	58	17.9	100
1977	7.2	41	10.4	59	17.6	100
1978	7.1	40	10.6	60	17.7	100
1979	7.0	40	10.7	60	17.7	100
1980	6.9	39	10.8	61	17.7	100
1981	6.8	39	10.8	61	17.6	100
1982	6.7	38	10.8	62	17.5	100
1983	6.6	38	10.9	62	17.5	100
1984	6.5	40	9.8	60	16.3	100
1985	6.4	39	10.0	61	16.3	100
1986	6.3	39	10.0	61	16.3	100

Source. MAFF: *Agricultural Statistics United Kingdom.*

Table 31.7. Average rents in England and Wales (£ per hectare)[1]

	England	Wales	England and Wales
1967	10.87	6.05	10.19
1968	11.71	6.30	10.97
1969	12.73	6.23	11.86
1970	14.04	7.35	13.23
1971	14.92	8.80	14.31
1972	15.86	9.67	15.22
1973	16.90	9.93	16.19
1974	19.17	10.90	18.31
1975	23.37	15.46	22.32
1976	23.34	15.66	26.52
1977	33.84	16.03	32.04
1978	38.22	40.15	21.04
1979	47.78	23.90	45.39
1980	56.34	26.23	53.39
1981	64.11	31.81	61.01
1982	71.92	37.57	68.67
1983	79.65	40.29	75.97
1984	85.88	45.46	82.14
1985	91.64	46.63	87.45
1986[2]	95.53	46.85	90.99
1987[3]	97.34	48.14	92.75

[1]Figures relate to October each year.   [2]Provisional.   [3]Forecast.
Source. MAFF: *Annual Rent Enquiry.*

Table 31.8. Indices of average rents per hectare (1986 = 100)[1]

	England		Wales		Scotland		Great Britain	
	Actual	Real	Actual	Real	Actual	Real	Actual	Real
1970	13.7	72.3	14.3	75.5	15.2	80.3	14.1	74.4
1971	14.9	71.8	16.5	79.5	15.8	76.2	15.2	73.3
1972	15.9	71.6	19.3	86.9	17.3	77.9	16.4	73.8
1973	16.9	70.0	20.9	86.3	18.7	77.2	17.5	72.3
1974	18.3	65.1	21.8	77.6	20.1	71.6	18.9	67.3
1975	21.1	60.3	24.6	70.4	22.3	63.8	21.7	62.1
1976	25.7	63.2	29.2	71.8	26.4	64.9	26.1	64.2
1977	31.1	65.9	33.1	70.2	30.1	63.8	31.2	66.1
1978	37.2	72.9	37.7	73.9	36.4	73.9	37.1	72.7
1979	44.0	76.1	46.5	80.4	44.0	76.1	44.3	76.6
1980	52.2	76.2	52.4	76.5	52.2	76.2	52.2	76.2
1981	60.9	79.8	59.2	77.6	62.4	81.7	61.3	80.3
1982	69.1	82.9	71.2	85.4	74.2	89.0	70.4	84.5
1983	77.6	89.2	76.9	88.4	83.9	96.5	78.4	90.2
1984	85.4	93.9	86.9	95.6	91.8	101.0	86.4	95.0
1985	92.5	95.3	91.2	93.9	96.4	99.3	92.9	95.7
1986[2]	100.0	100.0	100.0	100.0	100.0	100.0	100.0	100.0
1987[3]	101.7	97.5	102.4	98.2	104.0	99.7	102.5	98.3

[1]Information collected on basis of visits to individual farmers, not aggregated rents for whole estates.   [2]Provisional.   [3]Forecasst.
Source. MAFF: *Departmental Net Income Calculation.*

Appendix 32: Miscellaneous expenses

Table 32.1. Miscellaneous expenses (£ million)

1937–38	11	1954–55	60	1971–72	186
1938–39	12	1955–56	62	1972	219
1939–40	14	1956–57	67	1973	247
1940–41	16	1957–58	70	1974	309
1941–42	20	1958–59	78	1975	389
1942–43	23	1959–60	92	1976	448
1943–44	24	1960–61	98	1977	517
1944–45	26	1961–62	106	1978	585
1945–46	26	1962–63	110	1979	710
1946–47	28	1963–64	118	1980	785
1947–48	32	1964–65	123	1981	847
1948–49	38	1965–66	126	1982	1006
1949–50	41	1966–67	132	1983	1064
1950–51	49	1967–68	142	1984	1113
1951–52	52	1968–69	150	1985	1221
1952–53	55	1969–70	158	1986	1269
1953–54	57	1970–71	172	1987[1]	1283

[1]Forecast.
Source. MAFF: *Departmental Net Income Calculation.*

Table 32.2. Miscellaneous expenses in detail (£ million)

	1971	1975	1980	1981	1982	1983	1984	1985	1986	1987[1]
Vet expenses and medicines	31.0	48.2	88.1	99.4	109.9	117.5	121.9	133.3	146.3	150.9
Pesticides	17.3	58.6	175.2	158.7	245.8	260.4	269.2	314.2	309.5	285.0
Power and fuel: electricity	25.9	44.8	101.2	113.8	125.4	123.3	124.2	134.5	135.7	135.7
other[2]	3.3	4.9	9.5	10.7	12.5	13.4	14.8	16.8	17.1	18.2
Containers: horticulture	24.7	36.3	56.3	60.8	71.7	77.4	84.9	82.6	88.8	93.1
others[3]	4.0	7.9	14.8	15.6	15.8	14.1	15.6	17.0	13.9	15.7
Overheads: drainage and water rates	9.9	18.7	36.8	42.0	46.4	49.2	51.7	57.2	61.9	65.9
general rates and insurance	12.0	22.0	41.9	51.5	58.0	61.5	63.9	76.0	80.3	87.3
professional fees	16.7	30.1	67.0	74.2	81.6	89.4	95.4	102.9	112.3	121.0
telephones	9.4	17.0	27.7	35.7	42.0	41.7	43.1	45.5	47.5	48.1
other[4]	9.8	25.2	52.3	60.4	68.1	75.4	82.8	88.1	92.5	93.8
Sundry equipment: small tools	11.1	19.2	36.4	41.1	43.0	47.0	47.0	49.1	51.6	53.8
binder and baler twine	7.2	15.7	23.8	25.4	26.2	30.4	33.8	36.2	37.5	37.3
other[5]	5.5	7.9	10.6	11.3	12.1	12.5	12.5	13.0	13.2	13.6
Fees[6]	7.7	12.1	22.0	22.7	24.6	26.0	26.6	27.2	29.0	29.3
Other miscellaneous expenses[7]	23.4	20.5	21.3	23.5	23.4	24.9	25.9	27.7	31.4	34.1
Total	219.0	389.1	784.9	847.0	1 006.4	1 064.1	1 113.3	1 221.3	1 268.5	1 282.8
In 1986 money values	985.5	1 112.8	1 146.0	1 109.6	1 207.7	1 223.7	1 224.6	1 257.9	1 268.5	1 230.2

[1]Forecast.   [2]Batteries, coke, coal, kerosene and gas.   [3]Egg containers, grain sacks, potato boxes, pallets and sacks.   [4]Landlords' managerial and statutory charges, periodicals, postage, subscriptions, stationery, subsistence.   [5]Dairy equipment, hop requisites, fencing, barbed wire, etc.   [6]AI fees, Low cost milk production scheme and Pig records.   [7]Minor unclassified items.
Source. MAFF: *Departmental Net Income Calculation.*

Table 32.3. Plant protection products and veterinary services purchase price indices (1986 = 100)

	Plant protection products		Veterinary services	
	At current prices	In 1986 money values	At current prices	In 1986 money values
1970	21.4	113.0	17.9	94.5
1971	21.6	104.1	20.0	96.4
1972	23.0	103.5	21.4	96.3
1973	24.1	99.5	22.5	92.9
1974	32.6	116.1	29.4	104.7
1975	43.8	125.3	36.3	103.8
1976	52.8	129.9	40.1	98.6
1977	61.1	129.5	43.5	92.2
1978	66.2	129.8	48.4	94.9
1979	69.5	120.2	54.0	93.4
1980	80.4	117.4	63.6	92.9
1981	86.3	113.1	73.8	96.7
1982	89.6	107.5	79.7	95.6
1983	97.1	111.7	83.5	96.0
1984	95.8	105.4	87.6	96.4
1985	97.1	100.0	91.9	97.5
1986	100.0	100.0	100.0	100.0
1987	103.8	99.5	101.6	97.4

Source. MAFF: *Agricultural Statistics, United Kingdom.*

Table 32.4. Electricity and general expenses purchase price indices (1986 = 100)

	Electricity		General expenses	
	At current prices	In 1986 money values	At current prices	In 1986 money values
1970			14.4	76.0
1971			16.2	78.1
1972			19.1	86.0
1973	23.7	97.9	21.6	89.2
1974	26.7	95.1	23.2	82.6
1975	35.2	100.7	30.1	86.1
1976	43.2	106.3	38.1	93.7
1977	48.8	103.5	42.0	89.0
1978	53.8	105.4	48.1	94.3
1979	58.8	101.7	53.3	92.2
1980	73.1	106.7	62.1	90.7
1981	87.6	114.8	71.5	93.7
1982	95.1	114.1	78.8	94.6
1983	98.8	113.6	83.3	95.8
1984	97.7	107.4	88.2	97.0
1985	97.4	100.3	93.7	96.5
1986	100.0	100.0	100.0	100.0
1987	98.3	94.3	108.1	103.7

Source. MAFF: *Agricultural Statistics, United Kingdom.*

Table 32.5. Materials and small tools purchase price indices (1986 = 100)

	At current prices	In 1986 money values
1970	17.5	92.4
1971	19.4	93.5
1972	20.8	93.6
1973	23.6	97.5
1974	29.6	105.4
1975	37.7	107.8
1976	43.0	105.8
1977	50.8	107.7
1978	55.4	108.6
1979	62.2	107.6
1980	72.5	105.9
1981	77.4	101.4
1982	81.9	98.3
1983	85.6	98.4
1984	90.7	99.8
1985	96.6	99.5
1986	100.0	100.0
1987	104.2	99.9

Source. MAFF: *Agricultural Statistics, United Kingdom.*

Sources of Information

General

MAFF, 1968. *A Century of Agricultural Statistics, Great Britain 1866–1966.*
Mitchell B. R. and Deane, Phyllis, 1962. *Abstract of British Historical Statistics,* Cambridge University Press.
Mitchell, B. R. 1978. *European Historical Statistics, 1750–1975,* Macmillan References.
Peters, G. H., 1988. *Reviews of UK Statistical Sources – Agriculture* (Volume 23), Chapman and Hall.

Agricultural holdings, areas and livestock

Agricultural Statistics, United Kingdom.
Annual Review of Agriculture.
Agricultural Statistics for Scotland.
Welsh Agricultural Statistics.
Statistical Review of Northern Ireland Agriculture.
General Report of the Department of Agriculture for Northern Ireland.
Digest of Welsh Statistics.
Regional Trends.
Statistical Statements: MAFF, DAFS and DANI.

Farm structures

Annual Review of Agriculture.
Farm Classification in England and Wales.
Welsh Agricultural Statistics.
Statistical Review of Northern Ireland Agriculture.
Statistical Statements: MAFF, DANI.

Area of crops and grassland: livestock numbers

Agricultural Statistics, United Kingdom.
Annual Review of Agriculture.
Monthly Digest of Statistics.
United Kingdom Annual Abstract of Statistics.
Regional Trends.
Scottish Abstract of Statistics.
Agriculture in Scotland, Annual Report.
Welsh Agricultural Statistics.
Statistical Review of Northern Ireland Agriculture.
General Report of the Department of Agriculture, Northern Ireland.
Digest of Welsh Statistics.
Statistical Statements: MAFF, DAFS and DANI.

Horticulture

MAFF Basic Horticultural Statistics for the United Kingdom.
Annual Review of Agriculture.
United Kingdom Annual Abstract of Statistics.
Agricultural Statistics, United Kingdom.
Economic Report on Scottish Agriculture.
Agriculture in Scotland, Annual Report.
Digest of Welsh Statistics.
Output and Utilisation of Farm Produce in the United Kingdom.
Statistical Statements: MAFF, DANI.
Horticultural Crop Intelligence Reports: MAFF.

Agricultural output
Output and Utilisation of Farm Produce in the United Kingdom.
Annual Review of Agriculture.
Agricultural Statistics, United Kingdom.
Economic Report on Scottish Agriculture.
Agriculture in Scotland, Annual Report.
Statistical Review of Northern Ireland Agriculture.
General Report of the Department of Agriculture, Northern Ireland.
Ulster Year Book.
Monthly Digest of Statistics.
United Kingdom Annual Abstract of Statistics.
Scottish Abstract of Statistics.
Digest of Welsh Statistics.
Northern Ireland Annual Abstract of Statistics.

Farming net income
MAFF Departmental Net Income Calculation.
Annual Review of Agriculture.
Farm Incomes in the United Kingdom.
Economic Report on Scottish Agriculture.
Farm Accounts in Wales.
Farm Incomes and Investment in Northern Ireland.
Statistical Review of Northern Ireland Agriculture.
General Report of the Department of Agriculture, Northern Ireland.
Northern Ireland Abstract of Statistics.
United Kingdom Annual Abstract of Statistics.

Feeding stuffs and fertilisers
Annual Review of Agriculture.
Output and Utilisation of Farm Produce in the United Kingdom.
Survey of Fertiliser Practice ADAS/Rothamsted Experimental Station
Fertiliser Manufacturers' Association.
Fertiliser Review.
United Kingdom Annual Abstract.
Statistical Review of Northern Ireland Agriculture.

Agricultural machinery
Agricultural Statistics, United Kingdom.
Welsh Agricultural Statistics.
Agricultural Statistics, Scotland.
Statistical Review of Northern Ireland.
General Report of the Department of Agriculture, Northern Ireland.
Statistical Statements: MAFF, Welsh Departments, DAFS, DANI.

Agricultural workers
Agricultural Statistics, United Kingdom.
United Kingdom Annual Abstract of Statistics.
Monthly Digest of Statistics.
Economic Report on Scottish Agriculture.
Welsh Agricultural Statistics.
Statistical Review of Northern Ireland Agriculture.
Regional Trends.
Scottish Abstract of Statistics.
Northern Ireland Abstract of Statistics.
Press notices: MAFF, DAFS, DANI, Welsh Department.

Earnings and conditions of employment
MAFF Agricultural Labour in England and Wales.
Annual Review of Agriculture.
Department of Employment Gazette.
Annual Abstract of Statistics.
Regional Trends.
Welsh Agricultural Statistics.
Agriculture in Scotland, Annual Report.
Scottish Abstract of Statistics.
Northern Ireland Annual Abstract of Statistics.
Press notices: MAFF.

Stocks and capital expenditure
United Kingdom National Accounts.
Annual Review of Agriculture.
United Kingdom Annual Abstract of Statistics.
Regional Trends.
Scottish Abstract of Statistics.
Statistical Review of Northern Ireland Agriculture.

Agricultural prices and subsidies
Agricultural Statistics, United Kingdom.
Annual Review of Agriculture.
United Kingdom Annual Abstract of Statistics.
Monthly Digest of Statistics.
MAFF Agricultural Market Report (Weekly).
DANI Northern Ireland Market Report (Weekly).
Economic Report on Scottish Agriculture.
Statistical Review of Northern Ireland Agriculture.
General Report of the Department of Agriculture, Northern Ireland.
Northern Ireland Annual Abstract of Statistics.
Welsh Agricultural Statistics.
Digest of Welsh Statistics.
Government Supply Estimates.

Land prices and rents
Annual Review of Agriculture.
Agricultural Land Prices in England and Wales.
Inland Revenue Statistics.
Economic Report on Scottish Agriculture.
Statistical Review of Northern Ireland Agriculture.
Farm Rents in England and Wales.
Welsh Agricultural Statistics.
Press notices: MAFF Current Agricultural Land Prices.

Food supplies, consumption and expenditure
Annual Review of Agriculture.
Annual Report of the National Food Survey Committee.
Department of Employment Family Expenditure Survey.
United Kingdom National Accounts.
Department of Employment Gazette.
Northern Ireland Family Expenditure Survey.
United Kingdom Annual Abstract of Statistics.
Digest of Welsh Statistics.
MAFF Food Facts.

Imports and exports
Overseas Trade Statistics of the United Kingdom, Monthly.
Overseas Trade Statistics, Annual.
United Kingdom Annual Abstract of Statistics.

Forestry
Forestry Commission, Annual Report and Accounts.
General Report of the Department of Agriculture, Northern Ireland.
Statistical Review of Northern Ireland Agriculture.
Monthly Digest of Statistics.
United Kingdom Annual Abstract of Statistics.
Regional Trends.
Scottish Abstract of Statistics.
Digest of Welsh Statistics.
Northern Ireland Annual Abstract of Statistics.

European Community (EC Statistical Office, Luxembourg)
Year Book of Agricultural Statistics.
The Agricultural Situation in the Community.
Crop Production, Quarterly.
Animal Production, Quarterly.
Agricultural Prices, 1977–87.
Agricultural Prices, Quarterly.
Hill, B. 1988. *Total Incomes of Agricultural Households,* Euro Stat., Theme 5, Series D.

Other publications
Milk Marketing Board: Dairy Facts and Figures.
Home Grown Cereals Authority: Cereal Statistics.
Meat and Livestock Commission: United Kingdom Handbook.
Meat and Livestock Commission: United Kingdom Market Review.
Meat and Livestock Commission: UK Weekly Market Survey.

Main agricultural holdings in England and Wales

The following changes have been made in the thresholds below which minor holdings have been excluded from the census from time to time.

1955–67
All holdings with an acre or more were included, except where agricultural activity was known to be small.

Main holdings ('000)

1955	376.3	1962	340.5
1956	371.4	1963	335.7
1957	367.9	1964	328.8
1958	362.0	1965	323.8
1959	357.3	1966	318.1
1960	350.9	1967	306.6
1961	344.7		

1968–69
Main holdings defined as those with
- at least an acre in total and at least 10 acres of crops and grass
- or at least one full-time worker
- or a standard labour requirement of at least 26 standard man days a year

Main holdings ('000)

1968	254.3
1969	245.9

1970–72
Main holdings defined as those which met one of the following criteria:
- at least 10 acres of crops and grass
- at least one full-time worker
- a standard labour requirement of at least 26 standard man days a year.

Main holdings ('000)

1970	233.4
1971	228.6
1972	220.2

1973–79
Main holdings defined as those which met one of the following criteria:
- at least 10 acres of crops and grass
- at least one full-time worker
- a standard labour requirement of at least 40 standard man days a year.

Main holdings ('000)

1973	212.8	1977	199.1
1974	211.4	1978	198.0
1975	206.2	1979	197.5
1976	204.4		

1980 onwards
Main holdings defined as those with
- at least six hectares of total area
- or a standard labour requirement of at least 100 standard man days
- or at least one regular full-time worker
- or a glasshouse area of at least 100m^2.

Main holdings ('000)

1980	185.2	1984	182.9
1981	185.1	1985	183.6
1982	185.4	1986	184.7
1983	186.0		

Source. Based on Parliamentary Question, Hansard, 9 May, 1985.

Scotland and Northern Ireland
There have also been changes in Scotland and Northern Ireland but not necessarily at the same time.

—